1st
pg

Williams Haynes HAS ALSO WRITTEN

◇◇

MEN, MONEY AND MOLECULES
Popular Story of Chemical Business

CHEMICAL PIONEERS
Lives of American Chemical Industrialists

SULPHUR
An Industrial Romance

CHEMICAL ECONOMICS
A Textbook for Colleges

CASCO BAY YARNS

SANDHILLS SKETCHES

THE SQUAW AND OTHER ONE-ACT PLAYS

THIS CHEMICAL AGE

THIS
CHEMICAL
AGE

The Miracle of Man-Made Materials

BY

WILLIAMS HAYNES

ALFRED · A · KNOPF

NEW YORK · 1942

Gratefully to

ISABELLE ALEXANDER ROBEY

A WORD WITH THE READER

◇◇

THIS BOOK definitely does not need any Introduction. It docs need an Index, and my wife is attending to that.

Which reminds me that my old friend Richardson Wright assures us in his delicious *Gardener's Bed Book* that while Adam did name the flowers in the Garden of Eden, it was Eve who went about after him and stuck labels in the beds. Yet I am sure — and you will get the connection at once — that Clifton Fadiman is quite right when he says that the author who dedicates his work to "my severest critic" is unduly optimistic.

You, my Prospective Reader, will find in the first chapter the story of an English nobleman who, when his banker came asking him what he wanted done with forty thousand pounds sterling, did not care to bother with such trifles because he was very busy proving that water is H_2O. How he did that, and just what it means, explains to us a great deal about the fundamentals of chemistry.

In the second chapter you will read about a pernickety Quaker schoolmaster who drew pictures in his notebook which revealed to him, and to us, what the atoms are and how they combine. Here also you will learn about two young Germans, one working in Paris, the other in Stockholm, who quarreled over their simultaneous discovery — the discovery that showed how the atoms group themselves in different compounds in definite patterns.

When you know about these things, you know all the chemistry you require to enjoy reading about iceless ice, about synthetic rubber that is not rubber at all, and how nylon can be made of coal, air, and water; and why sulphanilamide is harmless to germs in a test tube, yet slaughters them in the human body. And that is the sort of thing that this book is really about.

Some of my good friends in the chemical fraternity are going to get cold shivers when they read the following pages. No doubt they will berate me for " thoroughly unscientific over-simplification." I shall not mind much. Indeed, I am rather proud how little chemistry there is in this book which deals with all the new synthetic chemical products.

After all, this book is not written for chemists and engineers. It is written for you, and for your particular benefit every chapter has been read by at least two critics outside my family.

All the chapters have been read by the delightful wife of a distinguished physician, a lady who knows no more about chemistry than you and I do about Cherokee grammar. Whatever she has not found clear and understandable has been rewritten. Then, each chapter has also been read by one or more of my technical friends who are experts in that special field. Whatever they questioned as to its essential accuracy has been corrected. My grateful acknowledgments of their great services to you will be found in the back of this book along with some suggestions about other books on this same general subject which you might like to read; definitions of some technical terms; the Index Mrs. Haynes is preparing — all exceedingly important and useful parts of this volume.

What I wanted to say to you, Gentle Reader, is that if you can stick Chapters I and II, where you will learn all the chemistry you need to enjoy what follows, you will not find the other chapters heavy going. I hope you will enjoy the reading and that you will learn a good deal about what is probably the most significant and certainly the most fascinating development of our times: the production of man-made materials, not substitutes for natural products, but new materials, better and cheaper and more adaptable for our use.

WILLIAMS HAYNES

Stonecrop Farm
Stonington, Connecticut

CONTENTS

◇◇◇

ILLUSTRATIONS

◇◇◇

THIS CHEMICAL AGE

CHAPTER I

NOT DIFFICULT NOR
DANGEROUS

◇◇

ALMOST everybody knows that water is H_2O. You may test this for yourself quite easily by a sort of personally conducted Gallup poll. But do not ask only such likely people as taxi-drivers, butchers, and manicurists. Ask distinguished members of the bar and of the League of Women Voters. Ask also college professors of English or Latin who disdain the sciences as a chemist shuns Greek verse. It is surprising how many people can tell you that H_2O means water in the chemical language.

A few know, too, that H_2SO_4 is sulphuric acid. But generally such knowledge is either pure swank or evidence of a good memory for high-school chemistry.

Yet a hundred and fifty years ago everybody believed that water was an element: one of the four great elements, earth, air, fire, and water, as was guessed by Empedocles — 450 B.C. — who taught it to Plato, who passed it on to Aristotle. And for twenty-one hundred years of course nobody questioned Aristotle till in 1781 an English nobleman, who was so timid that he dared not speak to his own maidservants, had the temerity to prove that water is not an element at all, but a chemical compound of two parts hydrogen and one part oxygen.

[3

This H_2O is the beginning of all chemical wisdom. Tucked away in that simple symbol are the most important basic laws of the science. Accordingly, if you not merely know that it is the chemist's shorthand for water, but really comprehend what the chemical combination of these two atoms signifies, and how it can be effected, and why it is not easily broken, then you know about all the chemistry necessary to understand how, for instance, nylon can be made out of coal, air, and water.

In these days it is pleasant at least to be in the know, as it were, about such things as iceless ice and soapless soaps and the other new products of chemical research which the Sunday supplements delight to hail as modern miracles. This magic of the chemists is performed, not by any slick trick of a Houdini nor even through Aladdin's command of supernatural power, but by applying imagination and hard work, brains and sweat, to the unchanging laws of chemical reactions. Neither legerdemain nor necromancy has any place in chemistry.

Without at least a rough working knowledge of the simple rules of the chemical game we live in this modern world deaf, dumb, and blind. Technical chemical terms flash in the headlines. The latest chemical discoveries are cocktail-hour gossip. Wall Street discounts the sales of that new synthetic chemical product which you and I will be purchasing next spring. Today the metamorphoses of cellulose into paper and rayon, into Celluloid and Cellophane, into photographic films and lacquers and high-power explosives, mean more to us than the tales told of old by Ovid. What is Jason's quest of the Golden Fleece to the search for synthetic rubber by Father Nieuwland, the American priest who taught chemistry at Notre Dame while the Four Horsemen made football history.

The simple fact that water is H_2O was first learned a hundred and sixty years ago. It was an epochal chemical discovery, and it was made by the most nobly born, fabulously wealthy, highly eccentric chemist who ever held a test tube or balanced the scales.

Henry Cavendish, the chemical discoverer of aqua pura, was the grandson of two dukes, first cousin of another, the nephew of two more and also of an earl. Generations of good, hard-working, democratic scientists have snickered scornfully at the biographer of Robert Boyle who wrote: " He was the son of the Earl of Cork and a father of British chemistry." Cavendish caps this anticlimax. His place in *Burke's Peerage* was higher than Boyle's and his chemical discoveries more important. Admittedly this is a very, very rare combination.

Something must have gone askew in the childhood of this strange genius. Had his fair lady mother lived, the whole life of Henry Cavendish might easily have been so different that he would never have touched a test tube.

The marriage of his parents, Lord Charles Cavendish, son of the Duke of Devonshire, and Lady Anne Gray, daughter of the Duke of Kent, was a brilliant affair. King George II sent the bride a necklace. The omnipotent Walpole was a witness. Off to Italy in coach and four posted the happy couple, not to return until three years later the bride, now the mother of one frail little baby boy and soon to be brought to bed with a second son, returned to the land of her noble ancestors to die. The elder of those two infants was Henry Cavendish.

In the record of his life are two mysterious, ten-year gaps, before his schooldays and following his residence at Cambridge University. We can guess that the childhood of this motherless little boy in the busy world of high society was full of fears and frustrations. At eleven years of age he entered the fashionable boarding school at Hackney whose worthy headmaster, the Reverend Dr. Newcombe, has been characterized by Lord Campbell as " a sound classical scholar and a strict disciplinarian." All this sounds a bit formidable. Though his brother and four Cavendish cousins were at school with him, the shy, ugly Henry, passionately devoted to mathematics and natural science, could well have been terribly miserable in such an environment.

At eighteen he escaped to St. Peter's College, Cambridge, where on December 18, 1749 he matriculated in the first rank. Accordingly, we may be sure that he was a better-than-average student. He accepted no invitations to house parties, which was unusual for a young gentleman of his position, nor did he slip away on holiday trips with any chums. The college records show that he was in residence almost constantly till February 23, 1753, when he left without taking his degree. Since he could not have feared the examinations, he must have been quite indifferent to the formal labels of education. His later life confirms this deduction. Certainly there never lived a prominent scientific man so careless of the credit due him for important original discoveries.

After he left Cambridge, Henry Cavendish lived rigidly within the limits of a niggardly allowance of fifty pounds a year, but how and where he lived we do not know. At all events he fixed upon himself habits of miserly frugality which clung to him after he had inherited three fortunes, one from a sort of fairy-godmother aunt, another from his father, and the greatest of all from an uncle, a fabulous, mysterious military gentleman who was one of the first of the wealthy Indian nabobs. For the last thirty-nine years of his life, therefore, he was, as M. Bigot said in a pretty French epigram, " *le plus riche de tous les savants: le plus savant de tous les riches.*"

Long before he became " richest of the scholars " he had begun his chemical experiments. After he had command of princely wealth his sole extravagances were scientific books and instruments. He was no amateur dilettante, but a technician of rare dexterity and patience who delighted to work in the delicate and tricky analysis of the gases. Capturing and purifying and weighing these imponderable, often invisible vapors is today no task for a careless bungler. In the crude apparatus of his time he demonstrated that two of the four ancient " elements " — air and water — are not simple, indivisible chemical elements at all; but that the one is a mixture, the other a combination, of different chemical substances.

With no knowledge of chemistry it is not always easy to mark clearly the distinctions between chemical combinations and physical changes. When milk sours, that is clearly enough chemical change due to the formation in it of a new substance, lactic acid. When cream rises to the top of the bottle, the fat globules originally thoroughly mixed have simply separated and, being lighter, float on the surface, which is a physical change. When the ice cubes form in your refrigerator or the steam floats away from the teakettle, the water has changed its form to the solid or the gaseous states. But it is still the same water. Your cook, if she ever thought about it at all, probably never identified ice, water, and steam as the identical chemical substance, and she would be apt to question your sanity if you assured her that the rust on the bread knife and the dark stains on your egg spoon are the results of chemical changes in iron and silver.

For thousands of years the human race has taken for granted the chemical realm in which we live and move and have our being. For this good reason chemical discoveries such as Cavendish's have never created much stir. We are amused that our hardheaded forebears assumed that a flat world was the foundation of the whole universe and that they protested vigorously when first told that the sun does not cross the heavens to give them day and night. Yet we blissfully ignore the fact that we cannot boil an egg or step on the accelerator without starting a great many highly involved chemical reactions, and with charming inconsistency we flare up when the biochemist informs us quite soberly that the thoughts of our heads and the emotions of our hearts are the result of the same sort of chemical reactions. Like Molière's bourgeois gentleman, who was astonished to learn that he had been talking French prose all his life, we are startled to remember the chemical basis of our entire physical existence.

For chemistry is much more than bad smells and poisonous fumes generated in a bottle-lined laboratory. It is the science of matter; its composition, its properties, and all its transformations. In that they all have a definite chemical composition, every part of the chair you are sitting in is just as much a chemical product as the contents of every bottle in the family medicine chest. Every material substance is chemical. As a matter of fact, there is a more complicated chemistry involved in the wooden handle of the old-fashioned penholder than in the synthetic plastic barrel of your fountain pen. The chemist is therefore concerned not only with acids and alkalies, chloroform and alcohol, indigo and turpentine, but also with anything from sawdust to stardust.

Æons ago some shivering, fear-ridden caveman made the first great chemical experiment. He caught the wild forest fire, born of the erupting volcano, and tamed it.

Fire and then the wheel! The two greatest of man's discoveries, symbols of chemistry and physics, the archetypes of all processing and all fabricating, the fertile tools that have begotten our civilization.

When that low-browed genius brought fire into his gloomy den, cherishing its light and warmth, he put chemistry to work. Generation after generation his children's children, without an inkling of the simplest principles of chemistry, learned how to carry on many chemical reactions in order to make over all sorts of materials more to their liking.

They liked wine better than fruit juice — this primitive taste persists in many of us — and alcoholic fermentation must have been an early discovery. A wise anthropologist has assured us that although races have been found so ignorant of the facts of life that they never knew the relationship of father to child, no tribe has ever been discovered that did not know how to make some intoxicating beverage.

Tanning is accomplished by the lowest savages. No doubt that was a chance discovery: a green hide lying in a swampy pool turned to leather which did not become soft and putrid. Nevertheless it was a fine piece of research, for while the advantages of leather are obvious enough to impress any thick-skulled flint-chipper, it takes close observation to trace out the cause of this desirable effect upon the raw skin, and logical reasoning to prepare tanning extracts by steeping barks in water. Any bark will not do: it must be one, like oak or sumac, rich in tannic acid. Though this is the chemical that turns hide to leather, no tanner ever even heard of tannic acid till 1797 when it was first isolated by Sequin.

Many such lucky accidents must have helped. However, there must have also been a great deal of cut-and-try experiment to have perfected dyeing and bleaching, glass-making, metal-working, brewing, and embalming. No possible happy combination of coincidences could ever have contrived the complicated preparation of Tyrian purple dye from shellfish nor brought together the combination of sulphur, saltpeter, and charcoal, the gunpowder with which an unknown Chinese blasted a new course for history. Many first-class chemical processes were worked out without any help from chemistry.

The alchemists also helped. For while their searches were misdirected and the theories they concocted were as weird as their brews, nevertheless they did learn many of the tricks of the laboratory trade and they devised quite a lot of handy apparatus. They discovered distillation, the process of converting either a liquid or a solid into a vapor and then, by cooling, of recondensing it back to its original form. By doing this over and over again, they learned that different substances have different boiling-points and that liquids mixed together can be separated by controlling the temperature of the boiling mixture. The first use they made of that discovery

ALCHEMISTS' FRACTIONAL DISTILLATION
APPARATUS

Woodcut frontispiece from *Philosophi ac Alchimistæ Maximi* published by Johannes Greininger, Strassburg, 1531. The book is attributed to Geber (Abu Musa Jabir), the Arabian alchemist of the eighth century. The artist is unknown, but his engraving admirably illustrated a very early form of fractional distillation. Print from the collection of D. D. Berolzheimer.

was to get a crude alcohol, and they knew what they were about for they called it " spirit of wine." We still call brandy and whisky " distilled spirits."

The alchemists perfected several types of closed vessels with long necks in which to carry on this useful operation of distillation. When they wanted a gentle, steady heat they set their vessels in larger ones filled with water — the same principle as the double boiler of the kitchen — or placed them in a pan filled with sand over a fire. Both water-bath and sand-bath methods are employed by chemists today. The test tube, the alembic, that handy glass ball with the neck, and the closed crucible or little metal pot with a lid, were all used by alchemists centuries before they became real chemists.

Most important of all, in a world where classical authority and the dictates of the church were the not-to-be-disputed last word, they were learning by doing and observing what happened. This is the key to the scientific method. By means of it they found many facts about the properties and trans-formations of their favorite materials: sulphur, salt, alcohol, lead, quicksilver, antimony, silver, and gold. If at worst they were unblushing charlatans, playing on the greed and fears of man with fine promises of wealth and health, gold and the elixir of life, at best they were competent workers in the metals. Out of their alchemy, about two centuries ago, was born our chemistry.

It was that son of the Earl of Cork who was hailed the father of British chemistry, the witty, polished, scientifically minded Robert Boyle, who straddles like a colossus the gap between alchemist and chemist. He believed firmly in the transmutation of the base into the rarer metals. Yet he wrote a popular best seller, *The Skeptical Chemist*, in which he flayed with sarcasm the senseless jargon used by the alchemists to describe their purposeless experiments. This tickled the readers, already a little suspicious of such hocus-pocus, and they chortled when he likened these impostors to the brave but foolish traders, described by Solomon, who brought back from their perilous voyage to Tarshish not only good gold and valued ivory, but silly peacock feathers and ridiculous apes.

Mentally Boyle was a real chemist. Most of all we are in

his debt for the first modern conception of the chemical elements. More clearly than his predecessors he distinguished between the physical mixtures and the chemical combinations of matter. He taught also that in the final analysis all matter is made up of millions of these mixtures or combinations of a comparatively few elemental substances which cannot be broken down into any simpler material. He reached out so far ahead of his time as to guess that the elements are made up of tiny particles of identical matter as the grains of sand make up the sea beach. With his walloping sentences he was able to pound into his contemporaries some conception of his own clear ideas about the composition of matter: " A few simple, indivisible elements . . . many mixtures and combinations of the same few elements."

Boyle suspected quite rightly that many substances then considered simple and indivisible would yield to better chemical methods and be broken up, proving thus that they are not true elements. In the skillful hands of Henry Cavendish water and air were to furnish sensational proof of this chemical foresight. Boyle also prophesied that some elements then unknown would be discovered. Again he surmised correctly. Sixty of the ninety-two elements have been found since his death.

This frail, slender aristocrat moved mountains of mental inertia. He changed search into research. Prodded by his witty sarcasm, the natural philosophers, as they were pleased to call themselves, gave over searching for alchemical peacock feathers and became scientists digging out the good gold of chemical facts. Vast differences in both purpose and method appear when an alchemist and a chemist perform the same experiment.

A prince among the alchemists was the brilliant, egotistical, avaricious medicine man of the sixteenth century, Theophrastus Bombastus von Hobenheim, who rechristened himself Aureolus Paracelsus. One of the first of the great real chemists was the shy, industrious millionaire misanthropist, Henry Cavendish. Both men dropped bits of iron into sulphuric acid. Both observed, as many others had, the violent bubbling up of a colorless gas. The results of their observations were, however, quite different.

Paracelsus, being a very great alchemist, went a step further. He found out that this gas burned with a hot, blue flame; but he failed to realize that it was " pregnant with vast consequences, teeming with grand result, loaded with fate." He recorded his observation in the elaborate mumbo-jumbo of his craft, and so far as he was concerned, that was the end of it.

Cavendish began the same experiment by cornering the London supply of pig bladders. He needed lots of them, for he proposed to collect a goodly supply of this bubbling, colorless gas since he wanted to study it and compare it with other gases.

Into a narrow-mouthed flask he poured sulphuric acid, dropped in some bits of iron, and stoppered the flask with a tight cork pierced with a glass tube over the free end of which he had securely tied one of the pig bladders. Small bubbles appeared on the surface of the metal. Slowly at first, soon rapidly, they began to rise. The flask began to heat up, so violent was the reaction, and the bladder began to inflate with the gas liberated from the stream of bubbles arising from the metal. When the bubbling ceased and the chemical reaction was over, Cavendish tied up the neck of the bladder, pulled out the stopper and tube, washed up his apparatus, and set it up again with a fresh bladder, ready to repeat the experiment.

The second time he dropped in, not iron, but zinc. The same heat and bubbling — were the gases the same?

He repeated the experiment using tin. Then he began all

over again with iron, but he dropped it, not into sulphuric, but into hydrochloric acid. From the two acids and the three metals he collected six bladderfuls of gas.

Carefully this persistent investigator worked a thin metal tube through the knotted bladder-neck, and as the gas escaped, he touched it with a lighted taper. All six burned with the hot, bluish flame that Paracelsus had observed.

It would certainly appear that the gases were the same from either acid or any of the three metals, thus Cavendish reasoned; but he was not so easily satisfied. The extreme lightness of this gas had impressed him. Even the heavy pig bladders inflated with it almost floated in the air. This suggested that he try to determine whether the gas from all six experiments weighed the same. So he set to work weighing acid and metal and pig bladders before and after each experiment. He filled reams of paper with calculations. At last through the forest of figures he came to a clearing. His carefully checked calculations began to make sense.

Though much lighter than air, this colorless gas did have weight and he determined that weight accurately. Moreover, he had learned just how much of this light gas was generated from so much of each acid and so much of each metal. Furthermore, he rechecked this experiment with nitric acid and also with other metals. He found that other, different gases were generated, gases that were not colorless and that did not burn.

Here at last was real chemical research. First get the facts, as many of them as possible; then check and compare them. Fit them together like the pieces of a jigsaw puzzle till they make a clear understandable picture, a logical interpretation of just what these facts mean. This is the core of research. No wonder the scientist is devoted to facts. For any fact, scrupulously determined and explicitly recorded, is another brick in the building of knowledge.

Cavendish suspected that this gas which bubbles up when

either sulphuric or hydrochloric acid is brought into contact with zinc, tin, or iron was one of Robert Boyle's simple, indivisible elements. Accordingly he began a long, long series of experiments by which he discovered ten years later that this hydrogen, when it burns in the air, combines with oxygen in the proportion of two parts of hydrogen to one part of oxygen — the familiar H_2O. In pursuing these researches, he demonstrated also that the air we breathe is a mixture of one fifth oxygen and four fifths another gas that remains unchanged while the hydrogen and oxygen are combining to form water.

Water is not an element, but a compound formed of two gases! It was a pronouncement as surprising and as upsetting in its effects as Copernicus's proof that the earth is not flat, but round.

The evening of January 15, 1784 was stormy, but that did not keep any able-bodied member of the Royal Society in London from attending the meeting. It had been announced that Henry Cavendish was to read a paper on "Experiments on Air." The modest title fooled nobody. All England's leading scientists plowed through the snowdrifts that blocked the narrow streets, for this unfriendly recluse had a reputation. He seldom read a paper, but when he did — well, it was sure to be full of new important facts. They were to be well repaid for venturing forth that blizzardly night.

Indeed, they could hardly believe their ears when they heard the startling statement that water is a compound of two gases. Cavendish had anticipated their skepticism and was prepared with triple proofs.

He made no parade of the thousands of experiments he had performed to learn just the correct proportions of the various gases involved. He told nothing at all about how many times these elusive gases seeped out and upset his calculations, nor how often he escaped blindness, even possibly death, when violent explosions burst his thick glass vessels. He skimmed for them the cream of his hours of labor and reported briefly on three epochal experiments.

First he had wired a heavy glass cylinder so that an electric spark could be liberated in it after it had been sealed. Withdrawing all the air with a pump, he put into the cylinder 400 measures of hydrogen and 1,000 measures of air. He touched off the spark.

Flash! The inside of the vessel became covered with " dew."

By careful weighing, he demonstrated that all the hydrogen and a fifth of the air disappeared from the cylinder. Four fifths of the air remained — and the dew. The dew weighed exactly as much as the hydrogen and the one fifth of the common air which had vanished.

Was that dew really water? Plainly he must collect a sufficient quantity for very thorough testing.

He took another glass cylinder, eight feet long, three quarters of an inch in diameter, and fitted two copper tubes through a brass plate which sealed the end of the long glass cylinder. Through these copper pipes he slowly fed " 500,000 grain measures of hydrogen and 1,250,000 grain measures of air," burning them slowly, passing the burnt gases through the long tube. In this way he cooled the hot gases and condensed the dew which began to drip from the open end of the glass cylinder. He collected " upwards of one hundred and twenty-five grains " of this colorless liquid which had no taste or smell and left no sensible sediment when evaporated to dryness; neither did it yield any pungent smell during evaporation. " In short," he concluded, " it seemed pure water."

One other question remained unanswered. He could be certain about the hydrogen. Had he not prepared it himself from zinc and sulphuric acid just as he had done ten years before? Therefore he knew what it was and was confident that it was pure. But how could he be certain that the gas which combined with his hydrogen was oxygen?

Luckily it was no great trick to prepare pure oxygen. One of his scientific acquaintances — Cavendish had no friends — had learned how to do this. Joseph Priestley several years before had discovered this element by heating red oxide of mercury, which by this simple treatment gives up oxygen. Fortunate, too, that Cavendish had ample means to buy all the red powder he needed, for in the 1780's it was too expensive for the average chemist's thin pocketbook.

One of the choicest scientific relics preserved at the University of Manchester is a great glass globe, big enough to hold 8,800 grain measures. Its short neck is furnished with a brass stopcock. Attached to it is a primitive apparatus contrived to generate electricity and hooked up so as to discharge a spark within the vessel. In this identical glass globe it was proved that water is H_2O.

Cavendish sucked the air out of this big globe with a pump and then filled it with two parts of hydrogen and one part of oxygen. He was positive because he had made both gases. He fired them with the electric spark. The hydrogen and oxygen disappeared, to be replaced with an equal weight of pure water.

Again and again he repeated the experiment, varying the proportions of the two pure gases. Invariably the result was that two volumes of hydrogen combined with the one volume of oxygen, and the weight of the water was always equal to the combined weight of the two gases that had united. In France another skeptical, nobly born chemist, the Comte de Fourcroy, verified this water-from-gas business in a big way. For a week he left burning two fine jets of hydrogen and oxygen gases. He got water and nothing but water, and it required two parts by volume of hydrogen to one part of oxygen to complete the reaction.

Then a few years later (1789) a couple of brilliant Dutch chemists, Van Troostwijk and Diemann, turned these experiments completely inside out. Instead of forcing hydrogen and oxygen to combine by means of an electric spark, they forced water to dissociate or separate into hydrogen and oxygen by passing through it an electric current from a powerful static machine. The two gases appeared separately, the hydrogen at the negative and the oxygen at the positive poles. Again two volumes of hydrogen were produced to one of oxygen. By synthesis or electrolysis, whether built up or torn apart, always the same ratio: two hydrogen and one oxygen, never more, never less. That is exactly what the chemist means when he tells us that the formula — that is, the chemical composition — of water is H_2O.

What Cavendish had done was an immensely stimulating accomplishment. His feat set a fashion among chemists of taking to pieces all sorts of things and putting them together again, like the little boy and the alarm clock, to find out what they are made of. One of the amazing things they discovered was that you could never be sure till you really knew. That is a splendid start for anybody on the long rocky road of chemical research.

Who ever would have suspected that two gases would have combined to produce a liquid, H_2O? But curiouser and curiouser, as Alice exclaimed, it was soon found that common salt, the salt of the salt cellar on your dinner table, the healthful, savory condiment and preservative, is made out of two poisonous substances, one a metal and the other a gas. For salt is sodium chloride, NaCl, sodium-chlorine; and sodium is a light white metal that burns in water and so is a favorite ingredient of naval incendiary bombs, while chlorine is a yellowish-greenish gas that chokes and smarts — kills if you breathe too much of it — used to bleach cloth and paper and to purify water. There is nothing very salt-like in the properties of either sodium or chlorine, so it was found that the chemical combinations create quite new and distinct substances that bear no relation to their component elements.

You simply must know. But knowing, you begin to see at least how it might be chemically possible to make a purse out of a sow's ear — which a smart American chemist, Arthur Little, actually did as a chemical publicity stunt — or, for that matter, to make stockings out of coal, air, and water.

CHAPTER II

MOLECULES MADE TO ORDER

◇◇◇

A GAUNT, ugly man sat in a rickety rocking-chair fondling a big, tortoise-shell cat. Plainly he was poor. The room was small and bare. His clothes, the somber grays and black of a good Quaker, were rusty and worn. The man, too, looked worn. Though he was only thirty-five he appeared to be ten years older. As he idly rubbed the cat's ears he gazed off into space. But he was not daydreaming.

John Dalton, Quaker schoolmaster of Manchester, England, was concentrating on the hardest work a man can do. He was really thinking, thinking out a clear explanation of a conflicting jumble of facts, thinking to great effect also, since his thoughts were to furnish the clue to chemists for understanding how chemical changes take place and to provide a tool enabling practical businessmen to make chemicals to order.

At this time, the opening of the last century, even the most brilliant, erudite chemist had no better notion than the caveman who captured fire what happens in a chemical reaction. Hundreds of these chemical changes had been watched, as Paracelsus had observed the bubbles rise from iron dropped into sulphuric acid; and just as Cavendish had studied the light, colorless gas, so the results of many chemical reactions had been carefully recorded. What had happened, however, and why, and how, were all a tangle of riddles snarled up with a lot of bad guesses. Dalton's thoughts, like the keen, flashing sword of the youthful Alexander, were to sever this Gordian knot.

At this time, too, practical craftsmen were employing the most amazing chemical means to make over materials more to their liking. With no knowledge of how these wanted chemical changes came about, rule-of-thumb operations were carried on because it had been noted that the desired results were obtained.

Buttermilk and vinegar, for example, were then the standard acids used in bleaching cloth. Pigeon and dog dung were popular alkalies employed in tanning leather. The former do contain lactic and acetic acids, and these animal excrements are notably rich in ammonia. They are all, however, weak chemical tools for either acidulating or alkalinizing operations, full of useless impurities unnecessary in the chemical reactions of bleaching and tanning. Results had to be obtained by the good old " by guess and by gosh " method. Dalton's thoughts changed all that and gave birth to the business of making definite chemicals to modify all sorts of materials better for mankind's use.

As this methodical old bachelor sat there rocking, his cat on one knee, a stiff-covered notebook on the other, he was hunting for a logical explanation why the four gases in the atmosphere do not separate into four levels. He knew they had different densities. The heaviest, carbon dioxide, should hug the earth, covered by successive layers of oxygen and nitrogen, with the lightest, water vapor, up above the highest mountain tops.

Nevertheless they do remain remarkably mixed. He knew that fact very well, for the weather was his absorbing hobby. He had traveled from London to the Scottish Highlands sampling air from city streets, the open fields, high mountains, and deep glens. He left a stack of notebooks, crammed with over 200,000 exact meteorological observations; and throughout his life the more he learned about the weather, the more he wanted to know. This puzzle of the mixed gases in the atmosphere kept him awake nights — thinking.

He had often picked up extra shillings tutoring in Latin and Greek, so he knew at first hand that the classical philosophers had formulated the theory that all matter is composed of tiny particles which the Greeks called " atoms," meaning " uncut, indivisible." He was familiar, too, with the hint thrown out by the brilliant Robert Boyle that these atoms might well prove to be the innermost secret of the chemical elements, those indivisible substances that could not be broken down into anything more simple.

The more he pondered, the stronger became the conviction that in Boyle's elements was the true explanation of the ultimate composition of matter. And yet why do not the gases in the air separate by weight as oil and water float in distinct layers?

He began to draw pictures in his notebook, pictures of the gases in the air. To represent them he must adopt arbitrary symbols, so he chose an asterisk for the water vapor, diamonds for oxygen, little dots for the nitrogen, and solid triangles for the heavy carbon dioxide. Combining them as one might spread out on a sheet of paper a very thin mixture of salt and pepper grains, he drew:

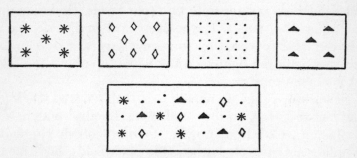

The pictures John Dalton drew to represent the mixture
of the four chief gases in the atmosphere.

In his mind's eye this picture visualized the rapid motion of the particles of the four gases in the air, diffusing through each other, this way and that, maintaining constantly a uniform mixture. Out of this vision Dalton formulated the atomic theory:

Every element is composed of these exceedingly minute atoms which are indivisible in the sense that they are the smallest units of that element which can exist as such.

This was essentially the thought of the Hindu and Greek philosophers which Boyle had guessed in his bold simile of the sand on the beach; but Dalton went further than this. He postulated that the atoms of a given element are all identical in size and shape and weight, but that each differs in all these properties from the atoms of all other elements, each of which has its own distinctive characteristics.

Dalton went another step. He pointed out that these atoms are the units by which chemical reactions take place, that every chemical change is a recombination of the atoms that make up the elements, or the compounds, or the mixtures involved in that particular reaction. The atoms are the building bricks of chemistry. The union of two or more atoms makes a chemical compound.

Furthermore atoms never unite save as units. The carbon atom, for example, combines with one or with two atoms of oxygen, but never with fractions or parts of an atom: CO and CO_2, but never $CO_{\frac{1}{2}}$. Carbon monoxide (CO) is the poisonous gas that kills the poor despondent who shuts the garage door and sits down in his car with the motor running. Carbon dioxide (CO_2) is the beneficent gas which, dissolved in beverages, gives them their sparkle or, solidified by great pressure, becomes the ultra-cold " dry ice." Carbon semi-oxide — there just ain't no sich animal.

Dalton was an eye-minded thinker, and to visualize this theory he drew a new set of symbols for the known elements, little circles distinctively identified with dots and lines:

Oxygen O   Nitrogen ⊙

Hydrogen ⊙   Sulphur ⊕

Then he could express the reactions between oxygen and hydrogen in a way that was crystal-clear even to the doubting Thomas among the bigwig chemists of his day:

⊙⊙ + O → ⊙⊙O

2 Hydrogen + 1 Oxygen = Water.

It is always exceedingly difficult to get a new idea into a very thick skull and it is often equally hard to demonstrate it effectively to certain exceptionally brilliant brains. No doubt you have noticed this yourself when you try to sell your friends some pet theory of your own. Not all the great chemists welcomed the atomic theory. It did, however, provide the first understandable explanation of the chemical elements and how they combine. It still does. It remains, therefore, the working rule for the research chemist in building up new chemical combinations, be they dyes or medicines, plastics or rayons; for the chemical manufacturer whether he is making simple, inorganic sulphuric acid or complex, organic sulphanilamide; for the citizen who wants to know about the new synthetic chemical products.

Dalton's symbols were clear enough, but they were clumsy; not so clumsy as the elaborate hieroglyphics the alchemists employed to mystify their dupes, but too clumsy for workaday use in lecture room, laboratory, or factory. Two smart chemists, an Italian, Amadeo Avogadro, and a Swede, Jöns Jakob Berzelius, came to the rescue with simplifications.

Avogadro coined the name " molecule " (Latin for " little mass ") for a group of atoms collected and held together in a chemical compound.

Berzelius suggested that the elements be identified by their initials, the first letter or two letters of their names.

Since many of the older elements, like gold and silver, had

quite different names in different languages, Berzelius proposed to use their Latin equivalents. Hence Au, for the Latin *aurum*, and Ag for *argentum*, are the accepted chemical symbols for gold and silver. Names coined by the chemists, as Lavoisier named hydrogen (the water-maker), and those of recently discovered elements like radium, are used all over the world, so the symbols H and Ra are universally understandable.

Why not, suggested Berzelius, group the letters closely together to represent the elements in a molecule with little subfigures to indicate more than one atom of a given element? His simple system was adopted with amazing promptness. Our old friend H_2O means: two hydrogen atoms and one oxygen atom chemically combined to form one molecule of water.

A lot of chemical mysteries began to clear up when studied and explained in terms of atoms and molecules, and of course much more has since been discovered about their properties and reactions. The physical chemists are smashing the atoms nowadays, discovering how they are put together, counting them, watching their bewilderingly swift motions, photographing them.

Dalton was wrong when he assumed that the atoms are indivisible, solid particles. They are miniature solar systems in which the sun is a central, positively charged proton about which, like planets, revolve electrons, positons, and neutrons — infinitely minute specks of negatively charged electrical energy.

In his atomic theory Dalton presupposed that the atoms and molecules are exceedingly tiny. They are far more minute than he imagined. It has been quite accurately determined that if all the H_2O molecules in a tumbler of water were by some magic each turned into a grain of sand, they would bury the entire United States in a sandbank a hundred feet deep. It becomes understandable that the molecules in a drop of indigo dye will tint a ton of water, and a grain of musk will scent a large room for months.

The atoms are smaller still. One atom of hydrogen measures 1/250,000,000 of an inch. Within this infinitesimal space an electron revolves around a proton at a speed of 1,400 miles per hour. That " earth " revolves about its " sun " 7,000,000,-000 times in 1/1,000,000,000 of a second. And we complain that our own years slip by far too quickly!

Let us return to earth as we know it.

Dalton's atoms and Avogadro's molecules are still the building bricks of chemistry. Ignoring the dizzy digits of the protons and their swirling electrons, the research chemists put together out of the atoms about four thousand new chemical combinations each year.

Dalton's atoms had given a new, a definite meaning to chemical analysis. Something more than idle curiosity now impelled chemists to take apart all sorts of things to discover what elements they contained and into what kind of molecules these elements had been combined. Every new fact emphasized that, despite the miraculous diversity of materials, matter obeys a few simple laws. Nothing happens by chance. Atoms combine in definite proportions. Nothing is lost when a chemical reaction takes place. It became possible to foretell how atoms would unite in new combinations. Thus chemistry, as we know it and employ it in the workaday world, developed out of these stimulating ideas.

Avagadro's molecules naturally suggested that it was practical to make a less common or more useful combination of the elements out of cheaper, more abundant molecules. Why bother with weak, unreliable vinegar and buttermilk when one could make strong, uniform sulphuric acid by burning sulphur and collecting the fumes in water? Why not use the sodium in common salt (sodium chloride, NaCl) to make soda ash and use it as an alkali in place of the potassium

leached out of wood ashes in big iron pots and called pot-
ashes?

Hundreds of similar questions were prompted by the growing industrial demand for cheap, dependable chemicals to
change materials into others better suited to men's needs.
This demand grew enormously as machines took over the
work of muscles in providing for man's wants. In answering
these questions, the chemical industry, the great business of
making molecules to order, was developed.

Adolf Hitler did not invent the idea of national chemical
self-sufficiency. Napoleon took special pains to encourage
chemists to supply him with all sorts of munitions made in
France, out of French raw materials; and before his time the
French Academy of Sciences dangled a fat purse of 2,500
golden louis before their molecule-makers as a reward for the
answer to that soda ash and potash question.

France had no great forests and she was dependent upon
America, Russia, and Scandinavia for pot-ashes. At that time
we cut a big slice out of the world's potash trade. We were
still clearing the forest for the plow and to burn the slash
and slab was a simple, profitable by-product industry. Many
a big iron kettle which the antique-dealer tells you was used
to boil soap and maple syrup was used also as an ash pot in
which this crude chemical was leached out of wood ashes.
In fact, the very first U.S. patent was granted to Caleb Wilder
of Massachusetts for a bigger, better potash kettle.

Chemical common sense, born of some knowledge of what
happens in chemical reactions, told the French scientists that
soda ash could be used for potash in making glass, soap, and
paper, in tanning, in scouring wool, in doing a great many
other useful chemical jobs. Their idea was a good one. Soda
ash was destined to become second in importance only to
sulphuric acid, but ironically the process which should have
won the French prize won for England during the last cen-

tury first place among the chemical-producing countries. Today we make in America about 3,500,000 tons of soda ash — more than England, Germany, France, and Japan added together.

Fourteen years after the prize was offered by the Academy of Sciences it was claimed by the Duc d'Orléans's private physician, Nicolas Leblanc. On the grounds that no process submitted was practical, the prize was outlawed. However, Leblanc did get a fifteen-year monopoly from the Government and the Duke advanced 200,000 francs to build a factory. Operations began in the early winter of 1791. They were just nicely under way when the little plant, along with the rest of the Duke's property, was confiscated. In the name of "liberty, equality, and fraternity" the Committee of Public Safety offered the chemist-physician his choice of giving up the secret of his process or else. His noble patron had been hurried to the guillotine and the inference was plain enough.

Eight years later, by way of compensation, Napoleon handed back the wrecked works to Leblanc. He tried in vain to raise capital to restore the plant. Disheartened, the broken man slunk away to his refuge in the village poorhouse and committed suicide.

In that sordid tragedy vanished the opportunity of France to have become the world's chemical headquarters during the nineteenth century. It was a friend of the pathetic inventor who transplanted his famous Leblanc process to England, became the father of the British alkali industry, and did much to establish English leadership in the field of the heavy, or industrial, chemicals.

Dublin-born of English parents, James Muspratt was a unique figure among the pioneer chemical manufacturers. Tall and strikingly handsome, bold, witty, adventurous, a lover of music and paintings, friend of actors and authors, he was certainly not cut according to the customary pattern for the grubby Victorian industrialist. Apprenticed to a drug-

gist, young Muspratt, after his parents both died, quarreled
— accidentally on purpose — with his employer and ran away
to join Wellington's army in Spain. For five years he actually
lived all the adventures of a rollicking historical novel. Then
returning to Dublin, he salvaged a bit of his modest inheritance from the chancery court and determined to capitalize
his drug-store experience by manufacturing chemicals. This
business flourished like a milkweed in a rose garden; especially so after he made prussiate of potash, which was in lively
demand for making blue paint pigments and as a mordant
to fix dyes.

Muspratt had a rare sense of chemical values. He looked
across the Irish Sea, observed the explosive expansion of English manufacturing initiated by the Industrial Revolution,
and decided to move into that lucrative market. He recognized, too, the commercial possibilities in using soda ash for
potash and foresaw that a cheaper alkali would mean cheaper
paper, leather, glass, and soap.

Cheaper and better goods — the opportunity to make
money, not by grinding down costs, chiefly labor costs, and
holding up prices; but by lowering costs through increased
output and then stimulating demand by lower prices. Thus
he preached the modern business doctrine that it is more
profitable to sell 1,000 at $10 per unit than 500 at $20, and
he proved it too in chemicals, as Henry Ford years later
proved it in automobiles. To him this conviction was far more
than an effective sales argument, for when a protective tariff
was proposed on prussiate of potash he scorned such assistance.

" If we cannot hold our own," he told his fellow manufacturers, " we deserve to be beaten."

That was years before the Germans made international
chemical trade a subsidized adjunct to commercial diplomacy and military preparedness. Muspratt never foresaw
that development, else he would never have supported free

trade so vigorously. His business philosophy, while it built up
the British heavy chemical industry to a commanding world
position, left the British coal-tar chemical industry defense-
less against the insidious attacks of the German Dye Trust.
This, as we shall see, had momentous effects in 1914.

When Muspratt moved to England in 1822, he was already
planning to make soda ash. He therefore picked a site near
Liverpool where sulphur from Sicily could be docked at his
front door and where he was in a limestone country, close
to Midlands coal and the Cheshire salt deposits. Sulphur,
coal, lime, and salt would be his raw materials. Here in an
old glass factory he duplicated his Dublin operations and
plowed his profits back into expensive lead chambers in
which to manufacture sulphuric acid, another step closer to
his goal.

He did not, however, immediately produce soda. Staggering under the burdens of the Napoleonic Wars, England
levied a tax of fifteen shillings a bushel on salt — twenty times
its value. Salt could not then be an industrial raw material,
but even as a luxury condiment such a tax load is in these
days something awesome to contemplate.

In 1823 that tax was reduced to two shillings. Muspratt
immediately began to operate the Leblanc process. This famous operation is obsolete now, but we owe it a great debt.
It put panes into the windows of every man's house. It made
the penny newspaper possible. It took soap out of the class
of luxury articles. Finally it taught the chemical manufacturers their first lessons in large-scale production.

It taught them also that it is hard to introduce a new chemical to an old trade. Soda ash makes better, harder soap more
quickly and at less cost than potash. But at first the soapmakers would have none of it. The good old natural wood
ashes, so they said, had been good enough for their grand-
fathers. This new chemical alkali, it was rumored, would
make soap so caustic that it would ruin anything from a

ship's deck to that schoolgirl complexion. It would certainly ruin the world-renowned reputation of the great English soap trade. So Muspratt literally gave soda away and then, to prevent those honest craftsmen the soap-boilers from playing tricks on his material, he was forced to go to their kettles with them and show them how to use it. Ten years later English production of soap — almost every pound of it made with soda — had increased twentyfold.

If, as some chemically minded philosopher has noted, the civilization of a people can be measured by their use of soap, then the British Isles made vast progress during the past century and we Americans must be at once the most civilized and the most godly people on earth. One may doubt that, though the statistical proof is perfect — per capita soap-consumption a year: U.S.A., 25 pounds; Netherlands, 24 pounds; Denmark, 22 pounds; Great Britain, 21 pounds; and the rest trailing down to China, 2 ozs.

The rough and rocky road lying before new chemical products is now a familiar trail. Once fairly started, however, the demand for them is apt to accelerate rapidly. In 1920 we produced some 5,000,000 pounds of synthetic plastics of all kinds; in 1930 about 45,000,000 pounds; in 1940 more than 250,000,000 pounds. It took the American rayon industry nineteen years (1910–29) to reach an output of 100,000,000 pounds. In the next eleven years, to 1940, it reached a total of 470,000,000, nearly five times as great.

While Muspratt was hounding prospective users of soda ash, two young Germans, the one working in Stockholm under the inventive Berzelius, the other in the Paris laboratory of the great Gay-Lussac, made a notable double-barreled discovery that led to a brisk quarrel which ended in a Damon and Pythias friendship. In Sweden the calm and cautious Friedrich Wöhler in his painstaking way had been studying a white powder, silver cyanate, trying to find out why it decomposes when heated. It is composed of the ele-

ments silver, carbon, nitrogen, and oxygen. He assigned to it
the formula AgCNO. The nervous, impetuous Justus von
Liebig was enthusiastically interested in fireworks and he prepared, at the risk of his eyesight, the slender, colorless crystals of silver fulminate, which if heated explodes violently.
He found its formula to be AgCNO.

"What ho!" he exclaimed. "Is that lanky chap in Berzelius's laboratory crazy or am I?"

He rechecked his analysis of the fulminate. It was right as
a trivet. Wöhler must be a butter-fingered analyst, and Liebig wrote in his emphatic style pointing out to his colleague
the error of his chemical ways.

"This is a bumptious boy," thought Wöhler, "telling me
I am all wrong and he is all right. But possibly it is so. Two
different substances certainly cannot have the same formula."

So he rechecked his analysis of the cyanate. He found it
correct. Then he analyzed Liebig's silver fulminate. He found
that the formula AgCNO, as Liebig had found it, was also
correct.

Something must be wrong, and taking extraordinary pre-
cautions, he repeated both analyses, not once, but ten times.
Ten times both formulas came out AgCNO. He took this
puzzle to his master, Berzelius, and that great analyst cor-
roborated his results.

Here was an important new fact: substances quite different in their chemical and physical properties can be composed of the same number of atoms of the same elements.

"Very important indeed," said the famous inventor of our
chemical symbols, "and we need a name for this significant
phenomenon. Let us call it 'isomerism' from the Greek
meaning 'having equal parts.' Silver fulminate and silver
cyanate are therefore 'isomers,' materials made up of equal
parts of the same elements."

How could this strange thing be — the same elements in

the same proportions, yet the two substances so different?

Plainly the atoms must be arranged differently in the cyanate and the fulminate, as a child with the same four blocks might pile them on top of one another to make a tower or arrange them in a square flat on the nursery floor. Put in another way, our Star-Spangled Banner and the tri-color of France are isomers in that both are composed of red, white, and blue. You could paint neither flag by indiscriminately mixing pots of red, white, and blue pigments; you can picture either if you follow its distinctive design.

Even Berzelius did not realize how important isomers and isomerism were to become after the riddle of organic chemistry had been solved by this same tall young German who stood at his elbow when he coined these useful words. With the highly complex formulas of the organic compounds the number of possible isomers is very great. For example, over a thousand isomers of protein are possible, and several hundred have been found. It is isomerism, therefore, that in a great measure accounts for the enormous multiplicity of organic compounds in both natural products and the synthetic combinations.

At that time, however, it was firmly believed that a vast gulf separated all organic compounds, the creations of animal and vegetable life, from the mineral compounds of inorganic chemistry. Wöhler bridged that gap with a test tube. He was still working with the cyanide compounds and by pouring ammonia water into cyanogen produced ammonium cyanate. He proceeded to evaporate the water in order to recover this colorless crystalline material in dry form, and he noted at the end that on continued heating the ammonium cyanate changed to smaller, needle-shaped crystals which on analysis proved to be urea.

Out of mineral materials and in a test tube he had made the chief nitrogenous waste product found in the urine of all animals. He could not believe what he had done. The vital life force unnecessary! No basic difference between animal, vegetable, and mineral materials!

It was a stupendous discovery and all its religious and social implications struck this meticulous scientist like a punch on his jaw. Not till three years later did he dare write his old teacher: "I can prepare urea without requiring the kidney of an animal, either man or dog."

In his cautious studies Wöhler found that ammonium cyanate and urea are isomers. The formula of both is N_2H_4CO. Continued heating had changed the arrangement of these atoms from the ammonium cyanate molecule structure to the pattern of urea. Wonder piled upon wonder — a mineral and an animal product both composed of the same number of atoms of the same elements. The gulf between inorganic and organic chemistry had been completely closed.

The very great differences in the properties of ammonium cyanate and urea must certainly be due to a different arrangement of the atoms in that N_2H_4CO combination. This was now clear to chemists. Accordingly, as Dalton drew pictures of the atoms in the air, they began drawing diagrams of the molecules to show more vividly and accurately their composition. Thus H_2O became $\begin{smallmatrix} H \\ H \end{smallmatrix}\!\!>\!\!O$. In like manner the old empirical formula for methyl alcohol, C_2H_6O became $\begin{smallmatrix} C_2H_5 \\ H \end{smallmatrix}\!\!>\!\!O$, which really gives some idea of what happens, for example, when a second methyl radical, C_2H_5, replaces the second H, or $\begin{smallmatrix} C_2H_5 \\ C_2H_5 \end{smallmatrix}\!\!>\!\!O$, dimethyl oxide, which we commonly know as ether, the anæsthetic which is manufactured by this reaction out of ethyl alcohol.

Such graphic formulas were exceedingly illuminating. With them came the conception that molecules have definite structure. The atoms and little unit groups of atoms, the radicals, are literally building bricks which cannot be dumped out of a hod on the ground, but which must be laid in a definite pattern if either a wall or a walk is to be built.

The pictures of molecules in the graphic formulas became more and more complicated. It was discovered that their basic structure follows not only the flat pattern of chains and rings, but also the solid patterns of cubes and pyramids. However, as the pictures became more complex, it became paradoxically much simpler for the chemist to understand how the intricate molecules of the organic compounds are put together. Knowing their structure, just how the atoms and radicals are grouped, it became easier to break them apart or to build them up into an almost infinite number of new compounds, some of them found in nature, others entirely original combinations of matter.

Dalton had inspired the analysts to determine the kind of atoms in the molecules of all sorts of materials from salt and sugar to oysters and opals. This architectural conception of the molecules set chemists to work anew studying their structure.

Then a century ago a great French chemist, Marcellin Berthelot, opened up an entirely new field. By turning analysis inside out he developed synthesis. Instead of taking the molecules apart, he began to build them up.

If Wöhler could make urea without a kidney, why could not the product of any animal organ or of the leaves or roots of plants be prepared in the laboratory? Berthelot, sharing the religious skepticism of his lifelong friend Ernest Renan, devoted himself zealously " to do away with life as an explanation whenever organic chemistry is concerned." He began by synthesizing acetic acid (vinegar) and he went on to carbolic acid and benzene. He prepared fats and oils. He made alcohol from ethylene, which is now being done commercially in this country from the ethylene in natural gas. He coined the word " synthesis " to describe hundreds upon hundreds of these experiments that he successfully carried through.

Berthelot created a new job for the molecule-makers. In laboratory and plant they had been making chemicals to tan hides and dye fabrics, to alloy metals and feed crops, to turn fats to soap, sand to glass, to transform salt into soda, molasses into alcohol, brimstone into sulphuric acid. Now instead of chemicals to change the properties of materials for man's benefit, they began to make new materials, cheaper, purer, more uniform than natural materials, or especially useful for properties not to be found in any product of nature.

The synthetic age had arrived. Since Berthelot's day more than 400,000 new combinations of the molecules have been constructed. Millions are theoretically possible.

Some of them are exact chemical duplicates of natural products. Common salt is sodium chloride (NaCl) whether it is dug out of rock-salt deposit, evaporated from sea water, or made by reacting caustic soda and hydrochloric acid.

Other so-called synthetics have properties similar to those of natural products which enable them to be used in their place. Amyl acetate is popularly known as " banana oil " from its smell and taste. Neoprene, Thiokol, Buna, and other synthetic rubbers replace natural rubber, though chemically they are not closely akin, because they have rubberlike physical characteristics.

Finally, no materials in nature even remotely resemble such familiar and useful synthetics as the drugs aspirin, barbital, and sulfanilamide; the fibers Celanese and nylon; the dyes methyl violet, malachite green, or rosaniline; the plastics Celluloid, Bakelite, or Lucite.

By constant use we have stretched the meaning of that up-to-date word " synthetic " to cover a great many materials that really belong in a number of different categories.

But all of them are the products of chemical reactions, all are man-made molecules.

Whenever a new synthetic appears on the market it comes into competition with some natural product, and the battle of land and laboratory has developed a technique as obvious as the *Blitzkrieg*. It is an economic pattern with which we will become familiar in the pages that follow.

Back in 1875 one of the first of these wars was declared when de Laire in France and Tiemann in Germany almost simultaneously patented different processes for the preparation of vanillin. Here was a simon-pure synthetic in the strictest sense. Vanillin is the exact chemical duplicate of the active flavoring principle of the vanilla bean. Vanillin was offered at $80 a pound — a handsome price till you realize that this is equivalent to the flavoring power of 175 pounds of natural vanilla pods, selling normally at about $2.50 a pound. At this price natural vanillin in the bean costs $447.50 a pound. During the following fifty years the price of synthetic vanillin, as always happens in these man-made molecules, was steadily brought down to $8 a pound.

Just at this time (1924) the price of natural vanilla beans went off on a periodical sky-ride, climbing up to $9 a pound, equivalent to $1,500 for pure vanillin. There were reasons enough — a revolution in Mexico; droughts and a hurricane in other tropical countries where the vanilla vine, which is a member of the orchid family, is cultivated. Supply was cut down and the planters of Madagascar naturally took advantage of the monopoly bestowed on them by the mere fact that their crop had come through unharmed and their yield was normal.

Their perfectly human selfishness stimulated a great planting of vines all over the world. Accordingly, three years later, when the new plantations began bearing, the price began tumbling. By 1932 it was down to 50 cents a pound, which did not pay for cutting and curing the crop. Plantations were neglected. By 1934 another vanilla famine skyrocketed the price to $3.50. But note that the price went only a third as high as in 1924.

During those ten years, the consumption of synthetic vanillin by cigarette makers, bakers, confectioners, and ice cream manufacturers had grown. With larger output and more experienced technique, the price of the synthetic flavoring material has been reduced from $8 to $2.75. Since then a new chemical process, employing a wood waste product as the initial raw material, has brought the price down to $2 a pound.

Our use of vanilla flavor has enormously increased. The growth, however, has been wholly in the use of vanillin. For thirty years our annual imports of vanilla beans have averaged close to 800,000 pounds, no more, no less. In 1913 we consumed 55 pounds of vanillin; in 1938, 454,948 pounds. That is a healthy increase. In actual flavor it equals 90,000,000 pounds of vanilla beans, beans that we did not import from the tropics. In 1913 all our synthetic vanillin was imported; in 1938 it was all made in the U.S.A. But that's another story.

An old Hindu saying warns us that the dyer's fingers are always stained, and certainly the chemical people — scientists and businessmen alike — are prejudiced witnesses when they testify that the synthetic age will add more to our wealth and health than did the age of power, that the Chemical Revolution will have more drastic economic, political, and social effects than did the Industrial Revolution. Certainly new materials are quite as important to our ways of living as new machines. Indeed, we could not have many of our machines — airplanes and streamlined trains, for instance — were it not for new lightweight metals and plastics. A solemn statistician has calculated that, if it were not for artificial leather for our automobile upholstery, porterhouse steaks would be a drug on the market because we should then have to devote the whole of the Mississippi Valley to raising cattle for their hides to supply the body factories of Flint and Detroit.

Plumb-crazy economics! Of course, admittedly so; but do not forget that chemical discoveries have long since proved their disruptive force. That unknown Chinese who learned to mix sulphur, saltpeter, and charcoal into what we call gunpowder literally blasted the powerfully entrenched feudal system out of history. We shall find that there is a lot more than pretty ashtrays and neat electrical gadgets, runless stockings and fender finishes that do not chip off, behind these new synthetic chemical products.

CHAPTER III

BLACK TAR TO BRIGHT DYE

◇◇

IT is thoroughly symbolic of the career of the handsome Baron Justus von Liebig that he blew himself out the back door of an apothecary shop into the University of Bonn. He was always an explosive individualist with an abiding interest in chemical education.

He had slipped through school, paying as little attention as possible to the regular lessons. But in the public library he had read in their order on the shelves every book on chemistry. His father, a small dealer in dyestuffs, apprenticed him to the local apothecary, who found him completely unsatisfactory as a drug clerk. But he calmly adapted the prescription counter to his own uses as a laboratory till one of his experiments with silver fulminate violently exploded, breaking the shop windows and abruptly closing his career in pharmacy. He persuaded his father to send him to the university to continue his chemical studies. Within two years he had won his doctor's degree.

"Now," announced the fledgling Ph.D., "I am going to learn some chemistry," and off he went to Paris.

This bombastic statement contained more truth than sarcasm. At the time Paris was the world capital of chemical science. Chemical education in Germany was poor and provincial. That these were plain facts did not mollify the indignation of the authorities at such brazen disrespect; and in another two years, when young von Liebig wished to return to Germany to teach, even the weighty influence of Alexander von Humboldt, whom he had met in France, was able to secure for him a post only in the small, poverty-stricken, undistinguished University of Giessen.

Liebig set to work with characteristic gusto to teach chemistry as he wished he had been taught. He laid out a course of lectures and in deserted barracks set up a laboratory. Out of nothing he created the model for all future chemical instruction. While he delivered spirited lectures most of the real work was done in the laboratory. Original research problems were assigned to each student and he learned, not by reading or listening, but by doing. Under an inspiring professor this system is highly successful, and till early in this century serious-minded youths flocked from all over the world to study in the laboratories of a score of distinguished German chemists.

Not only was this an admirable method of chemical instruction, but it was also perfectly geared to advance German chemistry. It taught the pick of the world's chemically minded young men not only chemical science, but also the German language. While giving them the feel of laboratory technique it gave them under the most favorable auspices a generous taste of the most attractive aspects of German life. It promoted an enormous amount of original research, expertly directed, pursued *con amore* by eager young enthusiasts. These young men joined the German chemical societies and after the meetings sat around great wooden tables, drinking good beer and discussing chemical problems. They read the German chemical journals from cover to cover. They went to the library to search the stout leather-bound files for all the background of their own projects, and when their research was completed their findings were published in some

Annalen, or *Berichte,* or *Jahresbuch,* thus adding their bit to the fast-growing monument of German chemical literature.

In the early days all this good German propaganda was quite innocent, a by-product of the German scientific spirit. But long before 1914 the Germans, being good nationalistic chemists, had learned to work up this by-product into what we shall discover was a very valuable asset.

Back in 1845, however, Victoria's German-born Prince Consort certainly harbored no sinister designs when he wrote Liebig for help in reviving English interest in chemistry. Set off to a flying start a century earlier by such real scientists as Boyle and Black, Cavendish and Priestley, British chemistry had slowed down after Davy and Faraday. Socially, the sciences were snubbed by the classics. Commercially, mechanics, offering, as it did, immediate and handsome profits in applying the new-found steam engine to all sorts of industrial opportunities, made chemistry seem a pretty impractical avocation.

Only a few in England sensed that Arkwright's wonderful spinning machine would have flooded the land with " gray goods " had not a French chemist and a Scotch chemical maker between them found a way to bleach cloth with chlorine in six hours any day of the year. Previously, back to beyond written history, cloth had been whitened by exposing it to the summer's sun for six weeks or more. Just as quick-drying lacquers made automobile mass production on the belt-assembly-line possible, so in a score of ways chemicals made the Industrial Revolution practical. Yet Englishmen of that day failed to appreciate this, as many of us fail to realize that without chemicals we should have no airplanes, no iceless refrigerators, no radios.

Prince Albert had, however, a true German perception of chemical values, and he was naturally conspicuous among the small band of devotees who wanted to retrieve English leadership in the sciences. The recently founded Royal College of Chemistry owed its high-sounding name to his interest, and he was no figurehead patron. He personally solicited funds and wrote to Liebig to recommend a head for the laboratory. Liebig suggested August Wilhelm Hofmann, one of his promising recent graduates, and it was Prince Albert who persuaded Hofmann to come to England.

Hofmann was a born teacher. His warm personality inspired trust; his enthusiasm was infectious. He was a prodigious worker and his fertile imagination kept his students well supplied with worth-while problems. He turned out an amazing number of men who made their mark, some as original investigators, others as great teachers.

Among the latter was "Tommy" Hall, who became the first chemistry instructor at the City of London School, the first English school in which experimental science was taught. Among Hall's pupils was a precocious lad, William Henry Perkin, son of a well-to-do builder.

Young Perkin must have been a serious-minded youth, for in telling of his own boyhood he confessed: "as long as I can remember the kind of pursuit I should follow during my life was the subject that occupied my thoughts very much." Not unnaturally his father wanted him to become an architect, and to this end he did a little carpentry work and learned to copy plans. This led to painting; but when a young friend showed him some chemical experiments, all other careers were erased from his thoughts. Under the spell of Tommy Hall, he resolved to follow his teacher's footsteps to Hofmann at the College of Chemistry.

There were a couple of stormy scenes with his father and an amusing one with Hofmann. Hall pleaded eloquently with Perkin senior, so effectively, indeed, that he later became a staunch supporter of his son's chemical career. Hall then took him to Hofmann, introducing him as his " first English grandson," a promising student of one of Hofmann's own students.

So friendly a launching did the boy no harm. He had the ability to make good the joking boasts of his school-teacher. Within a year he had come to grips with original research problems, and Hofmann had appointed him one of his laboratory assistants under Billy Crookes, the senior instructor, who years later became Sir William Crookes, president of the august Royal Society.

Assisting the energetic Hofmann to instruct a laboratory full of young enthusiasts proved to be pretty nearly a full-time job, so in order to carry on his own studies young Perkin fitted up a rough sort of laboratory in the attic of his father's house. Here during the Easter vacation of 1856 he set himself an ambitious task in coal-tar synthesis.

At that time only a few chemists knew anything at all about coal tar. Certainly nobody suspected that it consisted of a mixture of more than two hundred different, definite substances, six of which would shortly become the source materials for the manufacture of many thousands of new chemical products. Inky black, evil smelling, oily, it is nasty to handle, and with the apparatus then available it was hard to work with — not at all a tempting material for neat, clean-cut laboratory experiments. Accordingly, only a few of its constituent compounds had been isolated, identified, and christened.

A dozen years before, Hofmann had dabbled in this tarry mess. He was the first to isolate benzol from it. Furthermore, by treating benzol, C_6H_6, with strong nitric acid he had replaced one of the hydrogen atoms with the nitro radical, NO_2, and obtained $C_6H_5NO_2$, or nitrobenzol. He went even further: he "reduced" nitrobenzol; that is, he removed the two oxygen atoms and replaced them with two hydrogens, obtaining $C_6H_5NH_2$, which is aniline.

Hofmann's chemical vision ranged far, but he did not foresee that he had found one of the most important of the so-called coal-tar crudes and prepared from it two exceedingly important coal-tar intermediates. The second of these was destined to be the Adam of the great coal-tar dye family. He was, nevertheless, strangely attracted to this aniline. He studied its reactions with many chemicals. His first published paper reported these researches, and years later he affectionately called aniline " his first love." After Hofmann came to England in 1845, he continued this work, and he inspired one of his earliest and most brilliant English students, Charles Mansfield, to undertake the first systematic investigation of the constituents of coal tar.

In his report on the work at the college Hofmann had pointed out that chemically and commercially it would be a notable feat to make the alkaloid quinine in the laboratory. Characteristically he threw off a hint which Perkin determined to follow up:

" It is a remarkable fact that naphthalene of which immense quantities are annually produced in the manufacture of coal gas, when subjected to a series of chemical processes, may be converted into a crystalline alkaloid. This substance, which has received the name of naphthalidine, contains 20 equivalents of carbon, 9 equivalents of hydrogen, and 1 equivalent of nitrogen.

" Now if we take 20 equivalents of carbon, 11 equivalents of hydrogen, 1 equivalent of nitrogen, and 2 equivalents of oxygen as the composition of quinine, it will be obvious that naphthalidine, differing only by the elements of two equivalents of water, might pass into the former alkaloid simply by the assumption of water. We cannot, of course, expect to induce the water to enter merely by placing it in contact, but a happy experiment might attain this end by the discovery of an appropriate metamorphic process."

It sounds reasonable enough, but in the first place Hofmann did not have the correct formula for quinine, and even if he had, this idea of simple addition, then very popular, is not the way complex organic molecules can be built up. In fact, to this day no chemist has ever successfully synthesized quinine.

Not at all daunted by his ignorance of chemical architecture, the eighteen-year-old Perkin set to work by the " additive and subtractive " method to make quinine. Since several others had found that Hofmann's naphthalene hint led only to a dead end, he began with toluidene. He reached the point where by adding two oxygens and subtracting one water he should have the pretty white crystals of quinine in his test tube. He poured in a solution of potassium bichromate, which seemed to be the likely chemical to accomplish this oxidation step, and got, not quinine, but a dirty reddish-brown powder which precipitated to the bottom of the liquid.

Of course he was disappointed; but he was more curious than downcast. He did exactly what characterizes the good research worker. He wanted to find out what and why. So he started all over again, beginning not with toluidene, but with a simpler compound, aniline. Thus he hoped to understand more clearly what was happening in the series of reactions. Carefully he repeated each step. At the final one — again no quinine, but this time a black precipitate.

What was this black powder? He started to dissolve it in boiling water. Presto! a beautiful purple color. He had discovered aniline purple, the first coal-tar dye.

Other chemists working with coal-tar derivatives had from time to time found their flasks and test tubes filled with colors. Like Perkin they were seeking nice white crystals of " pure " substances. To them these reds and browns and blues were only signals of impurity. They threw them into the sink and began over again. Not so young Perkin. He wanted to know about this purple product.

Its brilliancy suggested a possible dye, so he dipped into it some narrow strips of silk. They sopped up the color like a blotter. And the color stuck fast. It could not be washed out with soap and water. It was, then, a real dye, not merely a stain. He hung the cloths at the open window in the warm spring sun for a week. It did not fade. It was a sun-proof dye. He showed his dyed silks to an artist friend and at his suggestion sent a little bundle of them to Messrs. Pullar, proprietors of the great dyehouse in Perth.

A week went by. Then a brief note acknowledging the receipt of the samples. Three weeks passed. Perkin was on tenterhooks. What could have happened? Had his dye stood the tests? On June 12, 1856 came this reply:

" If your discovery does not make the goods too expensive, it is decidedly one of the most valuable that has come out in a very long time."

And these canny and taciturn Scotsmen went on to tell him how much this particular color was wanted and how it had never been obtained fast on silk, and only at great cost on cotton. They enclosed a sample of the *best* lilac — underscoring the adjective — then available from only one dyer in all the United Kingdom. " Even this does not stand tests that yours does."

Perkin was naturally elated. But that opening " if " stood up big and threatening. Being remarkably realistic for his years, he determined to do a little research on costs. We should call it pilot-plant development work today, and any chemical man knows what a long, difficult task it often is to translate the laboratory chemical of the test tube into the commercial commodity in the tank car. From the date of discovery to the date of shipment — at least so says chemical-plant gossip — averages six years.

During the summer vacation Perkin set up small-scale apparatus for the technical production of his dye. With the assistance of his brother he made several ounces, and they agreed that the process appeared to be sufficiently practical to patent. Application was filed on August 26, 1856, and as soon as British Patent No. 1984 was safe in his father's strongbox, off he went to Scotland to try out the color under the actual working conditions of Pullar's busy dyehouse.

Results were not wholly satisfactory. The dye showed good affinity for silk and wool, but it was impossible on large batches to get "level" dyeings. The color did not take on evenly and the goods came from the vats patchy and spotty. On cotton the lack of a suitable mordant, or fixing agent, made it only possible to get weak shades of lilacs and violets. Because the new dye did not act like the vegetable colors, the old Scotch calico printer who tried it out shook his head skeptically:

"Verra, verra interesting," he commented dourly, "an' nae doot 'tis a grrand shade. But — weel, I dinna ken hoo we micht employ it. 'Tis too dear."

Thus at the outset Perkin, like Muspratt before him, ran head-on into the difficulties that beset the introduction of any new chemical into any established industry. He must either down or dodge all the prejudices of an ancient and honorable handicraft guild. The smug inertia, so dangerously akin to laziness, and the perfectly natural unwillingness of an established, prosperous trade to take chances are even today serious restraints upon industrial progress. In early Victorian days these drags were much heavier.

Robert Pullar helped greatly. He and Perkin independently worked out a new, successful mordant for cotton goods, tannin, the bark extract used in tanning leather. He gave his young chemical friend an introduction to a fellow Scot, Thomas Keith, who had migrated to London and earned a name for himself as a dyer of silks and satins. Keith made several experimental dyeings with the new color and, after exposing them to the sunlight for several weeks, pronounced it excellent. In fact, he was more encouraging than Pullar, who was frankly skeptical whether works such as Perkin was now planning to erect could be profitably operated for the demands of the dyers unless the calico printers also could use the new dye.

Grandfather's worsteds and homespuns never appeared in such a color array and his black coat soon faded to bottle-green.
— Courtesy American Cyanamid Company

This was a sketchy and inconclusive survey of his prospective market. Today no dyestuff-maker would dare to go ahead with a brand-new type of dye, which aniline purple certainly was in 1857, upon such conflicting reports of probable consumer demand. However, Perkin had no inkling of the many barricades, both technical and commercial, that blocked the road to ultimate success. He was inspired positively with faith in his aniline dye.

He must have been, else he could never have performed the next miracle. He persuaded his father and elder brother, Thomas, both hardheaded businessmen, to join him in this risky venture. Though Perkin senior was not predisposed towards chemical affairs, still he backed his youngest son in this new kind of chemical manufacturing. The brother forsook the profitable contracting business to become actively associated with the embryo firm of Perkin and Sons.

With this support assured, Perkin determined that no halfway measures would do, that he must give up his position at the Royal College. He called upon Hofmann and took a tongue-lashing. What a blazing young fool he was, his professor fumed, to abandon scientific research, for which he did have a bit of talent, to go into the manufacture of a chemical color of more than dubious value. Hofmann's devotion to pure science was deep and sincere, and when any of his promising pupils launched forth upon industrial careers he was as upset as a hen whose brood of ducklings have taken to the millpond. He did not succeed in dissuading young Perkin, but he did disturb him by raising doubts in his mind. These were quickly dispelled, however, by the absorbing work of building the new plant.

Perkin has confessed that at that time neither he nor any of his associates had ever set foot in any kind of chemical works. This was not so great a handicap as it now appears to us, since all they had to do was quite new. There was little to suggest either plans or procedure, nothing that could be copied. They were pioneering from start to finish. Each step had to be taken tentatively. New types of apparatus had to be devised and tested before more or larger-scale equipment could be ordered and installed.

Operating problems were not the only ones clamoring for answers. Raw materials were required and literally not a single one of these was readily available in steady supply at a low price.

When Perkin set out to make the first coal-tar dyes the coal-tar crudes were utilized in the manufacture of only one unimportant chemical product, nitrobenzene. This is artificial oil of almonds, sold as " essence of mirbane " to scent cheap soaps. Much coal was coked for metallurgical uses; but it was all made in pits similar to those used in the ancient method of burning charcoal or in little beehive ovens from which none of the by-products were recovered. The whole supply of crude coal tar came therefore from the gas works. Most of it was burned right at the gas plants as fuel, though some was shipped off for roofing tar and as a binder in the new Macadam method of road-building.

From the days of Gutenberg, who borrowed his formula from the Flemish artists and ground soot with linseed oil, the printing-ink makers had made no fundamental change in their process until their recent discovery that coal tar burned with a sooty flame which provided an excellent carbon black for their purposes. A little tar was so used. A very rough distillation of small amounts of coal tar yielded benzol mixed with varying quantities of toluol and xylol. This was used as a solvent for rubber, the basis of the first Macintosh waterproof cloth. Small quantities were also sold under the trade name of " benzine collas " as a cleansing fluid. Its evil, persistent odor and its dangerous aptitude for bursting into flames upon the slightest provocation did not make it too popular in the household. Therefore it was not easy to procure a regular supply of benzol in any quantity, and special arrangements had to be negotiated with Miller and Company of Glasgow.

The little dyestuff plant that was building during the summer of 1857 at Greenford Green, near Harrow, was thus to create the first industrial demand for the by-products from coal tar. Till then there was no substantial market for the coal-tar crudes, and the proprietors of the English coke and gas works naturally made no effort to recover them.

A similar situation existed right here in the United States prior to World War I. Without a synthetic coal-tar chemical industry, the now chemically valuable constituents were then about as salable as sand in the Sahara.

To brand those industrialists of the earlier years as wicked wasters of precious materials shows only a dull appreciation of the facts they faced. Every generation must live under conditions as they find them. In New England we wish wistfully that our Puritan forefathers had spared some of the great forests of murmuring pines and hemlocks that covered the land to the seashore. Had they tried to do so, they would have perished. Cut down the forests — that was their first imperative need. Land cleared for growing corn and wheat and beans, and logs to build a cabin, meant to them the vital necessities of food and shelter. The forests were fuel, furniture, and tools. A wide clearing around the settlement meant that cover in which the wolf and the Indian might ambush had been pushed away from the doorstep.

So too, our industrial grandsires burned coal tar or slithered it over their roofs and roads, or soaked railroad ties and telegraph poles in it. They were not always ignorant of the valuable hydrocarbons packed away in its black, odoriferous mass, but were wise in making no quixotic efforts to salvage what was then plainly a waste.

So we, also, will no doubt be bitterly criticized by our own grandchildren for wasting natural gas or cornstalks or what not. We know the chemical values of both gas and cornstalk. However, we know no profitable use to make of them since we have ready to hand other cheaper, more available materials. A wise chemical engineer pointed out years ago that it is silly to save wastes for our grandchildren. Most likely they will never want them.

The dye industry literally created a market for the former wastes of coal tar. Within a few years after Perkin began his factory the British gas works were buying up second-hand steam boilers and converting them into stills into which they poured the previously wasted tar. On applying heat, first the highly volatile products are driven off, the crude naphtha, or "light oils," so called because they float on water. After the light oils come the heavy or dead oils. The residue left in the still is thick, viscid pitch.

Both the light and the heavy oils are redistilled in order to separate their major constituents. Today this is neatly accomplished in tall fractionating columns which, utilizing the fact that each of these different constituents has its own distinct boiling-point, separates them with extreme precision. In Perkin's day the light oil was redistilled with steam and treated with sulphuric acid to yield benzol with traces of four or five other, less volatile bodies. In the modern by-product coke oven, the temperatures employed are higher than in the gas works because the object is to produce, not the gases, but a hard coke for the steel furnaces. The principle is the same.

A ton of coal yields roughly 1,500 pounds of coke, 2½ gallons of tar, and 10,000 cubic feet of coal gas, half of which gas is needed for heating the ovens, leaving 5,000 feet to be sold for fuel or illuminating purposes. The combined coke and by-products are worth four times as much as the original coal.

If we were as sensible as we know how to be, we should coke every ton of coal at the mine head, even turning most of the coke into gas. Then we would heat our homes and run our factories on gas piped straight from the coal fields. But neither the temptation of more-for-our-money nor the nuisance of the smoke pall over our cities can prod us into scrapping our old-fashioned and wasteful heating systems.

The chemists have found over two hundred distinct chemical substances in coal tar, analyzed them, and named them. Most of these constituents, however, are found in such minute quantities that the game of recovery is not worth the candle. Moreover, many of them can be obtained more economically from other sources or even synthesized. Only five, two liquids and three solids, are taken out and put to chemical work on a large scale.

A ton of coal yields about 3½ pounds of the liquids benzol and toluol, and of the solids, 1¼ pounds of phenol (carbolic acid), 6 pounds of naphthalene (moth balls), and 10 ounces of anthracene (which we do not meet in everyday life). Out of these five coal-tar crudes over 200,000 different products have been prepared in the laboratory. Some 3,000 of them, ranging from Perkin's aniline purple to the wonder drug sulfanilamide, are manufactured commercially and used as colors, as medicines, as scents and flavors, photographic developers, and war munitions.

The crude benzol that Messrs. Miller shipped from Glasgow to the Greenford Green plant of Perkin and Sons was crude indeed. Redistillation was necessary to rid it of other, unwanted ingredients that come along with it. Initially Perkin had to do this job himself, but later the gas works supplied a better benzol. Then his first chemical step was to turn benzol into nitrobenzol, a tricky reaction and much more dangerous than juggling dynamite sticks.

Whoever remembers using " benzine " as a cleansing fluid is not apt to have forgotten this white, greasy-feeling liquid which evaporates so quickly that like alcohol it seems cold to the touch, nor the indescribable but distinctive odor that it leaves behind. Anywhere within a dozen feet of a lighted

cigarette it becomes a dangerous fire hazard, exploding violently and burning with a bright, intense flame. Pouring
strong nitric acid into this volatile and unstable liquid is
a demand bid for trouble. This powerfully corrosive acid
causes flames to burst spontaneously from rags, straw, paper,
and plenty of other organic materials which do not have
half benzol's pyrotechnic proclivities.

When these two come together, the benzol undergoes a
quick and mighty change. First, as they blend, the mixture
warms up rapidly and becomes dark brown in color. In a
few moments thick clouds of choking brown vapors curl up
from the mixture, which now boils and bubbles like the
witches' cauldron. During this violent reaction the color of
the liquid pales to a bright, clear orange. The light, colorless benzol which floats on water has been replaced by a
dense colored oil that sinks. The benzol smell has vanished,
replaced by the pleasant odor of bitter almonds. Benzol has
been nitrated to nitrobenzol, or, as the chemist's shorthand
puts it:

$$C_6H_6 + HNO_3 = C_6H_5NO_2 + H_2O$$
Benzol + Nitric acid = Nitrobenzol + Water

It is all very well to carry on this boisterous reaction in a
test tube, but to nitrate benzol on a large scale and at reasonable cost was quite a different matter. At that time fum-
ing nitric acid was not on the market. Accordingly Perkin
had recourse to the chemical trick of manufacturing it during
the process. This worked, but it raised the risks of explosions.

Again he began experimenting. Into various types of open
kettles and closed tanks he gingerly poured benzol with
different mixtures of nitric and sulphuric acids or of nitrate
of soda and sulphuric acid. The former is now the favored
method of nitrating, but doubtless because he found it easier
to control, Perkin preferred the nitrate-acid reaction. He

never told how many times he blew up his makeshift nitrators, but there were several bad explosions, fortunately
without any serious accidents.

Again he sought the cause. These explosions came, he decided, when too much nitric acid had been released from
the nitrate by the sulphuric acid before the formation of
nitrobenzol had fairly begun. If this happened, when this
reaction did start, the chemical action was too vehement. By
putting the solid sodium nitrate into a big cast-iron cylinder
and then sealing the door before pouring the benzol through
a neck, the brown-red fumes gave fair notice that the operation was well under way. After that there were no more explosions. The first step had been taken.

The second was easier. For twenty-five years chemists had
known that nitrobenzol might be converted into aniline. His
own teacher had quite recently repeated this reaction. This
method required costly chemicals and Perkin had clearly in
mind the thrifty comments of the Scotch dyers. Luckily an
alternative process was ready to hand. A few years previously
a French chemist had learned that the two oxygen atoms in
nitrobenzol could be replaced with two hydrogens and so
become aniline, if it were heated with iron filings and acetic
acid. Save that this reaction on a plant-sized scale needed
caution in adding the acid, lest it burst bounds, the production of aniline was not too difficult.

Perkin had come triumphantly to his final chemical step.
The oily, sherry-colored aniline and enough sulphuric acid
to convert it into aniline sulphate were poured into a great
vat with sufficient water to dissolve the white crystals of the
aniline salt as soon as they were formed. Everyone breathed
easier at this stage, for here there were no risks of blowing
everything to smithereens. Into a second vat of water were
dumped the big, beautiful, ruby crystals of sodium bichromate, and then, after cooling, the two solutions were mixed
in a still larger vessel. Here they stood for forty-eight hours —

a tame climax indeed after a beginning of such dangerous thrills.

Out of the big vat they scooped a black paste which dried to a sooty powder. But digested with alcohol (to dissolve out certain impurities) this unpromising powder became bronzy in color with a pretty iridescent sheen — the dye aniline purple or mauve. Perkin sent it out to the dyers in three forms — a damp paste, in a solution in alcohol, and as crystals — and to this day coal-tar dyes are commonly on the market as both pastes and powders.

The four chemical steps from benzol to nitrobenzol to aniline to mauve that the youthful discoverer made so falteringly and at such risks are taken in a stride by his successors. Naturally enough he had found one of the simplest colors first. Some modern vat dyes are reached only after two dozen different chemical reactions. But they are made on the selfsame principle. Start with one of the coal-tar crudes, go on to so-called intermediates such as nitrobenzol and aniline, and thence by a series of chemical reactions to the finished product, be it a color or a medicinal or an aromatic chemical. It is a building-up process, far different from the popular notion that by some sort of magic all these different substances are picked out of the mysterious black tar. In this building-up process, however, there are rapidly diminishing returns on the materials used: a quarter of an ounce of dyestuff from a hundred pounds of coal. Perkin's own figures are:

	lbs.	ozs.
Coal	100	
Coal tar	10	12.0
Crude light oils		8.5
Benzol		2.75
Nitrobenzol		4.5
Aniline		2.5
Mauve		0.25

Inducing British dyers and calico printers to use this unfamiliar coloring material was another pioneering task. Perkin had to go out into the dyehouses and printshops, roll up his sleeves, and show them how to use effectively a synthetic coal-tar dye. Often he did not know himself. Though he had had no training or experience as a practical colorist, he learned. He even contributed to dyeing practice new mordants to fix these new dyes and new leveling agents to prevent splotchy dyeing of large batches. Some of these discoveries of his are used to this day.

His was a triple-threat genius. As chemist he synthesized a new, valuable chemical product and was clever enough to recognize its commercial possibilities. Not every good chemist is able to do that. As engineer he designed original apparatus for the first organic synthesis ever attempted on plant scale, including nitrators necessary to carry on the exceedingly hazardous nitration of benzol. As businessman he was the pioneer service salesman, the predecessor of those who today, backed by their companies' great application laboratories, go out to the textile man, the rayon spinner, the molder of plastics, the maker of paper, lacquer, linoleum, and what not, helping them bring more color into the American home.

Ironically Perkin was greatly helped in introducing his new dyestuff by his most unscrupulous rivals. His discovery of man-made dyes was like a gold strike. Hundreds of keen chemical prospectors rushed to find pay dirt in coal tar. From so rich a chemical mine they could not fail. Within five years half a dozen other colors had been synthesized. In hope of circumventing his patent, alternate methods of preparing Perkin's aniline purple were explored. Fortunately for him, he had hit upon the easiest, cheapest process, and with the advantage of " know how " he remained supreme. He was also fortunate in having found a much wanted color, exceedingly difficult, costly, and not too satisfactory when produced by the natural vegetable dyes, and one which was not quickly replaced by any better synthetic dye. He made a modest fortune out of mauve.

It was a grim joke, therefore, that his French patent, owing to a careless oversight in drawing up the specifications, had techincal flaws that made it invalid. Patent pirates took advantage of this situation. Soon aniline purple from several sources was offered in France. Unlike their British compeers, who did not fancy the changes in their processes required by the chemical color, the French calico printers welcomed the new dye. In fact they featured it, naming it "mauve" after the color of the deep-lavender mallow blossom. With the artistic skill for which they were famous the French printers worked this new color into their patterns. They created novel and striking effects. They forced their English competitors to use the new dye.

Mauve had a great popular vogue, and we still remember "the Mauve Decade." Queen Victoria, then in half-mourning for Prince Albert, wore a dress dyed with this lovely lavender shade at the 1862 Exposition in the Crystal Palace. The Government used it on the first "penny post" stamp. *Punch* published jingles about the dye, and it became a threadbare joke that even the London bobbies were telling people to "get a mauve on"!

Gradually, however, this popularity waned. Other coal-tar dyes came into use. Often these, while brighter in hue, were more fugitive. The willingness of both dyers and the public to sacrifice fastness for brilliancy distressed the scrupulous Perkin. It seemed to him a compromise with quality, abandoning what he conceived to be the greatest advantage of the synthetic colors.

As for fastness, Perkin lived long enough to see this quality he so cherished in coal-tar dyes perfected to a degree that has rendered his mauve quite as obsolete as its famous predecessor, Tyrian purple, the royal purple of the Roman emperors.

A century ago there were but three reasonably fast dyes — a black, a blue, and a red. Even logwood black did turn bottle-green on grandfather's overcoat. Indigo and madder mellowed in a manner suspiciously fugitive. Today we have colors so fast they can only be destroyed by destroying the goods dyed with them. And fast not only to tubbing and sunlight, but to perspiration, sea water, cleansing fluids, even to gin cocktails.

From Perkin's mauve to our rainbowful of colors we have come a long way. Quite a start was made during the first ten years, and while he contributed no other great new dye-stuff, Perkin continued his researches. He was able to simplify and cheapen the processes for manufacturing several early dyes. Most important of these was magenta or fuchsine, an aniline red discovered three years after mauve by Marcel Verguin, working in laboratories of Renard Frères at Lyon, the great French center for silks, satins, and brocades.

Eleven years after the discovery of mauve, a stolid scientific paper written by an ill-assorted pair of young German chemists again extended the frontiers of the color kingdom. Thirty-five years before, two French scientific collaborators, Robiquet and Colin, had separated from madder roots a substance they named alizarin and demonstrated that it was the active coloring principle of this dye plant. In 1868 Graebe and Liebermann prepared from natural alizarin the coal-tar crude, anthracene.

What goes up must come down. Anthracene from alizarin: why not alizarin from anthracene? The German research team had answered this question with an emphatic " It can be done."

They told in unadorned terms just how they had accomplished this synthesis. But it was plain as daylight that the chemical reactions they had employed were about as commercially practical as the large-scale production of marbles out of emeralds and rubies for the schoolboy trade. That question still remained a challenge to every chemical prospector of coal tar. Its correct answer became the rich prize in a great research race.

To no other chemist was this question of synthetic madder more provocative than to William Henry Perkin. It reawakened his college ambition to produce natural compounds synthetically — not quinine from the cinchona bark, but the red dye of the madder root. No living man was better equipped to take advantage of this discovery. Under Hofmann he had begun his chemical career with a research on anthracene. He had built a coal-tar dye plant and operated it for a decade. During this time he sold dyes to those thrifty Scotch colorists, and he really knew what imports of 120,-000,000 pounds of madder root at two shillings a pound meant in terms of both costs and markets. He locked himself in his laboratory and went to work.

The race was on. Could Perkin with his advantages overcome the handicap of immediate experience held by Graebe and Liebermann? The Germans called in a redoubtable ally, none other than Dr. Heinrich Caro, chemical director of the Badische Aniline Works. Perkin continued on his own, unassisted. It was a hair-line finish.

June 25, 1869, British patent No. 1936.

June 26, 1869, British patent No. 1948.

The first was issued to Caro, Graebe, and Liebermann. But Perkin, though a day late, was not beaten. The patents covered radically different processes, and in the end the synthesis of alizarin discovered by Perkin proved the better commercially. But there were profits and glory to spare for all four.

In a test tube, man had duplicated from coal tar one of nature's great colors. The opening skirmish of the battle between land and laboratory had been fought and won.

CHAPTER IV

THE RISE AND FALL OF THE GERMAN DYE TRUST

◇◇

TWENTY million dollars is still a tidy sum. Alongside a relief budget or a defense program it seems a trifle. None the less it would pay the wages for a full twelvemonth of all the workers in either our cigarette or our typewriter factories, or the Navy could for that money build three or four very up-to-date destroyers.

Twenty million dollars is more than all the good house-wives of America spend in a year for oilcloth or wallpaper or pianos. It would replace all the fountain pens we break or all the umbrellas we lose in a year. All the nails and spikes made annually in the United States are valued at less than half this sum. After all, a number of quite substantial in-dustries have been established to supply a market of twenty million dollars.

That was the prize, a market of twenty million dollars, in the race to synthesize the red coloring principle from the roots of the madder plant. It was a world-wide market with a demand as steady as that for wheat or millstones or pig iron. Madder was the standard red dye.

It was, moreover, a long-established market. The clever dyers of Thebes used madder to dye the mummy clothes of Tutankhamen. Theirs was an ancient craft, and the same dye, used for the same purpose, has been found in Egyptian tombs dating some seven centuries earlier. Who first dyed with madder is not now to be known; but he, or more probably she, no doubt lived somewhere in the Mediterranean basin in a remote day, long before mankind thought that any of the workaday tasks were worth recording. Throughout this region the madder plant (*Rubia tinctorium*) grows wild on the sunny hillsides. From the Pillars of Hercules to the Golden Horn, wherever the archæologists have come upon some faded-pink fragment of old, old cloth, it is most likely to have been dyed with madder.

Later the Phœnicians, who had an aptitude for using colors of animal origin, introduced kermes, the red juice squeezed from bushel upon bushel of tiny insects, so the cult of madder moved on eastward to India. From there it spread throughout the Orient, to be brought back to Italy by the Venetian traders. In Venice and Florence, during the Middle Ages, dyeing became one of the great arts, and the shrewd colorists so cherished their monopoly that " deepdyed secret " became a byword.

Secrets, however, cannot be kept forever. The conspiracy of the merchants, who brought the dye from the East, and the dyers, who produced the finest reds and pinks with it, was broken up by the Crusaders. They discovered the source of madder, and Charlemagne introduced the plant as a new and profitable crop for his French peasants to cultivate.

In France, Holland, Spain, and Turkey the madder plant became an important commercial crop. In these countries, at the time synthetic alizarin appeared, some 350,000 acres were planted to it. The yield was varying, as with any crop, but it ran from 150,000,000 to 180,000,000 pounds a year.

Within a decade this old, established, steady market had been quite lost to the madder-growers. The first pound of synthetic alizarin paste was shipped by Perkin and Sons on October 4, 1869. Five years afterwards three factories — one each in England, in Germany, and in France — sold over two million pounds. In another five years this output had risen to over twenty million pounds. So concentrated was the tinctorial strength of the synthetic color that in the dye vats a pound of it did the work of ten pounds of vegetable madder. The actual consumption of the red color had, therefore, increased a fifth.

As day follows night, so with the commercial introduction of a synthetic chemical product come lower prices. Before synthetic alizarin appeared as a competitor, ground Dutch madder, the finest grade of dye available, sold for $2.25 per pound. Ten years later the price was 70 cents. In the same period the price of prime Turkey roots, a standard grade of the raw material, tumbled from 75 cents a pound to 27½ cents a pound. At this price it did not pay to grow, dig, and cure the roots.

Meanwhile the introductory price of $2 a pound for synthetic alizarin had been whittled down to 35 cents. Color for color this represents a price of 3½ cents for roots. That price was just about 20 cents a pound below the planters' costs.

Such business arithmetic is devastatingly conclusive. The growers simply gave up, and madder has become one of agriculture's interesting historical relics. Today it is tenderly preserved in some of the larger botanical gardens.

Madder, the great red dyestuff of antiquity, had vanished from the plantation, the marketplace, and the dyehouse. Indigo, the great blue, still held its old position. No synthetic dye had appeared that even remotely threatened its grip on the dye trade, for none yet discovered was clearer in hue or more fast to soap and sunlight.

As with madder, so the early story of indigo is far too old to have been preserved for us. It appears likely, however, that the two followed somewhat opposite courses, indigo having come from the East to the Mediterranean countries, thence back to the Orient. For the past five centuries at least, world headquarters had been India. From Bengal the renowned blue was shipped to the big industrial dyehouses of Holland and Great Britain, to the handicraft dyers of Chinese silks and cottons, to the color merchants of Aleppo, Mosul, Bagdad, and Samarkand who peddled it out to the families of rug-weavers.

Like madder too, the active coloring principle of indigo had been identified. Long before the exact chemical composition and structure of indigotin had been determined, half a dozen chemists, chiefly famous French analysts, had recorded reactions that indicated rather clearly its chemical kinship with the coal-tar hydrocarbons. If alizarin could be synthesized, the suggestion that indigotin might be was as obvious as a blueberry in a bowl of milk.

The prize was even richer. The madder market had been twenty million dollars. The sale of indigo — China was, and still is, the largest consumer — reached a total of twice that sum.

Within a year after the commercial production of synthetic madder, two different methods of preparing indigotin had been found. It seemed that another swift chemical triumph was to be scored. But appearances are proverbially deceptive. Twenty years were to pass and one company alone was to spend five million dollars in this search before synthetic indigo was to threaten the long reign of the greatest of all natural dyestuffs.

As a matter of fact, the search goes back still another twenty years to when a thirteen-year-old schoolboy chemist got hold of a sample of natural indigo and gleefully performed the rather simple chemical feat of separating from it the active coloring ingredient, indigotin. Bursting with pride he brought the results of this little triumph to his teacher. In the Germany of 1848 schoolmasters drove their pupils with a tight rein and a cracking whiplash. Inhibited by no tender consideration of the self-expression so dear to

the adolescent boy, his teacher peered at the precious powder in the bottom of the evaporating dish and asked: " So
what? "

Then, to be quite sure that this precocious pupil was not
going to be spoiled, he added: " That, Adolf, is simple. It
has been done many times before. But that blue powder
there — what is it? It is easy to separate, but nobody has
analyzed it. Find out what it is. Then, my boy, you will have
something to show me; yes, something to tell the whole world.
But until you have done something " — he waved a depre-
cating paw and dismissed the matter.

By all the rules of child psychology and all the tenets of
Nazi propaganda, little Johann Friedrich Wilhelm Adolf von
Baeyer should have shriveled under such treatment into a
self-conscious introvert. He was thirteen years old, a critical
age. His father was a stout Teuton of some position, comfortable means, and impeccable pedigree. But his mother
was a Jewess. What courage, what tenacity, what vision was
to be expected of such a miserable little half-breed? Yet that
slip of a boy was inspired, not cowed, by these sarcastic
taunts.

He continued his chemical studies. Ten years later the
University of Berlin handed him a parchment scroll and he
became Doctor Adolf Baeyer. Always his interest centered
on organic chemistry, and throughout a long, active life he
was a college professor. Nevertheless, he was never the
theorist, but always the practical, workaday searcher. He
came back again and again to the problem of indigotin.

After twenty-two years he succeeded in the first synthesis
of that complex blue powder. Because of its high costs, the
process he found was obviously of no possible commercial
use. For ten years more he juggled apparatus and tried and
retried reactions, seeking to build up $C_{16}H_{10}O_2N_2$ from coal-
tar intermediates of reasonable cost by reactions feasible for
plant-scale operations.

In 1880 he discovered another synthesis from ortho-nitro-phenyl-propiolic acid, which, despite its formidable name, opened the way to definite industrial possibilities. It was not until July 1897 — seventeen years later and twenty-seven years after Baeyer's first synthesis of indigotin — that the directors of Badische Aniline and Soda Works, with whom he had been working since 1880 and to whom all his patents had been assigned, had before them a complete set of cost figures for the synthetic dye which they were certain totaled less than the lowest price at which vegetable indigo had ever been sold.

The long search was ended. The objective had been reached: synthetic indigo so cheap that it would surely replace natural indigo in the world's markets. The ensuing commercial battle was sharp and short. *Indigofera tinctoria* has joined the madder plant, an interesting historical specimen in the botanical gardens.

Through the scientific spectacles of the chemist, the synthesis of indigo was a stunning achievement. The patient perseverance, the chemical imagination, the clever technical dexterity that were called forth to reach this goal are among the greatest glories of organic chemistry. As the fine points of a polo game or of a polariscope can only be thoroughly relished by an expert, so the niceties of that complex chemical problem are only for the chemist's full appreciation. Nevertheless, along with this technical exploit, and intimately bound up with it, was a plain, cold, dollars-and-cents feat we can all recognize and value.

The core of the cost problem was raw materials. A few laboratory reagents that were expensive chemical curiosities could never replace 26,950,000 pounds of natural dye worth less than $1.50 a pound. For indigo came to the dyers after an elaborate preparation and quite highly concentrated as natural dyestuffs went. The Badische statisticians hardly needed a slide-rule to figure out that at least eleven million pounds of indigotin paste of hundred-per-cent strength would be needed. Remembering the diminishing returns of raw materials in dye-making — ¼ ounce of Perkin's mauve from 8¼ ounces of coal-tar crudes — no indigo process was going to be feasible unless it started from one of the cheap and abundant coal-tar intermediates.

Early in the eighties a process perfectly capable of large-scale operations was worked out. It started from toluol. The synthetic organic chemistry was a hundred per cent; the simple business arithmetic, zero.

Toluol, like benzol, is recovered from the light oils of the coal-tar distillate in the proportion of four parts of benzol to one of toluol. There were then available about 6,000 tons of toluol. All of this was already eagerly absorbed by the chemical industries in making other toluol derivatives. In fact, at that time the demand for toluol was growing more rapidly than the use of benzol, so that the toluol price was advancing.

That recently perfected indigo process — this was in 1882 — needed four pounds of toluol to make a single pound of the finished dye. If the natural dye was to be replaced, it would therefore require 44,000,000 pounds of toluol, which was just about 32,000,000 more pounds than the total supply. To make a bad case worse, 32,000,000 additional pounds of toluol meant that willy-nilly there would be a production of 128,000,000 additional pounds of its associated material, benzol, for which some market would have to be found.

In 1812 even talking about thirty-odd million pounds of toluol was akin to discussing a bushel of diamonds. It is vivid evidence of how our chemicals have grown to recall that, starting with an output of 10,000,000 pounds of toluol in 1914, we right here in the United States shoved up our production to a World War I peak of over 98,000,000 pounds. For when toluol is put through that same tricky, dangerous nitrating process that caused Perkin so much worry and trouble, it becomes trinitrotoluol, better known by its initials TNT. That was, as we shall see, a mighty chemical expansion, but it seems puny beside the figures that the Defense Commission wrote down for the 1941 " Munitions Wanted Budget ": toluol, 455,000,000 pounds.

In the eighties a twelfth of that quantity stopped dead the commercial development of synthetic indigo. Not till 1890 was another process found that even promised to break the log-jam of raw-material supply. This method of preparation started with aniline. It would also require quantities of acetic acid, chlorine, and ammonia. All of these chemicals were sufficiently cheap to meet the initial demands of supply and price.

Badische immediately secured the patents on this new synthesis and added its discoverer, Karl Heumann to their research staff. Enheartened by having at last a tangibly practical starting-point, the hunt went on with renewed vigor. It began early to develop along two lines, and a year was spent determining which would be the more efficient and economical. Now research had to reach out beyond the immediate scope of coal-tar crudes and intermediates into new work on two old familiar chemicals, chlorine and sulphuric acid. If new processes in staid and steady inorganic chemistry had not come to the rescue, even this promising new line of indigo synthesis would have again reached a dead end.

In fact, it very shortly developed that Heumann's original process, while meeting raw-material requirements, failed dismally when tried out in a pilot plant. It lacked the equally vital factors of easy operation and good yield of the final product. Seventeen possible modifications of the reactions were patiently tried out and a deal of ingenuity brought to bear upon the problem, but every new attempt ended in a fizzle. The bright hopes raised by Heumann's discovery grew dimmer and dimmer.

He had, however, discovered an alternate process before his untimely death in 1894, and though at the time this was discarded, it proved in the end the most promising of all. It had been set aside because it began with anthranilic acid, which was derived from toluol. Accordingly, whatever its other advantages, this process was commercially right back behind the old raw-material blockade.

Just as the whole long indigo research seemed to have bogged down again, two Dutch chemists announced a new process that, starting with phthalic anhydride, produced anthranilic acid. Badische grabbed up this patent in a hurry. For the initial material in the production of phthalic anhydride was naphthalene, and this coal-tar crude was so abundant that it was a drug on the market.

At that time some 30,000,000 pounds of crude naphthalene were being recovered from coal tar and at least 150,000,000 pounds were still being " wasted." For lack of any demand, naphthalene was simply left in the heavy oils. Here it was burned for carbon black or remained as one of the ingredients in the road and roofing tars. For the purposes of synthetic-indigo manufacture, even to supply the world's requirements, 100,000,000 pounds of naphthalene converted into anthranilic acid were more than a generous supply.

At last, victory! A synthetic process easy to operate, producing rich yields of indigotin out of cheap, available coal-tar intermediates. But no! commercial production, at a price that would be competitive with the vegetable dye, was still to be achieved.

In the first place, though Badische had been making phthalic anhydride for twenty years and thought that they had the world's most efficient processes, the cost analysis of the proposed indigo process indicated plainly that this material was still going to be too expensive. Off on a new research to lower these costs, and in due course one of their bright young chemists, Sapper by name, proudly reported to Director Heinrich Caro that he had succeeded in ferreting out an entirely new method of making phthalic anhydride. He heated naphthalene with highly concentrated sulphuric acid. Simple enough, and the company was in a position to take commercial advantage of this discovery, since they had but recently perfected a new sulphuric-acid process that gave them highly concentrated acid.

But — this indigo synthesis was becoming a grim and grisly joke. Twenty-five years of time and now close to twenty million marks in money were a heavy investment even if it brought the company the greatest of all dyes. The directors frowned and scratched their heads over these appalling figures. Out in laboratories the dogged Dr. Caro, having tasted blood in the hunt for artificial madder, stuck like a leech to the problem.

Naphthalene plus strong sulphuric acid worked like a watch in the laboratory. In the pilot plant, however, the yield was pathetically small for the amounts of reagents poured into the big metal autoclaves. Moreover, to keep the costs as low as possible the acid must be recovered. Both problems were subjected to a long series of experiments.

The climax was a joke that brought a grin to the sourest visage of the grimmest director. The acid-recovery problem was promptly cleared up in a pre-eminently satisfactory manner. To increase the yield proved stubborn work, and while carrying on the reaction in various apparatus and juggling the temperature, the pressure, and the time, another set of chemists were putting into mixtures of naphthalene and sulphuric acid various and sundry chemicals. They hoped to find some catalyst that would increase the yield of the phthalic anhydride.

Just how a catalyst works is one of the twenty-five questions that " Boss " Kettering, the research leader of General Motors, would like to have answered. We have learned much

In delicate artificial flowers, tough linoleum, candy, candles, toys, toothpicks, and what not, we demand more color; brighter, faster dyes. — Courtesy Calco Chemical Division, American Cyanamid Company

about how they work, but we know no more about the whys
and wherefores than did the Badische research staff in 1895.
A catalyst is a chemical that assists a chemical reaction without entering into it, for all the world like the parson at the
wedding. Sometimes catalytic action speeds up a chemical
reaction; often it makes reactions possible between normally
inert materials which would not react at all save for its
friendly acceleration.

Among the chemists seeking some catalytic agent to stimulate a more complete conversion of naphthalene to phthalic
anhydride was a careless chap who went off to lunch one
day leaving a thermometer in his apparatus. Somehow that
thermometer was broken. How this accident happened nobody knew. Soon nobody cared, though such carelessness is
not easily explained away in a well-managed chemical laboratory. The mercury from the thermometer bulb turned out
to be the long-sought catalyst. Within a year Badische offered
synthetic indigo at a price comfortably below the current
quotation for the natural dye.

Again the victory of the synthetic over the natural dye was
swiftly won. Within seven years nearly a million and a half
acres, chiefly in India, had passed from indigo to millet and
rice — a rather notable contribution to alleviate the horrors
of the recurring Indian famines. The market for 7,000,000
pounds of indigotin in the vegetable dye, worth $42,000,000,
has since grown to a demand for about 18,000,000 pounds
of synthetic indigotin. This costs the dyers, not $100,000,000,
as it would have at the old prices of the vegetable dye; but
$25,000,000 — more color for less dollars. That " more for
less " is an apt slogan for all sorts of chemical products.

Until the coal-tar dyes were available the dyers were never
able to produce bright, clear colors in many shades. Blue
from indigo and red from madder were shining exceptions to
the dirty yellows, coppery oranges, muddy greens, and dull

purples. No wonder the colorists rejoiced in their new-found opportunities and made the most of them. The stunning new shades captivated the ladies.

Sighing over "the good old days" is a persistent habit of ours, and every once in a while there is an epidemic of longing for "the good old dyes." The vegetable colors were so soft and warm and fast; the chemical dyes are harsh, glaring, and fugitive — so runs the lament. It forgets the realities. The dictionary distinguishes between "soft" and "dull" or "glaring" and "brilliant" in a way that the sentimental eye quite ignores.

About the time that synthetic indigo came upon the market an erudite German dye chemist thought up a splendid practical joke to play upon all the colorists in the world. By a clever bit of chemical substitution he would perpetrate a great color hoax. Practical jokes have become famous for taking unexpected turns. Yet who would have dreamed that all the worthy Dr. Friedlander of Biebrich on the Rhine would accomplish was to prove that the salesgirls in our dime stores are better judges of purple and fine linens than that distinguished voluptuary, the Emperor Nero of Rome?

Shortly before, Dr. Friedlander had discovered a beautiful new scarlet dye which his company was offering under the trade name of Thioindigo Red B. A chemist would at once expect from the prefix "thio" that this was a sulphonated indigotin, which in fact it was. Dr. Friedlander was making a special study of various substituted indigotins — that is, indigotin molecules into which some other chemical element, as sulphur, has been introduced. It had long been suspected that the glamorous Tyrian purple of antiquity had been some sort of an indigotin. His studies convinced him of this. To prove it he decided to reproduce the natural dye, analyze it, and then, if possible, synthesize it.

This Tyrian purple is the most romantic of all dyestuffs, the royal dye of Imperial Rome. The Emperor Diocletian, who went in for totalitarian control of markets in a really big way, set the price of a pound of wool dyed with Tyrian purple at $350. From the 57 cents for a pound of undyed wool that was quite a record " mark-up."

For nearly two centuries this dye was the object of probably the most perfect and longest-lived monopoly in all economic history. It was a monopoly backed by all the power of the Roman Empire. It began with the collection of the shellfish from which the color was prepared, and controlled each step in its manufacture, its sale, its application by licensed dyers; and finally decreed who might wear it, and when, and where, and in what garments. There was a monopoly that really did monopolize. It worked, as Mr. Thurman Arnold might well note, because it had the sanction of social custom, backed alike by trade and caste interests, and enforced by the strong arm of the Roman law. Few modern monopolies are so well buttressed.

Classical literature is full of references to this famous dye. Pliny and others set forth in detail how it was prepared and used. Accordingly Dr. Friedlander, having at great pains and considerable expense collected twelve thousand specimens of *Murex brandaris*, the shellfish from whose glands can be extracted a couple of drops of the raw material for making the dye, followed these directions and manufactured a few ounces of the genuine article. He analyzed it. It proved to be a brom-indigo. After his little journey to classical antiquity, here he was right at home again. Brom-indigo meant the introduction of a bromine atom into the indigotin molecule, and this was his specialty. It was at this point that his joke occurred to him.

He would synthesize the fabulous purple of Tyre as indigo and madder had been duplicated. Under some such nice scientific-sounding, thoroughly up-to-date name as Brom-indigo Purple R, his firm would offer it to the trade. No doubt, too, this would be a fine stroke of business. Tyrian purple,

more precious than pearls and rubies, must have been a
splendid color. He had something. He began reckoning up
his royalties.

For one so adept in the methods of chemical substitution
and so familiar with the indigotin molecule, the synthesis of
brom-indigo was a simple matter. His results were a miserable disappointment. Tyrian purple proved to be a weak,
reddish purple; a wine color, to be sure, but a wine reminis-
cent of the amateur vintners of our Prohibition era rather
than the glowing gleam of rich Burgundy. It did not cause a
ripple in the dye trade. It was a color so inferior to coal-tar
dyes already on the market that nobody was interested in it.
In all fairness it should be added that certain brom-indigos
have since found an important place in blending both rich
purples and brilliant cardinal reds. Likely enough the master
dyers of the Roman Empire did a little bit of smart color-
mixing of their own.

From the discovery of mauve to the duplication of Tyrian
purple an enormous change had taken place in the dye-
making industry. Such names among the leaders as Perkin,
Mansfield, Dale, and Nicholson had been replaced by von
Baeyer, Heumann, Brunck, and Duisberg. Born in England
and nursed there to industrial stature, the making of dyes
from coal tar had moved over to Germany.

Starting a poor third, for French chemists and chemical-
makers quickly followed Perkin's lead, the Germans in ten
years had been able to pass both their competitors. They had
many advantages, but they were helped, too, by British indif-
ference to the coal-tar chemicals and French ineptitude for
technical manufacturing. Perkin, who had conspicuous ability along these lines, might have furnished the leadership
that the English dye-makers certainly lacked; but he retired
before forty, with a comfortable fortune, to devote himself to
pure research. Prince Albert, who had caught the true chemical vision, was dead. Hofmann, the great teacher of coal-tar

chemists, went back to Germany. Although her great gas and coke works produced more than nine times as much coal tar as all the remainder of Europe, England slipped back into the easy and profitable business of supplying these raw materials to the German chemical plants. Once the German coal-tar industry won the place of leadership, they saw to it that no competitor was allowed to become a dangerously threatening rival.

By 1900 England was rebuying her own coal-tar crudes in the finished form at a handsome profit to Germany. About ninety per cent of the dyes and almost all the coal-tar medicinals that she used were imported. Fourteen years later she was bitterly to rue her dependence upon German-made synthetic chemicals.

The Germans, on the other hand, went in for all sorts of coal-tar enterprises with enthusiasm and determination. Their chemical industrialists, being themselves technically trained, valued research properly. Alert to every new chemical development, keen as terriers to grasp every commercial opportunity, they built upon a sound foundation an industry that grew rapidly and soundly.

Initially this was business pure and simple — yet not so pure, since there was a deal of spying and piracy. With characteristic ruthless thoroughness the German dye-makers adopted the familiar program of domination. They would control the world's markets for synthetic organic chemicals. To reach this end, they cherished no scruples as to the means employed. Gradually, too, this chemical business began to acquire political interests. As no other people at that time, the Germans were aware of the key position that these organic chemicals were fast assuming both in peace and in war. So profits were blended with patriotism. The Government began to lend a helping hand, building up a modern munitions industry with official subsidies for research and by preferential rates on the state-owned railways.

The dye industry was started in Germany, as elsewhere, by a few commercially minded chemists. Several score of men of this stamp started little plants. For some thirty years a merry battle among them served as an exceedingly efficient process for the elimination of the unfit.

By 1900, however, six companies began to emerge from this mêlée. By 1904 they began to form alliances which brought them into two groups. Badische, Bayer, and Agfa formed what was pleasantly called a " community of interest." They drafted and agreed upon the terms of a fifty-year agreement by which they allocated markets, exchanged basic patents, and shared profits. Among the other trio, stock control was employed to make more secure similar objectives. Hochst acquired 99 per cent of the Kalle stock and a 75-percent interest in Cassella.

It did not take these two powerful groups long to get together. In the now famous Dye Cartel they voluntarily pooled their patents and sorted out their customers, thus neatly eliminating destructive competition among themselves. Behind this united front they fared forth to complete their conquest of the coal-tar chemical markets of the world. They held those markets till 1914 when the war shut off their export business.

The word *Blitzkrieg* had not then been coined, but there are some striking similarities between the German war plans of 1914 and 1940. Both were preceded by the same carefully calculated planning, not only of the troop movements, but also of what were held to be the key munitions of the time. The Kaiser counted as much on his supplies of tri-nitrotoluol as Hitler did on his fleets of pursuit planes and bombers. Thus each held what he believed was a deadly weapon of such superiority that he could win a swift and crushing victory.

Having assured himself of a plentiful supply of the essential explosive element, nitrogen, by means of Fritz Haber's synthetic ammonia process, the Kaiser fondly believed that the dye industry had put into German hands a decisive weapon, the modern high-power explosives. Shells loaded with these destructive disruptants, so his General Staff assured him, raised the striking power of artillery to a crucial, dominating place in modern tactics. No other nation had adequate supplies of the coal-tar crudes and intermediates to munition a field army. Even if toluol and phenol were available, no other country knew the technique of organic synthesis. They lacked both the chemists and the trained operating personnel. They had neither the apparatus nor the equipment. Long before they could possibly be in production the war would be won. And just as an added assurance of victory, there were the poison gases, which possessed the stunning advantage of surprise and which would require, for both defense and offense, a degree of chemical knowledge and technical skill far beyond anything available outside of the Reich.

Substitute planes and tanks for explosives and gases and all this weaves the now familiar *Blitzkrieg* pattern.

The Kaiser failed to win a short and decisive campaign. In the final analysis he was eventually beaten because he lost " chemical control " of the military situation. In losing that, the Germans also lost their monopoly of coal-tar dyes and medicinals.

Francis P. Garvan, who was certainly in a position to know, was fond of repeating again and again: " The only thing the United States got out of the World War was a synthetic organic chemical industry; but it was worth all it cost."

CHAPTER V

MARS: CHEMICAL DICTATOR

◇◇

In 1898 we fought the Spaniards with gunpowder made by the same secret formula that the Moors stole from the Chinese and used themselves during their invasion of Spain in the twelfth century. It was formulated with less scrupulous care than the ink that printed this morning's newspapers and manufactured under less exacting chemical control than the red lacquer which the ladies smear over their fingernails.

Since then black powder has vanished as a military munition. There has been a chemical revolution in explosives.

The Boer War (1899–1902) marked the turning-point. The cartridges issued to Tommy Atkins in South Africa were loaded with cordite, a gelatinized combination of nitrocellulose and nitroglycerin based on the discovery of Alfred Nobel. Ever since, some sort of smokeless powder of this same general type has remained the standard military propellant charge. The Boer War also introduced a radically new species of explosives, the disruptants. These are used, not to discharge projectiles, but packed within them, to cause them to burst upon striking.

The artilleryman undoubtedly caught this idea from the naval technique of the torpedo. He welcomed it as a modernized adaptation of the murderous charges of grapeshot, old bolts, nails, and what not that he formerly crammed down his muzzle-loading cannon. He foresaw that explosive shells

would do a great deal to restore the tarnished prestige of his
branch of the service, and he was quite right.

When Tommy Atkins's vastly superior officers at their
polished desks in Pall Mall and Woolwich finally made up
their minds that the South African campaign was not going
to be " a Christmas party in Pretoria " they began shipping
out to him some new explosive shells. What the British toyed
with in South Africa, the Japs used in deadly earnest against
the Russians in Manchuria. The lesson taught was so perfectly plain that military minds the world over grasped the
idea that a new weapon had become available which greatly
increased the effectiveness of artillery.

This new weapon was a new kind of explosive. As a disruptant the old black powder was a pretty feeble affair. Guncotton (nitrocellulose) and blasting gelatin (nitroglycerin)
were not sufficiently stable to withstand the shock of the discharge. But now a really good disruptant had been found.

Military secrets leak out with amazing rapidity, and by
1900 everybody interested in such matters knew that England and France had both developed high explosives adaptable to shell loading. The British called theirs lyddite; the
French, melinite. The Japanese trailed along a couple of
years later with their shimosite. Lyddite, melinite, shimosite,
all three are essentially picric acid, the more exact chemical
name of which is tri-nitrophenol. And tri-nitrophenol is obviously a coal-tar intermediate, phenol being one of five important crudes. A pound and a quarter of phenol is recovered from every ton of coal coked.

If picric acid is to become the disruptive shell charge, even
the most torpid military intellect might have been expected
to comprehend the significant connection of modern munitions with the coal-tar chemical industry. Amazing as it
seems, nobody outside of Germany put these two facts together to a definite, purposeful conclusion.

In Germany, however, the General Staff and the high officials of the Dye Cartel very promptly got together. While England and France continued to favor tri-nitrophenol as their disruptive charge, the Germans investigated other, closely allied, coal-tar products. Some time before 1910 they selected tri-nitrotoluol, the TNT of the World War.

It is not quite fair to imply that the British were dumb or lazy in sticking to picric acid. While they may, or may not, have appreciated the superiorities of TNT, they had to be concerned over adequate supplies in event of war, and of all coal-tar products their chemical industry was best equipped to handle phenol. In fact, the English had made quite a specialty of disinfectants — remember that phenol is carbolic acid — and furthermore they were already working the process of synthesizing phenol from benzol, the crude that is about four times as abundant as phenol itself in coal tar.

The Kaiser's pride in the German coal-tar chemical industry now becomes quite pardonable. There is no longer any mystery in the favors — subsidies for research, remission of taxes, particular patent-protection, and preferential rates on the state-owned railroads — which the German Government granted so liberally to the dye-makers. And we may be quite certain, too, not only that the General Staff thoroughly approved of the Dye Cartel's military-like campaign for the destruction of effective competitors in Great Britain, France, and the United States, but that also, on occasion, they might not hesitate to put at their industry's disposal the exceedingly efficient assistance of the German espionage system.

To maintain their monopoly of coal-tar chemicals the German Dye Trust used every means at their command. Neither sentiment nor scruple tempered their ruthless vigor. Like a cat at a mouse-hole the Germans patiently watched for every opportunity and pounced upon it swiftly. In their hands each new, improved dye became a commercial weapon. Not only did they introduce these novelties at handsome prices, which provided ample profits to reimburse them for the high costs of their research; but they also refused to sell them at any price to dyers who were not regular customers for all their dyes. This " full line forcing " was particularly devastating competition to the struggling American dye-makers, who found to their dismay that these choking tactics were greatly aided by our own tariff and patent laws.

Back in the early days we had missed the chance of establishing an American coal-tar chemical industry. Tradition credits a shrewd Yankee chemical merchant, Henry Gould of Boston, with having piled up a snug little fortune in two years by being the first man in America to awake to the possibilities in coal-tar dyes. In 1862 he imported a thousand pounds, which New England dyers snapped up so quickly that he reordered $75,000 worth and the following year brought in dyes to the amount of $50,000. The story is that he made close to a quarter of a million dollars. This is possible, since he paid a dollar per pound plus thirty-five per cent ad valorem duty, and an exclusive trade was not an opportunity that he would be apt to fumble. His little flyer in the dye trade had natural results: dye-importers sprang up in all the larger textile centers; the foresighted Mr. Gould retired to his farm; and in 1871 the tariff on aniline dyes was cut in half to fifty cents per pound plus thirty-five per cent ad valorem.

Just about the time Henry Gould stretched himself out in a hammock under his apple trees, a Dr. August Partz was very busy soliciting sufficient working capital from his friends in Brooklyn to build a dye factory on the banks of Gowanus Creek in the Flatbush section. He proposed to import a mixture of aniline and toluidine with arsenic acid and by heating to convert them into the dye fuchsine. The record fails to tell of the outcome of this venture, but at least Dr. Partz made the first attempt and his plan of importing intermediates remained the favorite pattern of American dye-making till 1914.

Other pioneering attempts were more successful. By 1870 Brooklyn and Albany were both the home of modestly successful, small-scale dye plants. Away out in Parkersburgh, West Virginia, an energetic young German-American, who had had chemical training at Cooper Institute in New York, persuaded his partner to make aniline. Victor Bloede had gone west to extract bromine from the Ohio Valley brines, but he shortly became chemist for Oakes & Rathburn, manufacturers of sulphuric acid at Parkersburgh. When Oakes retired, the firm became Bloede & Rathburn, and the new head began vigorously adding new products to the line. Gas-house coal tar was available and this youthful enthusiast determined to make benzol and other coal-tar products. Having no experience with fractional distillation, he conferred with James Moffatt, manager of the local Standard Oil refinery, who became so infected with Bloede's zeal that he agreed to contribute not only his experience but also his hard-earned dollars. More than this, the Standard Oil junk-pile contributed most of the apparatus.

On a scale so puny that Moffatt, accustomed to oil-industry quantities, rocked with laughter over the operations, they produced benzol. This they proposed to nitrate, as Perkin had, to nitrobenzol. Out of an old thousand-gallon boiler they made a nitrator, which they mounted in a gully well away from the rest of their plant. Having a very wholesome respect for this explosive process, they invented a primitive cooling system out of a hose that sprayed water from a neighboring spring over the flanks of their apparatus. The flow of sulphuric acid, which Perkin had found was the critical factor in controlling the violent reactions, was governed by a long wire twisted round the lever of a stopcock. A thermometer inserted in the top of the boiler served as an indicator. The operator would rush to the edge of the gully, read the thermometer at a glance, give a tug or a shove at the wire, and scamper back to safety.

There were no accidents and they did make nitrobenzene. But there were also no customers, so perforce they went on another step and made aniline. The sole and only buyer of aniline dictated a lower and lower price till again they were shoved on to make another product, the dye fuchsine. At last in the great spring flood of 1881 the Kanawha River wiped out the whole works.

The following year a further reduction in the tariff barrier just as effectively destroyed four of the ten little dye factories that had sprung up in various parts of the country. Ironically this happened at a time when the prospects of establishing an American coal-tar industry had seemed quite bright.

The sensational advances of chemistry had begun to creep into the newspapers, and the chemical exhibits at the Centennial Exposition in Philadelphia during the summer of 1876 stirred up lively interest. The public ohed and ahed before two attractive arrays of display bottles filled with multi-colored samples of coal-tar derivatives. Artificial oil of almonds, synthetic vanilla, the scent of the violet and the geranium, colors of every hue; and in the center a great demijohn filled with black, oily coal tar! It caught the attention, fired the imagination, and made real the miracle of drugs, perfumes, flavors, and dyes which the chemist could create out of this unpromising-looking raw material. What if these brilliant bottles were filled with samples brought over from Europe for this show! What could be done abroad could certainly be done in the United States. Though for us it has now been sobered a bit, we all recognize the line of thought.

Less showy than these popular displays, but more substantial, were two modest exhibits of coal-tar products actually made in America. The Silliman Chemical Works of Philadelphia showed six quart flasks of aniline-dye solutions. Salicylic acid and a number of its derivatives were exhibited by August Zinnser, father of Hans, the bacteriologist of *Rats,*

Lice and History fame, and of Frederick, the chemist, who as the head of Zinnser and Company was to become a trailblazer in the manufacture of coal-tar chemicals in this country during the World War.

The 1871 tariff law provided protection behind which an American coal-tar chemical industry might have been built. Several firms which bought crude tar at the gas works refined a middle oil sold for creosoting railroad ties and telegraph poles, a heavy oil used on roads and roofs, and a soft pitch which was largely burned under their own stills. Since no tar was recovered from coking operations and much of the illuminating gas was made by the carbureted water process, the supplies of crude coal tar were not plentiful. Accordingly, the market for creosoting timber, road-building and roofing materials easily absorbed the supply. The situation was the same as in England before Perkin's dye factory created a demand for coal-tar crudes as raw materials for chemical processing. However, it was recognized that, eked out with importations of coal-tar intermediates, the needed raw materials for all sorts of coal-tar syntheses could be had in this country. Furthermore it was confidently expected that, given a demand for these chemicals, the recently discovered by-product recovery ovens would logically replace the old wasteful beehive ovens in which all the coke for our steel mills was then being produced.

When the tariff of 1883 whittled down the dye duties, all these hopes went aglimmering. It was twenty years before there were to be any installations of recovery coke ovens. Right up to 1914 the Germans were able to hold down coal-tar chemical manufacturing in this country to quite insignificant proportions. The powerful New England textile interests, which had exercised undue influence in writing that tariff, were then to pay dearly for the cheap, duty-free dyes for which they had pleaded so eloquently in 1883.

Later the dye tariff rates were raised, but it was futile to lock the barn door after the horse had been stolen. By then the German industry not only had established technical superiority, but had banded together in the cartel for united action. It had waxed strong and relentless. It was able to twist our tariff and our patents both to its own advantage.

Most of the dyes made in this country before the World War were manufactured from imported intermediates, and one of our well-established rate-making theories must have pleased the Dye Trust immensely. The tariff schedule read: 5 per cent ad valorem duty on coal-tar crudes; 10 per cent on intermediates; 35 per cent on finished dyes. In the end this meant simply that the net protection to the finished dyes of American manufacturers using imported raw materials was shaved down to 20 per cent.

At the time no indigo was made in America, so this important dye was put on the free list, with the result that the Germans sold it in Europe, where they had competition, lower than here. On the other hand, direct black paid a duty of thirty per cent and was made by the then largest American dye manufacturer. Accordingly, the Germans priced it at 17 cents a pound in the United States and 22 cents in Europe. The system was simple and bullet-proof. Where there is no domestic competition, make the American dyer pay a handsome premium. On the dyes that are made in America, absorb the duty and cut the price till the American maker is forced to quit. Never — and this was important from the military as well as the commercial point of view — never permit the production of crudes and intermediates to get a foothold. Accordingly, benzol, naphthalene, and anthracene were consistently offered here at such low prices that it did not pay American tar-distillers to separate them out from their creosote oils and their roofing and road-building tars.

To recover the losses of the savage price-cutting that such tactics required, the cartel found their patents, notably their patents on medicinal preparations, exceedingly useful. No

other nation is quite so liberal as we in the matter of patents.
We issue a patent on a product as well as on a process. A new
collection of chemical atoms put together in the laboratory
and useful as a dye or a medicine is plainly " a combination of
matter previously unknown in Nature." As such it is patentable under our law. For seventeen years such a patent blocks
anyone else from making this color or drug even if he dis-
covers an entirely original way of duplicating this product.
In other countries the process only is patentable. Perkin and
his German rivals in the race to synthesize alizarin, both obtained good British patents for their distinct processes, and
the same principle holds in German patent law.

With a U.S. patent on acetyl-salicylic acid, the product,
and a U.S. trade-mark on the trade-name " Aspirin," the
Bayer Company was doubly fortified to exploit the American
market. Just prior to the World War they sold this popular
drug in this country for 35 cents an ounce. In Germany their
price was 2 cents an ounce. Today with the patent expired
and the trade-mark declared by the courts an open trade-
name, acetyl-salicylic acid is made by half a dozen American
firms and sells for even less.

Other smart ways of making good the losses of ruthless
price-cutting on coal-tar staple products and raw materials
had been devised. Methyl violet, the dye also known as gentian violet, was early found to be an excellent bactericide, especially for use on lacerated wounds, and it has a selective
coloring action which makes it invaluable as a stain in the
examination of micro-organisms. Not big uses these, but important; and ones in which price is not going to be a compel-
ling factor. Methyl violet was sold by the Germans in the
form of a dark greenish powder. It must be used in fresh solutions; they directed that as soon as it was dissolved, it was to
be filtered, and the filtrate discarded. Into the laboratory slop
jar had gone thousands of little cones of filter paper filled
with this violet-stained powder, and nobody gave it a thought.

When the supply of methyl violet was cut off, a young assistant professor of chemistry at Wesleyan was prompted to investigate a process for preparing it in this country. Naturally he was curious about this filtrate, especially so when his scales told him that it comprised forty per cent of the total weight of the dye. He began testing and soon found that it was nothing but starch; good, plain, cheap tapioca starch, sold at five dollars a pound and making up nearly half the weight of the dye.

With such generous extra profits on a goodly number of well-chosen specialties, the Dye Cartel was strongly reinforced for a long and bitter price war against its American competitors. By 1914 they had reduced the industry here to seven small companies. Only two of these produced more than twenty different colors. All of them added together had far less than a tenth of the financial resources, the technical staff, or the number of products of the smallest one of the six companies in the cartel.

With the war and the shutting off of imports from Germany came an American famine of all coal-tar chemicals. We were jolted by the sudden realization that despite our geographical isolation, despite our vast resources, we could be neither safe, prosperous, nor even healthy so long as we were dependent upon foreigners for these vital chemical supplies. Overnight Mars became our chemical dictator, the director of our chemical research, and the active manager of our chemical manufacturing.

The clamorous demands of the war for all sorts of coal-tar products cut two ways. German stocks in this country quickly vanished: the Allies' needs for high-power explosives became insistent.

Less than a quarter of our coke was then produced in by-product recovery ovens, and the first critical shortage was in phenol. The British Army was short of explosive shells, and their own supply of phenol proved woefully inadequate.

France had no coal, and both turned to us. Benzol must be converted into phenol, and quickly, and in enormous quantities. The price of benzol soared and the steel industry with a good reason for stopping their "waste" of the coal-tar crudes began feverishly to replace the old beehives with by-product recovery ovens. The supply began to grow rapidly.

	Benzol per month	*Toluol per month*
End of 1915	1,750,000 *gals.*	525,000 *gals.*
End of 1916	2,500,000 "	700,000 "
End of 1917	3,000,000 "	857,000 "
End of 1918	5,000,000 "	1,400,000 "

Meanwhile the synthesis of phenol out of benzol was being carried on in all sorts of makeshift plants. The waste was terrific, owing to poor yields, but time was all that counted, and as weeks passed the operations in the best of the dozens of plants that sprang up were gradually perfected. To ease the strain on the requirements for benzol, phenol, and picric acid, toluol was converted to tri-nitrotoluol for shell loading.

Into this swift-moving development the demand for dyes and medicines had to be dovetailed. They required the same raw materials as the explosives, and we had to make good the vanished German supply of ninety per cent of our colors and drugs.

The shortage of dyes threatened to throw 400,000 American textile operatives out of work. Salvarsan, specific against syphilis, was being doled out to hospitals and the Army Medical Corps at $90 an ounce. For 10,000 pounds of Metol, the photographic developer, a moving-picture firm advertised an offer of $200,000. The simple coal-tar derivative salicylic acid jumped from 22 cents a pound to $4. Antipyrene sold up to $19 a pound and resorcin at $30 a pound. The dyes advanced even more sensationally, and even at these very fancy prices supplies of all the coal-tar chemicals were pitifully small.

The new and lucrative profession of chemical salvaging

was created. Its members scoured the land, rummaging in the warehouses of mills and factories, grubbing about in drugstore cellars, seeking out odds and ends of old surplus stocks of dyes and medicinals. A lucky find meant a little fortune — one hundred-pound keg of the dye Rhodamine B, originally sold for $100, was bought for $5,000 and " salted " ten pounds for one, to be resold at $75 a pound: profits $70,000, less the cost of nine hundred pounds of common salt. And better stories are told at the round table of the Chemists' Club when some of the oldsters get reminiscing about the old World War days.

Seven distinguished, worried textile manufacturers called on Secretary of Commerce Redfield in Washington. Lest their mills be shut down for lack of dyes, they begged him to use the full influence of the nation.

" First," they complained, " England puts dyes on the contraband list. Now Germany puts dyes under embargo and refuses to sell through neutral countries."

So three-cornered negotiations began. Germany would be delighted to exchange dyes and medicines for American cotton. England pointed out that cotton plus nitric acid made smokeless powder. At last, as a polite bit of courtesy among the great powers, Germany generously agreed to ship from Rotterdam 600,000 pounds of dyes and Great Britain graciously consented to grant them free passage on the Holland-America liner *Nieuw Amsterdam* through her blockade in order that our Government Printing Office might not be forced to issue our postage stamps in black and white. With a blunt emphasis that irked our pride, that little diplomatic episode made our dye plight perfectly clear. The submarine *Deutschland* suddenly bobbed up in Baltimore and New London, having twice slipped under the British fleet and brought over dyes and medicines, but we were less impressed by the dramatic feat than by the fabulous prices asked for these chemical cargoes.

Dire necessity for these coal-tar products created an insatiable demand ready, even willing, to pay any price. Scores of hardy adventurers launched forth as chemical manufacturers. By the end of 1916 our dye industry of seven had grown to forty-two. They were struggling with all sorts of unsuspected difficulties, little dreamed of when they embarked on their quest. Equipped with copies of the German textbooks on dye manufacture — Friedlander's *Teerfarbenfabrikation* and Schultz's *Fabstofftabellen* were such favorites that second-hand copies in poor condition were selling for a hundred dollars, and if you were lucky enough to get one, it was kept in the safe — they set out the hard way to turn theoretical book-learning into practical plant operations.

One of their first lessons, learned by bitter experience, was that one could not always rely implicitly upon the facts and formulas which the German authorities set down in black and white on the printed page. The German literature of coal-tar chemistry, like the German dye and medicinal patents, was full of significant gaps. Vital steps in processes were sometimes entirely omitted. Essential bits of " know how " about time or temperature or pressure somehow failed to get into the record.

By hook and crook we began producing not only explosives, but also dyes and medicinals. Through some weird reactions in makeshift apparatus coal-tar chemicals actually resulted. At the end of 1916 we were making more than forty coal-tar intermediates and nearly one hundred dyes and medicines that had never been made here before. Yields would have highly amused the Germans. Quality gave the customers some headaches. But we were learning organic synthesis from the ground up.

It was a costly education. It wasted hours of what should have been unnecessary work and it ate up many a dollar. It was, however, a thorough education. Our infant dye industry learned that research is as necessary as bookkeeping in the

chemical business. As a result they had given us the basis of a synthetic organic chemical industry.

Along with all the factories, real estate, securities, and what not owned by alien enemies which the Government took over during the war were some 4,500 German chemical patents. These covered the latest dyes and medicinals, and also a number of key patents on processes picked with great skill to block the development of a synthetic organic chemical industry in America. If the German Dye Trust continued to control the most improved products and certain basic processes, their stranglehold could never be broken. It was vital to make these patents available.

If, however, they were auctioned off to the highest bidder (as the Alien Property Custodian did with the factories and real estate), a couple of large companies might buy them up. This would not greatly help build a rounded American chemical industry. In effect, it might merely transfer the coal-tar monopoly from the German to an American dye trust.

The very word " monopoly " sends a shiver up and down many American spines. Other nations have long encouraged cartels and trusts. They have been proud of the size and strength of their large corporations. For reasons that become more and more obscure the longer one observes their causes and effects, we Americans dislike large companies and seem to distrust strength. Accordingly, anything like the creation of a Government-backed dye industry, such as the Germans had and the English were organizing, was beyond the pale. Indeed, some device must be discovered to prevent absolutely any attempt to build up an American dye trust. Unless this could be done these valuable patents would be impounded to nobody's gain and the nation's great loss. How to use them so as to help build an American dye industry strong enough to fight off the assaults of the Germans after the war and yet not so powerfully centralized as to rouse the opposition of some trust-busting politician?

The right-hand man of Alien Property Custodian Mitchell Palmer was Francis P. Garvan, a young lawyer who had caught the vision of all that a synthetic chemical industry might mean to the United States. Before going to Washington he had had a grueling training in the office of New York's battling District Attorney Jerome and he had learned at first hand the utterly unscrupulous methods used by the German Dye Trust to choke off effective competition in America. With his interest riveted upon this problem, he characteristically flashed an inspired solution. Literally he dragged his chief to the White House to lay the proposal before Woodrow Wilson.

" Create," said Garvan, " a public, non-profit corporation to buy all the German chemical patents in a lump. License the use of any of these patents to any *bona fide* American chemical-maker. Set up a fund to protect American interests by prosecuting any German attempt to sell in this country any product covered by these patents. Finance the whole deal by selling stock in this Chemical Foundation, Inc., to the American chemical manufacturers themselves. Use the income from the license fees to educate politicians and bankers and other influential but dumb leaders of thought in what a well-rounded chemical industry means and to stimulate young men with prizes and fellowships to take up chemistry as their life work."

It was just as simple as that. President Wilson approved. The Chemical Foundation was created. Every American chemical company of any standing subscribed for stock, which was placed in a voting trust. The German chemical patents were bought for $250,000, and a like sum was put into the defense fund. Francis P. Garvan was elected president — honorary president in the British sense that he received no salary — and so began his outspoken, two-fisted fight for American chemical independence.

Twenty years later, when World War II again shut off imports from Germany, we had no chemical famine. Prices did not skyrocket. No speculators " salted " colors to their own inordinate profit. Not a corner drug-store but was well stocked with all coal-tar medicinals including such recent discoveries as sulfanilamide and sulfapyridine. Our vastly greater moving-picture industry and our army of amateur photographers suffered no lack of developers.

By the acid test we proved that the domination of the German Dye Trust, now greater and stronger and more nationalized than ever, is broken in this country. We do have the complete, independent chemical industry that Francis Garvan saw in his vision.

The wild, wasteful scramble out of which developed the great organic branches of that industry was the very antithesis of any planned economy. Men were prodded by war demands to take great risks and to labor day and night. They stumbled through a titanic task, the building in four frantic years, in the midst of the confusions and the shortages of the war, a coal-tar chemical industry which the Germans had patiently built up during half a century. When the war boom collapsed, they struggled in a bitter competitive fight that only the strong and efficient companies survived. But we do have today a score of companies — National Aniline, du Pont, the Calco Division of American Cyanamid, General Dyes, Dow, and others who successfully specialize in certain particular types — that are a complete dye industry.

That is a national asset of value to all of us. For the dyes are the industrial keystone of the whole arch of synthetic products from coal tar. Not big business in dollars or pounds; but vital business in products and processes. Without the dye industry we should have neither the experience nor the plants to produce the modern explosives or the modern medicines. Defense and health alike depend on products of coal-tar synthesis. To keep abreast of chemical progress we must search and research in the field of coal-tar technology.

This field has spread out and ramified tremendously. In the field of dyes alone the colors have become carefully specialized so that when chic Mistress Modern sallies forth to costume herself from hat to shoe all in an ensemble of a single shade, she unwittingly places an order for from fifty to a hundred different dyes. Her homespun jacket and gaberdine shirt, her Celanese blouse with its linen trimmings and wooden buttons, her straw hat and reptile-skin pumps and rayon stockings, to say nothing of her kid gloves, her patent-leather belt, and artificial leather handbag; all these, with her costume jewelry of plastics and enameled metals too, all must match. She demands that wool, silk, cotton, and linen, three types of rayon, as many distinct kinds of leather, straw, wood, and cellophane, several plastics, and what not besides, shall all be dyed to a given shade, or, what is just as complicated, dyed to prettily blending or strikingly contrasting hues. She gets what she demands. And she thinks little of it. Her grandmother could never have enjoyed what she accepts as a matter of course because thousands of skilled chemists have labored patiently building up new combinations of the atoms in coal tar, and because we have the industry that translates their test-tube discoveries into articles of commercial use.

CHAPTER VI

SWEET SMELLS AND SAVORY FLAVORS

◇◇◇

CLEOPATRA discovered that lotions and perfumes can be potent forces in international affairs, quite as powerful as the ironclad legion, as far-reaching as the war galley with its triple bank of oars. According to men who were not in love with her, she was not a pretty woman — a red-head with freckles — but she made the most of her opportunities and she certainly used paint, powder, and perfumes most skillfully. Her cosmetic diplomacy did things to the map of North Africa which Benito Mussolini, with appalling effort and at great cost of blood and treasure, has been endeavoring to undo.

It is fitting therefore that she, not Venus, should be the high priestess of the cult of feminine beauty. It is quite natural, too, that she should be credited with the discovery of many good perfumery recipes, including the secret that a heavy, ugly animal scent does wonders for the delicious delicacy of a floral perfume.

Of course, the glamorous Queen of Egypt did not invent cosmetics. They are one of women's earliest wiles, almost as old as vanity. In her day the grand ladies all painted their eyelids with kohl, an exceedingly sophisticated mixture of black lead with the oxides of iron and copper, brown ochre,

[95

malachite green, and chrysocolla, which is a blue ore of copper. For the five-and-ten-cent-store trade of Memphis and Thebes a kohl prepared from soot and bluish clay was in great demand, for not a peasant's wife nor a slave girl but darkened her eyes with black circles to achieve that languorous effect so esteemed in the Orient. A thousand years before her reign the mother of the wife of Egypt's first King gave her daughter a capital recipe for a henna hair-dye, and it has been broadly hinted that this same family formula accounted for Cleopatra's famous auburn tresses. Certainly this same henna was then used, as it still is throughout the East, to stain the palms of the hands and the bottom of the feet, the nails, and the ear lobes.

Back to the most remote antiquity we have perfumes and incense — the two words come from the same root-meaning of " smoke from burning " — all mixed up together. Myrrh and frankincense, cloves and cinnamon, sweet oils and precious ointments, these with salt were the first goods of commerce.

Of all these, frankincense, the gum of the olibanum tree, was most famous. Inferior sorts came from Somaliland, the Sudan, Abyssinia; but the genuine article was found only on trees growing in the inaccessible mountains of southern Arabia. There, in the country of the Sabæans, three hundred families claimed a hereditary monopoly of collecting. It was a holy and hazardous trade, according to Herodotus, for the olibanum trees were each guarded by a flock of little winged serpents which could be driven away only by the fumes of burning styrax resin; and if the frankincense was collected by any man who had not ascetically forsaken wife or sweetheart for a moon's rise and wane, it would become bitter and rancid.

In a more mundane mood, the priests of Sabota, whither the gum was brought by camel train, permitted it to enter the city through one gate only. There they collected ten per cent by measure. Another tenth was levied by kings of the

Gebanites, through whose ports it was exported. By the time it reached Alexandria, headquarters of the ancient incense and spice market, it was so precious that, to prevent stealing, the servants of the traders worked stripped naked save for a sealed clout. The good King Juba was forced by her avaricious father to pay for his favorite wife her weight in the milk-white gum. Out of such bright-colored stuffs is woven the romance of perfumery.

Cleopatra lived during the first great age of cosmetics. From Egypt the luxurious fashion crossed the Mediterranean to Rome. During the later Empire it reached such fantastic extravagances as gilding the nipples, rouging the knees and elbows, and even tracing the veins of male forearms with blue paint to heighten the effect of virility.

Then the barbarians descended upon the decadent city, and the art of the perfumer hid away in the heart of Arabia. There it was cherished by the great physicians and alchemists, who also preserved medicine and arithmetic for us. The great doctor of the eleventh century, Trotula, did not disdain to write three famous perfumery-recipe books, and it was this Arabian lore, spreading east and west, that became the basis not only of our modern art of the aromatics, but also of the science of their preparation.

In Italy perfumery flourished during the Renaissance. In 1562 Giovanni Marinello, a medieval forerunner of Lois Leeds and Florence Wall, wrote a monumental book that went through many editions, *The Ornamentation of the Ladies*. Catherine de' Medici brought to France the Italian arts of the toilet and initiated what was to become the Golden Age of Cosmetics, from the early seventeenth to the late eighteenth centuries. Literally thousands of different preparations appeared: pastes, essences, balsams, paints for the eyes, cheeks, nails; and an elaborate ritual grew up to have almost legal authority. There were established types of make-up for the lady of rank, the courtesan, the bourgeois wife. Gallants, who when knights were bold carried the colors of their mistress on their helms, now affected their lady's favorite scent. Louis XV ordered that the royal apartments be sprayed with a different perfume every day in the month. In Paris alone 50,000,000 francs were spent in the perfumers' shops, which in our money today would be some $25,-000,000, a lavish sum even when compared with our own national cosmetic bill of $132,336,000.

Anciently — that is, before the Arabians learned to put flower petals, buds, seeds, or whatever part of the plant yields the odoriferous principle, in a still with water, and by heat drive off the fragrant constituents along with the steam — the sweet scents were extracted by soaking the plants in oil or spreading them on fats, which both absorb perfume principles. These methods are still employed for delicate odors which might be spoiled by the heat of distillation.

Another process, still used for collecting rose oil, was discovered, so the legend has it, by the bride of the Indian Emperor Jehanger. She noticed a film on the surface of the petal-strewn canals in the royal rose garden and collected this oil. She named it Atr-i-Jehangiri, hence our attar of roses, the trade-name for Bulgarian rose oil. A fourth process of collecting the essential oils is by maceration, in which the odoriferous parts are steeped in a suitable medium, alcohol or a dry powder such as starch just moistened with a solvent. By all these ancient methods there comes into commerce a wealth of aromatic materials.

During the kindergarten days of the science, when chemists with the insatiable curiosity of a healthy six-year-old were taking to pieces all sorts of materials to find what they were made of, the rare, costly perfume oils and the pungent spices were great favorites. However, the early analysts found these complicated mixtures of complex organic substances beyond their skill and knowledge.

It was exceedingly baffling, for example, when the good

Bonastre found in the oil of cloves a pale yellow liquid with a strong clove odor that boiled at 254 degrees and whose formula he accurately determined as $C_{10}H_{12}O_2$, to discover that white, odorless crystals melting at 115 degrees could be separated out from the spice cumin, which also had the formula $C_{10}H_{12}O_2$. To make confusion worse confounded, more than a hundred substances with this identical formula, many of them aromatic materials, were isolated. Not till organic chemists had learned from Wöhler about isomers and knew a great deal about the structure of the molecules based on the arrangement of their atoms was much progress made with the aromatic chemicals.

Quite early it was discovered, however, that the majority of these essential oils are composed chiefly of one single dominating, aromatic substance. With it are often associated hydrocarbons called terpenes, having the formula $C_{10}H_{16}$, or polymers (that is, multiples of the same proportions), as $C_{15}H_{24}$ or $C_{20}H_{32}$. Thrown in for good measure are a whole flock of other aromatic principles in smaller, often minute quantities. The distinctive odor of any particular plant is thus a blend of scents.

The terpenes, however, were found to be often unnecessary, undesirable ingredients. They are easily affected by the oxygen of the air, so that the quality of the perfume oil is seriously affected. Chemically this means the formation of certain acids. Practically it results in objectionable odors. The fragrance of Limburger cheese, for example, is chiefly due to butyric acid, which is not a pleasing note in the symphony of smells.

Plenty of incentives tempted chemists to examine these aromatic materials and if possible to reproduce them synthetically. Myrrh and frankincense, precious gifts at the manger in Bethlehem; cinnamon, which paid the emperor's ransom to the fierce Mongol conquerors; sweet-smelling musk, the perfume of the dark-eyed houris of the Mohammedan paradise; rose essence, worth its weight in rubies, carried by camel caravan across deserts and mountains, eastward to Kabul and Jaipur, westward to Damascus and Aden — a fine net to enmesh the interest of any man with sufficient imagination to be a great creative chemist.

Who has not felt the power of scent to delight, to tempt, to warn, to rouse buried memories? What chemist but would be intrigued to learn just which combinations of the atoms produce these wondrous effects upon our olfactory nerves? That, and color and taste also, are still unsolved chemical mysteries.

To romance add greed. For even the commonest of these aromatics is not cheap, and many of them are fabulously expensive. Furthermore, the demand is insistent and increasing, and in the very nature of things their quality varies greatly from crop to crop. Their prices swing up and down from season to season so that the perfumer who skillfully blends a formula which today may cost him $35 an ounce may be bedeviled five years hence by costs that have risen to $200 an ounce. No chemical economist could plot a situation which chemically or commercially offers more glowing opportunities to a pure, staple-priced, synthetic substitute.

The fashion in toiletries that Catherine de' Medici introduced made Paris the cosmetic capital, and naturally enough in the south of France, where the climate is perfect for such crops, the cultivation of scented flowers for this trade gradually became a great industry. The ancient Roman city of Grasse, built in a beautiful amphitheater, facing southwards to the Mediterranean, is the fountainhead of this garden of perfumes. Throughout the region of Nice, Cannes, and Monte Carlo the industry employs twenty thousand people. It produces some five million pounds a year. The greatest crops are orange, jasmine, tuberose, bergamot, orris, mignonette, and violet; and you get a peek behind the scenes of this fragrant business when you know that it takes twenty-five tons of violet blossoms to produce a single ounce of the essential oil.

While the French Riviera is the single greatest center for the production of essential oils, it has by no means a natural monopoly. Sicily is famous for its bergamot and lemon oils. Sandalwood comes from India, citronella from Java, cloves from Zanzibar, lavender from England, bois de rose from Brazil, anise and cassia from China, licorice from Turkey, camphor from Formosa, rose from Bulgaria. Those curious, costly animal products used as fixatives, civet and musk, come respectively from a lean, long-legged wild cat native to Abyssinia and a graceful, excessively shy little deer found only in mountains of Mongolia.

In the globe-circling statistics of this trade, the United States has its modest place. American peppermint oil, chiefly from Michigan and Oregon, and oil of wormwood from Maryland and Louisiana, are both exported. We also produce supplies for our own needs of birch, wintergreen, and cedar; but these have been sorely hit by synthetic competitors, while the oldest and once most famous of such American products has toppled from a high place in medicine to be an ingredient in soft drinks.

Ponce de León and his helmeted Spaniards tramped the length of Florida and failed to find the Fountain of Eternal Youth. He did discover, however, that the Indians used as a medicine the bark of a pretty, smallish tree with dark leaves shaped like a child's mitten. The aborigines called it " pavane," esteeming it not only for its curative powers, but also for its aromatic flavor. For its pleasing taste they chewed the twigs and mixed the dried leaves with their smoking tobacco. This sassafras entered medical literature on page 51 of a stout tome printed in Seville in 1574, Monardes's history of the materia medica of the American Indians. Its fame spread over Europe. Sassafras tea became a favorite remedy for all sorts of ailments, from thinning hair to fallen arches.

When the fire-eating Captain John Smith was raising capital for his exploratory voyage along the New England coast, he told the good London burghers that he would return laden with gold. That failing, he very sensibly filled his vessel to the hatches with fish, furs, and sassafras. Henry Hudson, the Dutchman Adrian Block, Bartholomew Gosnold, who named Cape Cod, Matthew Pring, the first sea captain to nose an English ship among the islands and islets of the Maine coast, all engaged profitably in the sassafras trade. From their day till fifty years ago it was a very sizable business. But the fame of sassafras as a spring tonic and blood-purifier has faded and the once celebrated root is now used only in root beer.

Most of the many changes that have taken place in this old, old trade in aromatics have been caused, however, by the introduction of chemical substitutes. The first of these, nitrobenzene, was used for scenting soap at the time when Perkin began to manufacture it in quantity for the making of his mauve dye. It was sold as oil of mirbane and served as a coarse, rank replacement for the costly, illusive oil of bitter almonds. This was a rough and inauspicious beginning for the delicate, highly scientific business of synthetic aromatic chemicals as we know it today.

That nitrobenzene smells remarkably like almonds is, once that chemical has been prepared, simply a matter of " your nose knows." During the fifties and sixties of the last century, when the age of analysis in chemistry was followed by the great epoch of synthesis, many chemists found in their test tubes new compounds that pleased the senses of smell and taste. A few lucky finds led to whole groups of new and useful aromatic compounds. However, had progress depended upon these haphazard discoveries we should have but a small fraction of the two thousand odd synthetic odors and flavors now available.

Once chemists added to their knowledge of the percentage of the different elements contained in a compound a proper understanding of the structure into which these atoms were built in the aromatic compounds, their creation in the laboratory became a delicate but exceedingly fascinating jigsaw-puzzle game. When, for example, it was learned by analysis that the smell of almonds is due almost wholly to benzaldehyde, it was not a great feat to produce this coal-tar derivative.

One of the first of the deliberate discoveries in this field was made by the same Perkin who by chance found the first coal-tar dye. The tonka bean — really a nut from a tree native to South America — ground up and macerated with alcohol, yields a distinctive odor used largely to flavor snuff and in perfumes such as " Jockey Club," and to simulate the popular smell of new-mown hay. The tonka bean's chief aromatic principle had been isolated back in 1813 by Vogel, who determined its formula as $C_9H_6O_2$. He called it coumarin. In 1868 Perkin synthesized this material. Here was a true synthetic in the strictest meaning of the word, the chemical identity of the natural product reproduced in the laboratory.

This discovery suggested the line of much future progress. Coumarin is found not only in tonka beans, but also in sweet woodruff, clover, yellow melilot, and other favorite flowers of grandmother's old-fashioned garden. Just as Nature paints her glorious array of hues and shades from a palette of the six primary colors, so with similar economy she creates a multitude of odors and flavors by blending a few odorous principles. Once this secret was found in the laboratory, progress in making synthetic smells and tastes was speeded up greatly.

A most knowing manipulator in this field was Professor F. Tiemann of the University of Berlin, a genius with the infinite capacity to take pains. He spent a busy life taking apart the minute aromatic molecules and putting them together again. One of his many important triumphs was the synthesis of the odoriferous principle of the violet. The pulverized root

of the Florentine iris, known as orris, is one of the oldest
perfumery materials. It has been used for centuries in sachets
and powders for its clean, refreshing violet-like scent. From
orris Tiemann isolated irone. Seeking to synthesize irone
cheaply, he prepared from citral and acetone iso-ionone. By
heating this with sulphuric acid and glycerin he produced
ionone, which has the odor of the violet.

This was clever synthesis, and exceedingly important when
translated into dollars and cents. With violet blossoms worth
from 20 to 30 cents a pound, a pound of pure oil represents
some $6,000 worth of flowers. Even in the luxurious perfum-
ery trade such material is utterly beyond the realm of commercial practice. Therefore the perfumers are accustomed to
use a natural violet pomade in which the scent is extracted in
oils, paying at the rate of about $700 an ounce for the traces
of irone that it contains. All of which smacks of burning down
the house to roast a pig. By chemical synthesis ionone — a
capital substitute for the natural irone of the violet blossoms — is made and sells for from $2.50 to $3.50 a pound according to grade and chemical purity.

The high esteem we have for the fragrance of the violet is
bestowed in the Orient upon the scent of the rose, and these
queens among perfumes have strikingly similar stories. Both
are as costly as they are popular. It requires nearly two tons
of rose petals to produce one pound of attar of roses, the
pure, natural essence. As ionone, the odorous principle of
the violet, can be reproduced more cheaply in the laboratory,
so the geraniol, the basic scent principle of rose, can be obtained more easily and in larger quantities from the oils of
citronella or geranium or palmarosa grass. Indeed, the chemist is able to improve upon the natural attar by adding to
geraniol traces of phenyl-ethyl alcohol, for this chemical is
found in the rose petal and lost in the process of preparing
the natural oil.

Geraniol is one of the most widely used of Nature's perfume ingredients. It is the dominating element in roses and geraniums. Minute quantities are found in many other flower scents. The perfumer has naturally found it exceedingly useful in floral bouquets, creams, and lotions, even in soaps and lipsticks. It is also the bait that lures Japanese beetles into the glass-jar traps. Thus many a fair gardener who for years has used geraniol in her cosmetics has had the opportuntiy to know at first hand what an overpowering, un-rose-like odor this very heart of the essence of rose perfume is when even a few drops of the pure isolate are used undiluted.

When man sets out to make in the factory the alluring smells and enticing flavors that nature manufactures in her plants, he gets off to a flying start by employing a number of her natural aromatic chemicals. Like geraniol extracted from the oils of citronella or geranium these natural isolates he gathers from other cheap, abundant natural sources. Citronellol, for example, comprises eighty per cent of the comparatively inexpensive oil of citronella and is easily recovered from it. From citronellol is prepared hydroxy-citronellal, which makes possible artificial lilac and lily of the valley, two fragrances that nobody has ever been able to extract from the flowers.

Eugenol is likewise the main constituent of oil of cloves and quite simply isolated from it. Treated with caustic soda, it becomes iso-eugenol (an isomer of the same number of atoms but in different arrangement), which is the basis of the useful spicy carnation odors. There is, after all, a sound chemical reason behind the so-called clove pinks of our gardens. Iso-eugenol by oxidation becomes vanillin, the essential aromatic element in the vanilla bean. By this process vanillin is made from cloves, a startling result in flavor-transformations.

Iso-safrol is prepared in the same way from safrol. It in turn is extracted from crude camphor oil. Iso-safrol is by oxidation changed to heliotropin, the delightful scent princi-

ple of the heliotrope. Though now obtained commercially
from camphor, safrol itself is the chief constituent of our once
famous sassafras. Being cheap and notably efficient in mask-
ing unpleasant odors, safrol finds good utilitarian employment in laundry soaps, glue and paste, shoe polish, inks, and
many other similar smelly products.

Terpineol, like safrol, is comparatively cheap and pene-
trating. It has ability to withstand the action of alkalies, so
that it, too, is used in soaps, to which it gives a lilac-like odor.
As you might very well guess from its name, terpineol is extracted from turpentine. All things considered, it is the most
useful tool in the workbox of the aromatic synthesist. Treated
with acetic acid (the acid of vinegar), it yields an artificial
lavender; with formic acid (found in ants), an imitation of
the jasmine; with butyric acid (rancid butter), eucalyptus
odor. Several hundred of its derivatives are useful aromatics,
and terpineol itself enters directly into many famous perfume
blends, as in honeysuckle, jacinthe, Narcisse, sandalwood,
sweetpea, Jockey Club, cologne, and Bois de Nice.

At his best the most skilled perfumer imitates Nature's
blending of fragrances. Her materials and her technique
have both been revealed by the chemist. He has learned not
only the dominant odoriferous principle in natural scents,
but also the complex mixtures of supplementary elements.
Taken apart by analysis, natural jasmine oil is found to be 65
per cent of benzyl acetate, which is also found in gardenias
and jonquils, and which can be most economically prepared
from coal tar. The remaining 35 per cent has the following
approximate composition:

15 per cent linalol: a natural isolate, chief constituent of
linaloe oil and extracted from it, but also found in coriander,
cinnamon, sassafras, orange flowers, and bergamot.

7.5 per cent linalyl acetate: also known as artificial bergamot, and prepared from linalol by treatment with acetic acid.

6 per cent benzyl alcohol: a coal-tar derivative, but also

found naturally in several balsams, bergamot, lavender, hyacinth, and other flowers.

3.5 per cent jasmine: a compound found only in this natural oil, but prepared by chemical synthesis.

2.5 per cent indole: fifteen different chemical syntheses of this material have been worked out; it occurs in oil of cloves and jasmine and in animal excrement; a heavy, unpleasant, feces-like smell.

0.5 per cent methyl anthranilate: made from coal tar, known also as artificial grape flavor.

Brazenly copying Nature's own formula, an artificial jasmine oil is thus prepared in the chemical factory. It must be confessed, however, that if low cost is not the first object and a really high-class product is sought, about 10 per cent of the natural jasmine extract is necessary.

When the chemists set out to build up a thoroughly artificial perfume base, they steal another leaf from Nature's laboratory notebook and borrow her methods. The lovely June fragrance of lilacs in bloom cannot be wrung from the blossoms, but it is reproduced in the laboratory in this wise:

Hydroxy-citronellol: the dominant ingredient, prepared from oil of citronella.

Cinnamic aldehyde: made synthetically, but found in cinnamon and the balsams.

Anisic aldehyde: prepared from anethol from anise or fennel.

Rhodinol: a natural product in geranium, a mixture of citronellol and geraniol, used also as a bait for fox and mink traps.

Heliotropin: made from iso-safrol from camphor.

Phenyl-ethyl alcohol: produced by coal-tar synthesis; a trace is found in attar of roses.

Phenylacetic aldehyde and musk xylene: two synthetic coal-tar preparations which are not contained in the natural aromatics.

Rose absolute and oil of sandalwood: two natural products.

This reads a good deal like grandmother's recipe for mince pie, and as in the pastry so in the perfume, the quantity and quality of the different ingredients may be varied and are apt to be governed by cost. There is no guide save good taste: no rules save the test of the trained palate or nose. Remember, too, that this formidable list of ingredients is only for the lilac perfume base. This is but the foundation of the finished perfume. Very likely that will contain from twenty to as many as fifty different natural and synthetic products — odors, fixatives, diluents, solvents.

This art of the perfumer is one of exceeding great delicacy. The quantities he handles are minute; but their quality must be perfect. Costs are as fantastic as the perspective of Alice's Looking-glass Country. The nose — even a vulgar, uneducated nose — is a precision instrument that detects one one-hundredth of one per cent of bromine or chlorine left in a synthetic after the chemical processes of its manufacture. Infinitely smaller traces of sulphur are ruinous, for sulphur is the arch-enemy of perfume. It occurs naturally in the oils of garlic, onion, mustard, and asafetida, which explains a great deal.

Yet our most cultivated nostrils delight in curious fragrances which experts classify as " burnt," " goat," and even " putrid." Politely these thick, evil, animal odors are described as " Oriental," " heady," " alluring," " exotic." In infinitesimal quantities they heighten the floral fragrances as a dash of salt brings out the full chocolate flavor in fudge or cake icing.

Our modern taste veers away from the sweet flower harmonies popular in Victorian days towards these weighty, carnal odors. Whether this radical change is the effect of gasoline and coal gas upon our olfactory nerve, or of wars and depressions upon our psyche, might be a stimulating subject for debate to try on your next dull dinner companion.

What m'lady pays for the finished creation of the perfumer's art often bears little relationship to the cost of his raw materials. Naturally an ounce bottle on the ten-cent counter will not contain fifty high-priced aromatics even in ultra-microscopic portions. But the compounder's skill in harmonizing unique, tempting perfumes does not of necessity depend upon the use of the most costly ingredients. Furthermore, the charm of the container and the lure of a Paris label both count heavily. Then, too, the advertising man has his say. Many a woman, for the support it gives her self-confidence, will pay five dollars for what she would not otherwise buy for fifty cents. And all jumbled up in this luxurious and fastidious commerce is the belief that the best cosmetics are made exclusively from genuine, unadulterated, natural flower essences.

Nearly thirty-five years ago in the first college lectures on synthetic aromatics the pharmacy students at Columbia University were told by the pioneer American manufacturer of these materials:

" Not a single manufacturer of perfumery in the world today can get along without synthetics."

What was true in 1908 is more true today. That lecturer himself, Alois von Isakovics, did much to increase this use of synthetics by lowering their cost and raising their quality.

As a boy in his native Prague — his father was a Judge Advocate of the Austrian Army — young Isakovics rode two hobbies: chemistry and stamp-collecting. They went together well. For when his father wanted him to become an army officer, he achieved independence to follow chemistry by writing books on philately that sold like peanuts at the circus. Thus he earned his own way to America.

In New York the sixteen-year-old chemist, fresh from the University of Vienna, fell luckily into a curious opportunity. The R. H. MacDonald Drug Company had lost their chemist and with him the formula for their popular and profitable

Vinegar Bitters. Alois believed that he could duplicate their vanished recipe and he did. Three years later, in a loft up in Harlem, he launched the first exclusively synthetic aromatic chemical manufactory in the United States.

That same year, 1889, another young chemist, Francis Despard Dodge, scion of the old essential oil house of Dodge and Olcott, established in 1798, made the single, most important American contribution to the chemistry of aromatics. After graduation with honors from the Columbia School of Mines, then the best opportunity for a practical course in applied chemistry, he went to Heidelberg to study under that genial, joke-loving, bearded Hebrew genius, Victor Meyer, one of the great organic chemists of all time. The young American was by inheritance interested in aromatics and at the outset of his chemical career he began a thoroughgoing study of the then little known oil of citronella. From this he was the first to isolate the important citronellol and to distinguish its allied citronellal. Under his leadership the little laboratory of Dodge and Olcott expanded from testing and purifying essential oils. At the time one aromatic synthetic only was manufactured, methyl salicylate, but they soon added the preparation of safrol, citronellol, and terpineol.

Out of such modest beginnings grew, in answer to the aromatic famine of the first World War, a new American industry. In pre-war days several of the larger essential oil merchants carried on a little purifying and rectifying and blending of perfume bases. The Isermann brothers and Dr. Robert Fries had struggling synthetic chemical plants, hard pressed by ruthless foreign competitors. It was not the kind of business — small quantities of highly refined products — that most Americans choose, and what we needed in scents and flavors were supplied chiefly from France, Switzerland, and Germany.

Whether you consider cosmetics a necessity or a luxury depends almost wholly upon your sex. Most women, though they may know nothing of the history that Cleopatra lived, need no such classical example of the practical values of the smart toilet. Most men — ruling out barbers and beauticians, actors and movie stars as having professional prejudices — are of a different mind. All the difference here between the tactics of offense and defense in the battle of the sexes! But whatever you may think, it is a bald fact that this is a sizable industry. It totals close to $150,000,000, with twice that sum spent in hair-do's and manicures and similar beauty-aid services.

It is something tangible to have achieved independence in these aromatic chemicals. Commercially it cuts down the costs of glorifying the American girl. Chemically it adds one of the most advanced branches of organic technique to our industrial skills.

Just how tangible that accomplishment is was checked up for us in hard dollars by the second World War. Again we were largely cut off from supplies of both natural oils and synthetic chemicals from abroad. Between the end of 1938 and the beginning of 1940 the average price of the most important essential oils (citronella, geranium, peppermint, lemon grass, bergamot, thyme, cassia, cloves, orange, lemon, and vanilla beans) leaped up over 160 per cent. During the same period the average price of twelve representative synthetics and isolates (geraniol, terpineol, musk xylol, hydroxy-citronellal, benzyl acetate, heliotropin, methyl salicylate, phenyl-ethyl alcohol, cinnamic alcohol, coumarin, and vanillin) actually declined nearly 15 per cent.

But the true tale of progress in this new industry is told by the course of the synthetic prices per pound during the two wars, borrowed from the house organ *The Givaudanian:*

	1914	1918	1927	1933	1940
Citronellol	$12.00	$30.00	$4.00	$1.95	$1.40
Geraniol	4.00	8.00	2.50	1.80	1.30
Methyl anthranilate	8.00	55.00	2.00	2.00	2.35

	1914	1918	1927	1933	1940
Phenyl-ethyl alcohol	$17.00	$48.00	$4.75	$3.80	$2.40
Musk xylol	4.00	35.00	2.50	1.80	1.00
Musk ambrette	22.00	150.00	6.50	5.50	3.25
Terpineol	.30	1.25	.35	.35	.26
Average of group	9.20	49.60	3.23	2.45	1.56

To relish the full flavor of those figures be sure not to forget that the year 1927 was the peak of those booming days when American prosperity was guaranteed to be of a new, permanent brand and when all prices were on the upward spiral just before the snapback of 1929. Nor must you overlook that the year 1933 followed the depth of the depression and was in the heyday of all sorts of extraordinary efforts to shove up all American values — wages and prices — to the nostalgic normalcy of those vanished averages.

This business of making synthetic aromatic chemicals may be founded upon the sands of a vain and silly fad. It may be the most senseless of our extravagances, the most costly of our luxuries. Call it all the economic bad names that a great friend of the forgotten man can think of, and then tax it almost out of existence to pay farmers for not raising pigs or cotton, its record shows that it knows and practices the true economics of real abundance. The makers of these delicate scents and pungent flavors follow the same ultra-modern philosophy that inspires the makers of American motor cars, radio sets, chemicals, fertilizers, plastics, electrical gadgets, and what not. They know that more and better goods for less money makes good sense.

CHAPTER VII

IN VITRO: IN VIVO

◇◇

EARLY in January 1937 a young man, well known throughout the country, lay in a Boston hospital stricken with a double infection of those deadly killers the streptococci. He was dangerously ill. His mother came to his bedside by airplane from the White House. The guarded, scrupulously professional bulletins that his physicians gave out were rushed to the front page of every newspaper in the land.

In anxious consultation these doctors determined upon an audacious treatment. They would administer a new drug, so new that only a few of our most alert medical men had even noted the highly sensational clinical reports of its explosive potency in conquering streptococcic bacteria, and those who had done so were reasonably inclined to discount the claims. Discreet physicians in this country and England have learned to be a bit wary of the blasts of scientific publicity that call their attention to new chemical cures discovered in Continental laboratories.

In the case of Prontosil the carefully documented laboratory report in an important German medical journal appeared to be utterly fantastic. A thousand mice inoculated with "strep" germs, treated with this new, carefully patented drug—a thousand cures! Such results—one hundred per cent perfect—transcend all experimental and clinical experience.

[113

Moreover, it was confessed that this mighty destroyer of bacteria in the mouse's body had little or no effect upon them in a test tube. Such contradictions are familiar. Always they shout a taunting challenge to both the bacteriologist and the biochemist. Why, they cry out in the shop-talk of the laboratory, does this chemical have bactericidal action *in vivo* and none *in vitro;* why does it kill germs in the living body and do them no harm in the glass test tube?

If you think about that question, you will guess that within the body the chemical either stimulates some natural germ-killing agent or else it is itself in some way changed into either a poison for microbes or an inhibitor of their activities. But which of these alternatives happens, and again why and how?

Answer those questions correctly and another definite fact, possibly a vital fact of wide importance, will be added to our knowledge of the most delicately complex branch of all chemical science. Very likely, too, another weapon will be found to save thousands of us from our most persistent, most dangerous enemies. These questions plagued those physicians in their consultation. They had been raised about this new drug reported to be so powerful a streptococcus-slayer *in vivo,* yet quite impotent *in vitro.*

To a watchful medical man this " Prontosil " suggested another mystery. Prompt publication of chemical discoveries is good business sense in the pharmaceutical field, yet these astonishing results had been withheld from public print for three years. Even the signature of distinguished Dr. Gerhard Domagk of the Eberfeld plant of the German Dye Trust could not quiet certain lurking suspicions till reports almost as sensational, dealing with patients in English and French hospitals, began to appear in the foreign journals. Such reports were just reaching us at that time, confirming and encouraging; but disturbing too, since they described a number of serious after-effects noted when Prontosil was administered to human beings.

Nevertheless, the experienced and conservative Boston physicians decided to administer this potent chemical to young Roosevelt. The case may well have been more desperate than the country at the time suspected, for once committed to the bold course, they went the full way. Not only did they jab him with needlefuls of Prontosil, but they also gave him tablets of Prontylin, the German trade-name for a related drug which we now know as sulfanilamide.

The results were immediate and vivid. The patient's soaring temperature was pulled down as a boy reels in a kite. Within three days he was quite out of danger.

Even in the days when patent-medicine advertising, free of any restraints, flourished lush and lurid, no press agent ever dreamed of such a glorious introduction for a new drug. Overnight the country learned another of those outlandish chemical names.

" Sulfa — sulfa — " everyone was stuttering, " sulfa-you-know-what-I-mean," and everybody did.

This miraculous cure of a dangerous infection riveted attention. The patient, son of the nation's President; his distinguished physicians, leaders of the profession; the hospital with a famous name — the background for reams of favorable publicity was perfect.

Out of medical literature popped the word " chemotherapy," and the hope of finding definite chemical combatants of all the specific germ diseases, which had been deferred nearly half a century, sprang again to life. In scores of laboratories all over the world chemists began eagerly juggling the complex sulfa-combinations of the molecules.

Curiously this newest wonder drug traces back indirectly to the oldest medicinal specific. For sulfanilamide belongs to the family of coal-tar dyes, founded by aniline purple, which the boy Perkin found by chance when he sought to synthesize quinine, which had been used since 1638 as a true chemotherapeutic agent against the germs of malarial fever. We must confess, like the Spanish dowager who traced her ancestry back to Adam but was forced to admit that there were some dubious generations along about the time of Noah, that chemically speaking there are certain lapses in such a pedigree for sulfanilamide. Historically speaking, however, in the development of the idea of specific drugs to combat particular diseases, the sequence is as complete and logical as the precession of the equinoxes.

Save for dragon's teeth and unicorn's horn, eye of newt and tongue of frog, hair of the dog that bit you, and similar choice ingredients of the witch doctor's concoctions, the vegetable kingdom was our first medicine chest. There are few plants from oak to violet that have not some time or other been used as cures. Leaves and blossoms, seeds and berries, roots and barks, all have been appropriated by the medicine men. Every clime and all peoples have contributed their share to our stocks of drugs, so that it is quite remarkable that two of the most important of all, quinine and cocaine, both came from a single primitive tribe.

The Indians of Peru knew that when they munched coca leaves they killed hunger, deadened fatigue, benumbed pain. They found them excellent to chew on their hard journeys through the high, steep passes of the Andes and most pleasant when one lolled at ease in the warm shadows of the tropic jungle. They had discovered the effects with no understanding of the cause, the subtle habit-forming narcotic, cocaine. So too, with no knowledge of its active principle, quinine, they drank bitter brews of a certain powdered red bark in order to cure the misery of chills and fever. In their malarial country so cherished was this medicine that they named the stately tree from which it was stripped the quinquina, the bark of barks tree.

In glass laboratory apparatus molecule-making is tried out in miniature, and controlled heat is a vital tool of the research chemist.
— Natural-color photographs in Kodachrome

Francisco Pizarro and his conquistadores did little to endear themselves to the Incas, and while the habit-forming coca leaves could not be hidden, the precious secret of the fever-bark was kept from the Spaniards for a hundred years. Even then it was revealed, not for a profitable sale or bribe, but as a free act of charity. A Jesuit who lived and labored in the Indian villages was cured of malaria with the bark by a native medicine man. He returned to Loxa in 1638 with a bundle of quinquina bark and told his story to Don Lopez de Canizares, the corregidor of this Spanish outpost.

Now, just at this time the beautiful lady Ana, wife of Don Luis Geronimo Fernandez de Cabrera Bobadilla y Mendoza, Count of Chinchon and Viceroy of Peru, lay sick of the fever in the palace at Lima. Nine years before, Canizares had been one of the train of petty officials who had welcomed the Count and Countess of Chinchon to their vice-kingdom and he had been captivated by the gracious lady. Besides he was an old crony of her physician, Dr. Juan de Vega. He, therefore, promptly commandeered, in the name of His Catholic Majesty and humanity, the Jesuit's little store of bark; he wrote its strange story and described how it was administered by the Inca medicine man, and sent off the bundle and letter by an Indian runner to his old friend.

Dr. de Vega used the new drug as directed. The fair patient made a rapid and complete recovery. And two years later, when she returned to Spain, she carried back a generous supply of quinquina bark to distribute among the fever-ridden peasants on her husband's estates. The fame of the miraculous bark spread and in memory of the great service the Countess of Chinchon had rendered mankind, Linnæus named the botanical family which yields the fever-bark *cinchona*.

Dr. de Vega followed his patient to Spain bringing with him over one hundred pounds of bark, which he promptly sold in Seville for a hundred reals per pound. Thus began the trade in quinine, which shortly the Jesuits in Peru organized for the collection of the bark and its sale in Spain and Italy, so that cinchona came to be known as Jesuit's powder. This name created prejudices in Protestant England, but its healing virtues prevailed, and its reputation grew so high that in 1679 Louis XIV bought the secret of preparing cinchona powder from Sir Robert Talbor, an English physician, for two thousand gold louis, a pension, and a title.

Year after year the demand in Europe grew and on the slopes of the Andes little bands of native bark-gatherers fared forth to supply it. With never a thought for the time when such reckless methods must exterminate the species, they felled trees, stripped them, and left them to rot on the forest floor. By 1795, when Humboldt visited Peru, he reported twenty-five thousand quinquina trees were being destroyed each year. Half a century later, exhaustion of the vast natural supplies was in plain sight.

Foreseeing an opportunity to transplant the wild trees to plantations on their East Indian island of Java, the thrifty Dutch Government in 1852 sent the botanist of that colony, Justus Hasskarl, to South America to collect slips and seeds of all species of cinchona. He was not welcomed by any reception committees, and none of the customary diplomatic courtesies extended to a distinguished visiting scientist were proffered him. On the contrary he was guided into rough country where poor species grew sparsely; his young plants were continually being left to bask in the torrid sun; his seeds had a habit of getting water-soaked at every river fording. He reached good collecting territory after the seeds had ripened and so lay up in Arequipa, Peru, for the winter. Early in March he crossed the Andes, plunged into the forests of Bolivia, and eventually turned up in the little frontier village of Siva, where he introduced himself to the commandante as José Carlos Muller, a German-Brazilian traveler.

" Just an amateur naturalist, my dear sir, with a fondness

for mountain-climbing and interested in birds and butterflies and plants. And oh, yes, I should very much like to take home some seeds of the famous *Cinchona calisaya* to plant in my experimental botanical gardens. Could you help me get some of these seeds? "

No, the Governor could do nothing; but he introduced him to a good friend who might — well, for a price, almost anything could be bought.

This Clemente Henriquez was an able, unscrupulous rogue who fleeced the good Justus Hasskarl very thoroughly. However, he earned all his fees and bribes since he did produce four hundred living plants of the favored calisaya variety. Two months later these were packed on a sailing vessel at the port of Islay. One hundred and nine days afterwards, on December 13, 1854, they were docked at Batavia. Hasskarl thoroughly earned his honors — Knight of the Netherlands Lion and Commander of the Order of the Oaken Crown — and his post as director of the cinchona plantations in Java.

That was the adventurous beginning. By patient breeding experiments, skillful grafting, and painstaking cultivation, the Dutch botanists have raised the quinine content of wild cinchona bark of 2 per cent to 4–8 per cent in their cultivated product. And the end is that today Java has all but a complete monopoly of the world's quinine supply. That, incidentally, is not the least of the reasons why the fate of the Dutch East Indies is now important in world politics.

Meanwhile the chemists had been delving into cinchona bark. Half a dozen smart analysts suspected that it contained some active principle analogous to the morphine of the opium poppy and the atropine of the belladonna. These mysterious, powerful substances act chemically like an alkali radical to form salts with the acids, hence their name of alkaloids.

As a matter of fact the delicately refined technique of the modern analyst has found thirty-four different alkaloids in cinchona bark. Fortunately the most abundant, and most

valuable, is quinine. This was isolated in 1817 by a pair
of French pharmacists, Pelletier and Caventou who unrav-
eled the chemical mysteries of numerous drug plants. This
was a big forward step. No longer was it necessary for patients to gulp down great nasty draughts of the bitter powder of the fever-bark. The active principle might now be
extracted and administered in definite doses of known
strength and purity. Soon, too, it was discovered that the
alkaloid quinine is a specific poison to the germs of malarial
fever. After Pasteur had solved the riddle of the microbes
and the germ character of this disease was proved in 1880
by Alphonse Laveran, a French army surgeon who was a
mediocre physician and a first-class bacteriologist, this chemotherapeutic action of quinine *in vivo* was quickly demonstrated.

These discoveries set chemists and physicians to work seeking other drug specifics to fight all the germ diseases. The
Pharmacopœia was ransacked. Only one other was found.
The alkaloid emetine from ipecac root kills the parasite of
amœbic dysentery in solution as minutely dilute as one part
in a million.

Hope of finding specific drugs to cure all the diseases paled,
but this merely strengthened the unique position of quinine.
Small wonder Professor Hoffmann suggested that to produce
it synthetically would be important work. Small wonder, too,
that young Perkin failed to duplicate the alkaloid of cinchona
bark. As a group the alkaloids have still almost defied synthesis. But Perkin's chance-found dye blazed a new chemical
trail that led to the next great chemotherapeutic agent.

As the dyes from coal tar multiplied and microscopic technique improved, it was noted that many stains had a highly
selective action on different kinds of tissue and different species of micro-organisms. While such work was all quite new,
back in the seventies, a medical student at Strassburg University pumped a hypodermic needleful of methylene blue into

the veins of a living rabbit. Fascinated, he watched the color appear only in the nerves of the animal. It was a pretty experiment; exceedingly useful, too, for anyone wishing to dissect out the nervous system. It planted a new idea in young Paul Ehrlich's highly imaginative brain and it utterly ruined his medical career.

He had been a thoroughly unreliable student of medicine. No doubt he should have been lancing boils in the clinic when he was watching the tiny nerve ends of that rabbit turn bright blue. Measles and broken collar-bones left him cold. Neither materia medica nor obstetrics roused his interest. The whole race of patients rather bored him. But he would huddle over the muscle of a frog's leg by the hour, patiently paring away paper-thin slices, staining them with hundreds of dyes, slipping them in his microscope to observe and record the color effects. All this was his hobby — his professors counted it a vice and most reluctantly gave him his degree — till that methylene blue coursing visibly along the nerves of a rabbit gave him the inspiration of his life work.

If methylene blue acts only on the nerves, maybe it will kill pain. That idea was quickly disproved. Two others crowded into his head. If a good narcotic could be hitched to methylene blue, an ideal anæsthetic, not affecting any other part of the body, would be the result. If a certain dye will stain only one kind of tissue, why cannot another be found that will stain no tissue but kill the bacteria within the body?

So young Dr. Ehrlich got himself a job as a hospital laboratory assistant, and before long had discovered the tri-acid stain by means of which the white corpuscles in human blood are differentiated sharply, promptly into five varieties. The test is used to this day. It was a neat little triumph for a youngster. After this auspicious start, however, there was for a dozen years no following accomplishment of note. To all appearances Dr. Paul Ehrlich was slipping into the deep rut of a routine laboratory technician — not a very clever technician, at that, and one who would be handicapped with bad health. Threatened with tuberculosis, he went to Egypt and upon his return was invited by the great Robert Koch to work in his laboratory in Berlin.

Within this fertile incubator of bacteriological discovery Ehrlich's two great ideas, dormant since his student days, blossomed luxuriantly. Too luxuriantly, it seemed to his fellow workers at the test tube and microscope, for to explain his theory of chemicals that kill or cripple invading bacteria without injury to their host, he formulated another theory of side chains of groups of chemical atoms with highly selective likes and dislikes for each other. This was gilding the lily in fantastic style. Competent critics demolished his side-chain notions time and again, but he clung to them and defended them with vigor. Some of today's most plausible explanations of how sulfanilamide kills streptococci are suspiciously like the crazy-quilt pattern of Paul Ehrlich's side-chain ideas. All the while he was searching diligently for his " *therapia sterilans magna,*" the drug of drugs that in one gigantic dose would destroy all the microbes in the human body as the angel of the Lord smote down the army of Sennacherib.

The routine laboratory assistant had been transmuted into an archetype of the research scientist. Ehrlich had become a character, an eccentric, the beau ideal of the popular picture of the absent-minded professor. He worked twelve, fifteen, eighteen hours at a stretch. He smoked two dozen black Havana cigars a day and drank several gallons of charged mineral water. He wrote postcards to himself to remind him to have his hair trimmed, that his wife had a birthday, that he was due for dinner at Herr Professor Schmidt's at seven o'clock. His workroom — it could hardly be called a laboratory — was a chaos of multi-colored bottles of dyes, of books and journals. Yet he was a meticulous worker and one of the most patient, persistent researchers that ever tried and tried and tried again. He and his Japanese assistant, Dr. I. Shiga, tested the action of over five hundred different dyes on more than two thousand mice inoculated with trypanosomes in the preliminary work that led up to the beginning of the experiments that ended in his great discovery.

Ehrlich had selected the trypanosomes for three good reasons. They are comparatively large and quite distinctive, hence easy to see and to identify. They are hardy devils, easy to propagate and inoculate into mice. They invariably kill mice — one hundred per cent laboratory results — so that if he could find a single dye that would save a solitary mouse, he would have done something obviously significant.

Ehrlich needed a sensational victory, not to bolster his own extravagant theories or tighten his tenacity, but to show the world. At this time he was installed in a little laboratory of his own at Frankfurt, close to the headquarters and one of the biggest plants of the Dye Cartel. These good neighbors encouraged him in his work.

" This Ehrlich has some wild ideas," so the directors reasoned, " but who knows? He may hit upon something good."

So word went out to the order department to let the Herr Doktor have any and all samples he wanted and to the laboratories to co-operate with him and to humor his fancies. What the shipping clerks thought is not important, but the young chemists in the laboratory cracked nasty little jokes at the expense of this aging researcher who was always just going to make a great discovery, while the older men, though more tolerant, noted that he was neither a good physician, a trained chemist, nor a bacteriologist of any marked ability, and wondered at the faith and generosity of the higher-ups.

But " orders is orders " in a German organization, so when Ehrlich rushed into the head research man's office one morning with another brand-new idea, a competent chemist was told off to execute it. He had been trying out some benzopupurin dyes of the azo family, and while every one of the mice still died, nevertheless, it seemed to him and Shiga that the clotted blood of the little victims contained fewer of the snakelike germs with the distinctive fins. They smeared dozens of tiny slips of glass and under a powerful lens counted and compared. No doubt of it, these dyes did cut down the number of trypanosomes; not sufficiently to give the mouse a fighting chance of life, but here was the first real bit of evidence of progress.

"If only that dye were a bit more soluble in the blood," mused Shiga.

"*Ja, ja,*" interrupted Ehrlich impatiently, "if, if — "

He broke off and, tugging his short gray beard, sat staring at the clutter of microscope slides on the laboratory table before him. Suddenly like a jack-in-the-box he jumped to his feet, "*Gott im Himmel!* I have it! "

Out of the room he rushed and over to his neighbors the dye-makers.

"That benzopupurin dye, almost it works" he explained, pounding the desk. "If we modify it ever so little, maybe it works completely. Let us add to it another sulfonate group."

They did and it did work; not one hundred per cent, for not every mouse lived; but every mouse did not die.

It was the triumph he needed. No longer did the young chemists smile, not even behind his back, and the older men now clamored for a part in his work. Best of all Franziska Speyer gave him a fine new laboratory, a whole building, beautifully equipped, and with all the money he needed for mice and men. In memory of her husband Georg Speyer, this generous Jewess created him a real director of research.

Paul Ehrlich always claimed that he was lucky, but in this great good fortune he was doubly blessed. It brought to him Bertheim and Hata. He could not have found more faithful, skillful assistants than this clever German chemist and this skilled Japanese bacteriologist. Back in the dingy old laboratory, before he began testing dyes against trypanosomes, Ehrlich had tried out the killing powers of all sorts of chemicals upon these ugly, dangerous microbes. Among them was a complicated organic compound containing arsenic, known to chemists as para-amino-phenylarsonic acid, and nick-named atoxyl. Because in the test tube, *in vitro*, the hardy trypanosomes flourished in big doses of atoxyl, he had discarded it; but his old master, Koch, had shown in 1907 that *in vivo* atoxyl causes trypanosomes to disappear from the blood stream. After his partial success with the dye, trypan red, Ehrlich decided to attack these micro-organisms with arsenic.

Here was the fruition of his theory of chemotherapy: by combining arsenic (poisonous alike to trypanosomes and human beings) with an organic group of chemicals that acted selectively upon the micro-organisms, this deadly poison could be administered without danger to the patient. He selected atoxyl as the starting-point of a search for such a compound.

He and Bertheim went to work. He furnished the ideas, Bertheim the skill that built up all sorts of modifications and adaptations of complex organic molecules into which was always shoved at least one atom of arsenic. Their compound Number 1 was the sodium salt of an acetic acid derivative of atoxyl.

Over to Hata's laboratory went a sample of this new white powder for testing on mice inoculated with the fatal germs. Down the throat of two mice it was forced from a medicine dropper while two others were jabbed in the thighs with needlefuls. Nine days later, when all four mice should have been stone dead, two, the two that had been injected with compound Number 1, were alive. A week later, however, they were both blind.

So the patient Hata began all over again and, weighing out five different doses, injected each into two mice, seeking to find the smallest number of grains of No. 1 that would kill the microbes and spare the eyesight. Better results this time, but not good enough for Paul Ehrlich. He had set up a standard, a ratio of three to one for the curative and toxic effects.

Meanwhile Numbers 2, 3, 4, and 5 had come to Dr. Hata. Each was administered orally and by injection into four mice. Every one that saved the life of a single mouse must be scrupulously retested. Some had no effect on the murderous trypanosomes, but arsenic is a powerful poison to microbe and mouse — to man, too — and most did check or cure the disease. Most had dangerous effects also on the animals. They went blind; they had the symptoms of jaundice or dropsy; many had a sort of St. Vitus's dance and became involuntary waltzing mice. All the little victims, just as soon as the tests were checked, were quickly and mercifully disposed of.

Meanwhile the ingenious Bertheim kept on turning out new compounds of arsenic. He reached Number 100, 200, to 300; each in some way a different combination, on up to Number 605. Hata tested them all — good, bad, and indifferent — and rechecked the experiments on every one that kept a single mouse alive for nine days.

Number 606 was diamino-dihydroxy-arsenobenzene-dihydrochloride, $C_{12}H_{14}O_2N_2Cl_2As_2 : 2H_2O$.

For all that array of atoms, so great is the atomic weight of the metallic element arsenic that the As_2 represents 31.5 per cent of the compound. Thus Number 606 carries a big load of the poison, and Hata found that it killed the trypanosomes like a bolt of lightning. And it left the little mice frisking about their wire cages as merry as grigs; coats sleek and soft, eyes bright and beady, appetites ravenous; in a word, healthy, happy little rodents.

After so many hundreds of promising compounds fail, one becomes as cautious as a cat in a strange alley, and the painstaking Hata rechecked to see how close this 606 would come to meeting the exacting three-to-one safety ratio the chief had set up. As it met test after test even the calm, self-contained bacteriologist burned with excitement. Bertheim breathlessly repeated his synthesis of the double-barreled shot of arsenic in that complicated arrangement of carbon, hydrogen, oxygen, and chlorine which Paul Ehrlich had worked out on paper. As for the doctor himself, he was strangely quiet, but he smoked more black cigars than ever.

No doubt about it this time; at last, after 605 mistrials, Ehrlich had devised a killer for the deadly trypanosomes that was harmless to mice. But — and that " but " stood up as big as a mountain — would this 606 kill the trypanosomes that cause sleeping sickness in man? And a great new hope — would it kill the recently found *Spirochæta pallida*, a pale, spiral organism, thought to be closely akin to the trypanosomes and proved to be the cause of syphilis?

Against this great hope Hata had been carefully nursing some syphilitic rabbits. That dangerous plague is neither a pleasant nor convenient material for laboratory experiments. Unlike the trypanosomes of African sleeping sickness, the spirochetes of syphilis cannot be given readily to animals. The ape and the rabbit are the only experimental material easily available. Even when successfully inoculated, instead of killing in from three to nine days, the disease runs an exceedingly chronic course. Had Hata been testing those hundreds of arsenic compounds in rabbits on the spirochetes, the time involved would have strung out to twenty-odd years. The expense, despite Mrs. Speyer's bounty, would have been pyramided prohibitively. Nevertheless he was prepared, and now the moment for the trial had come. On August 31, 1909 half a dozen rabbits, ulcerous with the loathsome disease, were injected with the straw-colored solution of the six-o-sixth compound.

Almost overnight half of that big, mountainous " but " crumbled away. Salvarsan, as Paul Ehrlich lavishly christened his new compound, did kill the germs of both sleeping sickness and syphilis in mice and rabbits. It was safe, absolutely safe, for use on these small animals.

Only the last, thrilling, dangerous step remained. Out of the laboratory Salvarsan must go to the clinic, from the wire cages to the hospital bed.

Paul Ehrlich's old friend Dr. Conrad Alb made the first trials. He effected miraculous cures of the most dreaded, most dreadful of all diseases. Syphilis had been conquered, not to be wiped out of the system in one massive dose, as Ehrlich had dreamed, for the crafty tenacious spirochetes attack many organs and hide away in many tissues. Even the mighty Salvarsan does not poison them directly, but *in vivo* works with the human body to destroy these deadly invaders.

What if the last detail of Ehrlich's glorious vision had not come true? What if the final argument of all his broad theories was not proved? With Bertheim's chemical skill to weave the deadly arsenic into the complicated patterns that his brilliant imagination had pictured, he had created a drug in which the poison selectively destroyed the germs of syphilis. It was a stunning triumph over man's most insidious enemy. But even more than this, Paul Ehrlich's discovery created a new class of weapons against many deadly diseases, raising anew the hope of our ultimate victory over all germ diseases. For with Salvarsan the modern science of chemotherapy was born.

CHAPTER VIII

THE SULFANILAMIDE FAMILY

◇◇

PAUL EHRLICH's discovery of Salvarsan started a great hunt for other chemicals poisonous to invading microbes, yet harmless to the human body. With the devoted Bertheim, he himself continued to build up new, complex combinations of arsenic hoping to find an even more effective weapon against syphilis. Other researchers — chemists, pathologists, biologists — joined the quest. For several years the results were meager indeed, and the feverish interest in chemotherapy gradually cooled.

In one great laboratory, however, the search continued unceasingly. Day after day, year after year, all the elaborate technique of skillfully synthesizing new chemical compounds and then painstakingly testing them in test tubes and in mice and rabbits — *in vitro: in vivo* — was repeated innumerable times by his Frankfurt neighbors, the dye-makers. With the same persistency that kept them for twenty years at the task of finding a profitable process for synthetic indigo, they kept on constructing elaborate molecules and testing them against all sorts of noxious micro-organisms.

When Ehrlich gave up his hunt among the dyes and began concocting arsenic compounds, the dye laboratories went on from his trypan red. Knowing that this trypanosome-killer was an azo dye, they manfully determined to exhaust the possibilities of this organic series. It is said that in twenty-five years they synthesized — and tested too — over six thousand azo compounds, a monumental example truly of the patient, wasteful, slow, but certain experimental process of cut-and-try. In the end, as we shall see, they scored a brilliant triumph.

When Salvarsan proved to be but indifferently effective against the trypanosomes of African sleeping sickness, the German Dye Trust attacked this pernicious parasite in a carefully planned campaign. This research started about 1910, was carried on vigorously throughout the storm and stress of the World War, and was climaxed in 1920 by the announcement of Bayer 205. Amazingly clever molecule-building went into this drug. It boasts the enormous molecular weight of 1428.7 and a formula of $C_{51}H_{84}O_{23}N_6S_6Na_6$. In the grandiloquent manner of Ehrlich they christened it Germanin, and with a commercial skill as smart as their chemical technique, they wrapped it in a most enticing air of mystery.

After the stage had been carefully set Germanin stepped gingerly into world politics. Not through the usual diplomatic channels, but as one medical man to another, a distinguished German physician suggested to a British confrere that he believed it might be possible to exchange the secret of a drug that would abolish the terrible plague of tropical Africa for a return of the lost German colonies.

" Our German people," he argued, " would be proud to make such a splendid contribution to suffering humanity, to have a share also in redeeming the great Black Continent. Think, my dear colleague, what it would mean to the English to make Africa, all of Africa, a white man's land. It is the dreadful sleeping sickness that is the big obstacle blocking the exploitation of all the vast rich equatorial regions. Believe me, we can wipe out that plague absolutely; remove completely that barrier against progress. England would be the chief beneficiary, of course; but Germany would like, would well deserve, a part in that important work."

Somehow or other this proposal did not appeal strongly to the Englishman. He was sufficiently worldly-wise to know that the morals of international diplomacy are not as straightforward as the physicians' oath of Hippocrates; nevertheless, this proposal so smacked of wholesale medical blackmail that it left a sour taste in his mouth. He did agree, however, to take the matter up with a close friend high in the Government.

Just exactly what happened nobody now seems to know. The stories told in London and Berlin are quite contradictory. There are, of course, no official records. It is quite clear, however, that the English did not react to this suggestion as the Germans had anticipated. Nothing more than a buzz of rumors came of it, and shortly thereafter, when Fourneau in France succeeded in duplicating the elaborate synthesis of Germanin, even the rumors all died a natural death.

The hopes raised by this well-publicized chemical were not fulfilled. In spite of its potency in mice, it proved to be but weakly toxic to the deadly trypanosomes in human beings. Save for its little flurry in international politics, Bayer 205 was not greatly unlike a number of other elaborate coal-tar derivatives which in the twenty-five years following 1910 were hailed as epochal advances in chemotherapy. Some of these have become real weapons in our endless fight against disease. All have added their bit to our knowledge; knowledge of complex organic synthesis and knowledge, too, of the action of chemicals and groups of chemicals upon microbes and men; all of it knowledge that brings us closer and closer to Paul Ehrlich's *therapia sterilans magna*, the cure of cures which shall kill all the germs in one grand dose.

While Ehrlich and Bertheim were busy putting arsenic into over six hundred different combinations a young chemistry student named Paul Gelmo, hard at work for his doctor's degree at the Vienna Institute of Technology, synthesized a new coal-tar derivative with the formula $C_6H_8N_2O_2S$. In his thesis, published in 1908 — the date is important — he did a very thorough job of describing this new compound. He set forth its principal chemical and physical characteristics and detailed the method of its preparation. Very properly, from the chemist's point of view, he called this pretty, white, crystalline powder para-aminobenzene sulfonamide. It has since become famous and we have very sensibly nicknamed it sulfanilamide.

That tireless prospecting of the azo dyes which was going on in the Bayer laboratories of the German Dye Trust, was at this time engaging the skill and energy of an exceedingly competent chemist, Dr. Heinrich Hörlein, director of all the pharmaceutical research. Liberally backed by the management, he had plenty of funds, the best of equipment, and a competent staff of assistants. The research had been planned and organized with customary German thoroughness, and like the divisions of an invading army proceeded along several distinct lines to a common objective. One group twisted and turned the azo molecules — so called from the French *azote,* nitrogen — making all sorts of compounds and derivatives. Each new product was then tested as a dye and as a bactericide. No worthy product, either as a color or as a drug, was to be missed. All of which sounds quite simple, but every step requires a highly trained man, dexterous, patient, and scrupulously exact in his technique and his thinking.

Quite probably Dr. Hörlein, or some of his associates in the dyestuff department, knew all about the work that young Paul Gelmo was doing at the Vienna Institute. It is a responsibility of the good research director to keep an eye on likely students in the universities, and this Gelmo was plainly an up-and-coming chemist specializing in a subject right within their field. If not, we may be sure that the ink was hardly dry on his thesis before one of the " library researchers," whose duty it is to winnow out every new and significant fact from the current literature and see that it reaches the desk of the man in the organization best able to appreciate and use it, spotted that competent description of the synthesis of para-aminobenzene sulfonamide.

At all events, less than a year after the publication of Gelmo's paper Hörlein, using his new product as a starting-point, perfected an attractive brick-red dye, the first of a new group of azosulfonamide dyes. The record of the German Patent Office is clear on this point. It reveals also that during the next two years three other dyes of the same general group seemed to the Dye Trust promising enough to warrant patent protection.

These azosulfonamide dyes, containing the SO_2NH_2 chemical group, have had a respectable, but not sensational commercial career in the textile trade. They are level dyeing, which you remember was not one of the conspicuous virtues of Perkin's famous mauve, and because of their affinity for protein cells, they are exceptionally fast on wool to washing and milling.

Not a hint had yet been dropped that any of the products containing the now famous SO_2NH_2 group had shown the slightest bactericidal action. We know that those products which are patented and placed on the market are but a small fraction of the total prepared and tested. We know, too, that a very thoroughgoing investigation of all kinds of azo derivatives on various bacteria, both *in vitro* and *in vivo*, was being carried on simultaneously with the development of the dyes. It would seem curious indeed if some of these sulfonamide combinations had not been found to be fatal to microbes, especially since outside the Dye Trust this significant fact had been discovered and published. As early as 1913 Eisenberg had reported that chrysoidine, a brown dye of the azo family, destroyed certain bacteria *in vitro*, and six years later it was only through an unlucky mischance that two Americans failed to beat the whole world to the discovery that sulfanilamide is a master murderer of streptococci.

In our own Rockefeller Institute, right in New York City, Drs. Heidelberger and Jacobs were seeking an efficient chemical weapon to conquer the dangerous coccus bacteria of pneumonia. Jacobs, who had been graduated from Berlin just before the World War, suggested to his research teammate that Gelmo's sulfanilamide might well be a likely starting-point. First they worked in the direction of the azo dyes. They diazotized sulfanilamide — that is, they added to it two nitrogen atoms — and then coupled it with hydrocuperine. Dyes in this series, so they discovered, kill pneumococci with some success *in vitro*.

One hardly needs to be adept in biochemistry to surmise how " warm " these Rockefeller Institute chemists were in the great chemotherapy hunt when they struck this trail. They missed the right clues because they were sleuthing blindfolded without even the faintest notion of how the sulfonamide compounds they had just prepared acted on bacteria.

Since 1919 we have had a peek or two, but the men who have put in many, many hours of hard labor trying to discover why and how drugs of this family destroy bacteria seldom see eye to eye. The Rockefeller workers were looking for a poison that would slay the germs instantly as Robert Koch tried to kill the tuberculosis bacilli by injecting poisonous bichloride of mercury into the blood stream.

We at least know today that these sulfonamide drugs are not true germicides. They do not kill; they injure bacteria by interfering with their life processes. Then the natural protective and recuperative processes of our body are able to overcome these weakened invaders. We are quite certain that this mode of action is fundamentally chemical, that the drug upsets the normal reactions of the bacteria's life functions, though what these reactions are and how they are disorganized by the drug are subjects of hot debate. Furthermore, the experts disagree as to whether this chemical disorganization attacks the bacteria's reproductive system, or their powers of assimilation, or the elimination of their poisonous wastes; in other words, whether the invading germs are defeated because of compulsory birth control, starved out, or repelled by poison gases. Victory comes to the sulfa-drugs not from a direct attack on the micro-organisms, but from a sort of economic embargo, a chemical boycott. This information has meant a great change in the tactics of the research campaign.

Back in 1913, however, Drs. Heidelberger and Jacobs knew but few of the many facts that have since been arrayed to support these various theories. Therefore their plan of campaign was wrong. They could not even suspect which group of atoms in their complex chemicals was significant, although they did almost stumble over this secret. Maybe they sensed it, for from the dyes made from sulfanilamide they went on to link sulfanilamide to quinine. This led to a dead end. Discouraged, they went off the right track to pursue what seemed to be a more promising line.

What went on behind the scenes in the Elberfeld laboratories of the Dye Trust during the next few years is a closed book. Chemical manufacturers are generally about as communicative as the Sphinx, and one of their least favorite topics of dinner-table conversation is the research work that they are carrying forward. As for the laboratory notebooks of their research workers, they are kept locked up in the safe. It takes a lawsuit over a patent to open such records to public inspection.

This secretiveness is not wicked or sinister. It is perfectly natural, inherent in the business of making molecules for sale. For this is a bitterly competitive business, and, fortunately for the greater comfort and better health of us all, this competition is sharply focused upon improved processes that lower costs and upon new products that open up wider markets.

" Know how " is the best asset of any chemical enterprise. And " know how " is born in the laboratory and raised in the plant.

Christmas Day 1932 is the next known date in the chronicle of the sulfanilamide family. That day Drs. Fritz Mietzsch and Josef Klarer filed application for a German patent on an orange-red dye, a derivative of sulfanilamide. Their new dye was closely akin in chemical structure to the brown dye chrysoidine which nineteen years before had been found to be a good microbe-destroyer.

Nobody paid any particular attention to this newcomer. Since Drs. Mietzsch and Klarer were in the employ of the Dye Trust their patent was, as a matter of course, assigned to the I.G. Farbenindustrie. " Just another I.G. dye," said hundreds of those hawk-eyed library researchers who are continually scanning the patents of all countries. No doubt in a few of the bigger dye laboratories little sample batches were synthesized and a few trial dyeings made. Nobody took it into the pharmaceutical laboratories. Apparently, too, nobody noticed that when this dye was patented in the United States it was assigned to the Winthrop Chemical Company, which is the drug agency of the I.G. in this country.

The following May came the first inkling of the new dye's medicinal virtues. At a meeting of dermatologists in Düsseldorf a Dr. Foerster reported that it had cured a child of staphylococcic blood-poisoning. A single case of this sort seldom makes medical history, and still the new dye was not suspected to be chiefly important as a pharmaceutical. Even when the I.G. christened it Streptozon, which indicates clearly that the godfather knew something about its usefulness against streptococcus infections, nobody caught on.

The following year this name was changed to Prontosil, and during 1933 and 1934 at a number of German medical meetings several individual physicians made brief and not too detailed reports of the successful use of Prontosil against

From sulphuric acid to sulfanilamide, sulphur melted a thousand feet underground and pumped up to " freeze " in these vats is a most useful chemical element.   *— Courtesy Texas Gulf Sulphur Co.*

various forms of streptococcic infections. Still the drug was not officially sponsored by the I.G. No information on experimental work with mice or rats or rabbits was published. No elaborate, detailed reports of clinical experience appeared in the German medical journals. None of the customary favorable background for the great blast of scientific propaganda which precedes the introduction of another new drug was being built up. But by now a very few, very alert biochemists and bacteriologists outside of Germany had begun to take notice of Prontosil.

Behind the scenes in the Elberfeld laboratories the big, blond, blue-eyed research executive in charge of all pathological work had taken personal supervision of elaborate experiments with this little heralded Prontosil. This belied the lack of attention this new drug was apparently receiving. Back in 1933, shortly after the patents were issued, Dr. Gerhard Domagk jabbed into a thousand white mice a pure culture of streptococcus bacteria sufficient to kill a thousand cats. According to all past laboratory experience, and there is a huge stack of reports and statistics available on this infection in these animals, the life expectancy of those mice was exactly nil. Under any conceivable circumstances, the one-thousandth mouse would be dead within three days. No known drug could save a single one. But the brawny pathologist with the vigilant brain and the subtle fingers forced big doses of Prontosil down a thousand little throats. A gruesome holocaust of white mice was turned into glorious scientific triumph. Every last mouse recovered.

Prudently Dr. Domagk repeated the experiment with rabbits. The results were as sensationally successful. He observed that enormous doses of Prontosil apparently slaughtered the streptococci and obviously left his laboratory animals unharmed by any toxic effects. Here was the dream of Paul Ehrlich, of the massive dose that would kill all the baneful micro-organisms without hurt to the body, impressively turned into a fact demonstrated by carefully controlled experiment. He commissioned his assistants to recheck the results, varying the dose and extending the experiments to other bacteria.

Then his own daughter was stricken down by the same hardy, deadly strep germs that he was fighting in the laboratory. She had pricked her finger with a sewing needle. Somehow she caught a streptococcus infection. Tortured by the haunting nightmare that it was he who had been the cause, that one of those little chains of beadlike bacteria had escaped from his test tubes and been carried home on his fingers, his face, his hair, he rushed her to the hospital. Her alarming condition became threatening. The surgeons cut, and then cut again; still the infection spread. Domagk had seen the miracle of the thousand mice and he believed. Clinical experience was still far too scanty to justify the use of Prontosil on human beings. But Domagk believed. He had faith in his own experiments and the courage of his convictions. He administered one of Ehrlich's massive doses of Prontosil to the dying child and she lived. The researcher who had witnessed that glorious scientific triumph in the laboratory had himself brought it to a crowning conclusion at the bedside, a magnificent victory over the vicious streptococci.

Still there was no publication of those astonishing laboratory tests. One, two, three years passed. Suddenly in the February 1935 issue of the *Deutsche medizinische Wochenschrift* appeared a shortish article, "A Contribution to the Chemotherapy of Bacterial Infection." Beneath this modest title was the signature Gerhard Domagk. In the cold, clipped style of the professional scientific paper he reported the results of administering Prontosil to streptococci-infected mice.

Like a bolt from the blue those results — a hundred per cent perfect — left biochemists, pathologists, physicians thunderstruck. They were too good to be true. That percentage was more than miraculous; it was fantastic. Besides, all the progress made fighting microbes with chemicals had been against protozoa. No headway had been made against the more simple micro-organisms of the bacterial class, the streptococci, the bacilli, the pneumococci, the gonococci, the meningococci. Yet not only are these mongers of deadly diseases, but their attacks do not bring any immunity. It was quite reasonable that the eminent physicians caring for young Roosevelt should question the early accounts of Prontosil's stupendous efficacy.

Among the very few, exceedingly acute scientific men in all the world who before the publication of Domagk's bombshell report had suspected that Prontosil might be something more than a nice orange-red dye for woolens was the French bacteriologist Levaditi. He wrote the I.G. for a sample. They replied regretting that at the moment they were unable to comply with his request. After a decent interval he wrote again, and when he received another regretful and evasive answer he began to smell a rat of quite a different color from the rodents in his laboratory cages. He called in the chemist Fourneau. You recall him as the man who knocked the props from under any possible international deal in Germanin by showing how that very elaborate molecule might be synthesized. This Fourneau plainly rejoices that the French law specifically forbids the issuing of any patent for any chemical useful in medicine.

" Can you make Prontosil? " asked the bacteriologist, shoving the German patent under his nose.

The chemist skimmed over the disclosure sections and said that it appeared to be child's play, but one could never be quite certain about a German patent. "If you want some, my friend, I should be delighted to try. How much will you require? "

" Half a kilo or so would be splendid; more than enough to make a few little tests that I have in mind."

" *Eh bien,* we shall see what we shall see," and Fourneau went back to his laboratory.

In due course Dr. Levaditi received a wide-mouthed, glass-stoppered bottle containing a kilo of tiny red crystals and labeled: " Prontosil — *avec mes compliments* — Fourneau."

These red crystals Levaditi distributed among a team of his collaborators at the Pasteur Institute: Dr. and Madame Trefouels, Bovet, and Nitti. It did not take them long to discover that Prontosil possessed extraordinarily effective anti-streptococcus powers *in vivo* and was practically innocuous against the same bacteria *in vitro*. Here was the old puzzle of so many chemotherapeutic agents, but in a new material and against a new type of organism. Deadly in the living animal, harmless in the test tube — why? how?

Being good scientists they tackled these taunting questions. Being French, their method of attack was quite different from the laborious, painstaking, cut-and-try system of the Germans. They sat down around the table to consider the facts and then build a theory that would explain them. Afterwards it would be the proper time to test out the theory.

The first fact was as self-evident as sunlight. Something happened to the Prontosil molecule inside the body of the mouse, or the rabbit, or the man. So they drew a graphic formula of Prontosil and, pooling their combined knowledge and experience, pictured all the possible changes that were likely in such biochemical reactions. They drew similar pictures of all the azosulfonamide molecules that Fourneau could find in the literature and of a couple that he thought up in his own head. Each one certainly might break down to yield sulfanilamide, the parent substance from which all had been built up.

" *Eh bien,* let us try sulfanilamide, and we shall see what we shall see."

What they saw very promptly was that it was sulfanilamide, not the more complicated dyes made from it, that had the bactericidal powers. They published their findings to the world. The I.G. at once coined another trade-name and began offering sulfanilamide to the medical profession as Prontylin.

Slipping through that loophole in the French law, the dexterous Fourneau, aided and abetted by the able staff of the Pasteur Institute, had again broken a German medicinal chemical patent. In this case his blow was a knockout. Nobody would want the more complex, carefully patented Prontosil if the simpler, unpatentable sulfanilamide did all the work of germ-killing.

The importance of the date of Gelmo's doctoral thesis, 1908, twenty-seven years before, now becomes clear. His capital descriptions of sulfanilamide and his detailed directions for its preparation were all public property. Anybody who could might make sulfanilamide: it could not be patented.

Herein, probably, lies the explanation of the delayed introduction that Prontosil had to the medical world. No doubt the scrupulous, skillful exploration of the sulfonamide compounds had revealed to the Dye Trust scientists the secret that the French research team discovered by characteristically Gallic methods. Accordingly, the launching of their patented Prontosil had been held up by the I.G. executives either to accumulate such a stunning mass of evidence that its potency would stampede the medical profession (which in truth it did) or else in the hope that other new patentable sulfonamide combinations might be found (as has also happened in the development of sulfapyridine, sulfaguanidine, and others). After their long years of accumulated experience it is ironical that the best of these newest sulfa-drugs have come, not from the I.G. laboratories, but from English and American workers.

In England as well as in France work was now being done

on Prontosil and sulfanilamide. What the French research team by brilliant scientific deduction had discovered about the essential efficacy of sulfanilamide was confirmed by the painstaking experiments of Buttle, Gray, and Stephenson. In January 1936, thirty-eight women suffering from child-bed fever in Queen Charlotte's Hospital, London, were treated with Prontosil by Dr. Leonard Colebrook and his assistant Dr. Neave Kenny. All but three lived. Ten of the thirty-eight previous patients suffering from this same high-fatality disease had died.

These phenomenal clinical findings, and others, together with the report comparing results obtained with sulfanila-mide and its derivatives were the sensation of the Congress of Microbiologists at London that summer. This scientific gathering turned out to be a jolly little coming-out party for the sulfanilamide family, their debut into the high society of medical science.

The great gusts of applause that swept over that distin-guished, dignified audience when Dr. Colebrook folded up his paper and sat down had not died away before a tall, slender, loose-hung figure — an American as surely as the Bunker Hill Monument — might have been observed slipping out of the meeting. It was Dr. Perrin Hamilton Long and he was hurrying to a cable office. Trembling with excitement, he scrawled his message to the Johns Hopkins Hospital: that they should immediately get working samples of Prontosil and sulfanilamide; that he needed them on his return; that he was giving up a half-holiday trip to the Continent; that he would be back on the earliest possible boat.

The full force of the facts about these streptococcus-killing drugs hit Dr. Long squarely. For nearly three years he and Dr. Eleanor Bliss had been fighting those wicked, beadlike strep germs, poking them into rats and rabbits, making blood-tests and cultures, hunting for a serum that would cut down their high death-rate records. He had, therefore, a wholesome respect for the vitality and virility of the whole coccus tribe. He could appreciate more comprehensively than most of Dr. Colebrook's listeners that a victory had been won which would mean a new epoch in medical practice.

He had, moreover, the true scientific spirit, and he thrilled to the core of his being at this triumph. It threw into the discard hour upon hour of his thoughts and works, but his professional *esprit de corps* was spontaneous and sincere. For was he not the son of a physician, even unto the third generation of country doctors out in Ohio? Had he not been schooled in the laboratories of the Rockefeller Institute? There he did good microbiological work, and when Francis P. Garvan, the same who thought up the Chemical Foundation as a means of making the German patents available to the whole American chemical industry, raised the $350,000 J. J. Abel Fund for research on the common cold at Johns Hopkins, young Long moved down to Baltimore to join this hunt. Streptococcic infections are an ingredient in the devil's brew of germs involved in this apparently simple, often complicated ailment, and Dr. Long began studying the little shiny chains of cocci bacteria during the common-cold campaign. When the exhaustion of the funds ended that research without definite, successful results, Garvan, who liked this tall, dark-haired young researcher from Ohio and was drawn strongly to his work on the streptococcus, made him a proposal.

Francis Patrick Garvan never knew the meaning of defeat. He was a Celt: a rank sentimentalist and a joyous fighter, generous and tenacious; an enthusiast with a heart as big as a barrel and a legally trained brain as clear as quartz crystal. Into the battle against the common cold, as in the fight against the German Dye Cartel, he poured time, energy, and money; and when it came to no triumphant conclusion, he recognized that in research a negative fact is valuable and that all the dollars he had helped to raise had not been wasted. Furthermore he found something positive and useful to salvage, for he saw that the research had developed in young Dr. Long a scientific worker of real promise.

However, in 1933 it was not easy to get subscriptions to continue such work. In the best of good times patient money for long-haul research projects is hard to find even at the meeting of the directors of a company that invests in research as insurance of future profits. The common-cold campaign could no longer be financed, but Mr. and Mrs. Garvan decided that, if Dr. Long would take command in the field, they would wage a private war against the streptococci. It would be a memorial to their little daughter Patricia, a victim of this same murderous germ; a practical expression of their hope that other children might be saved. So they inquired whether Drs. Long and Bliss would be interested in concentrating on the extermination of the wicked strep clan.

Of course they were interested, terribly interested, so interested that for two years they worked uncounted hours in a hard, minute, exacting, disheartening battle against the microscopic enemy. And here in London they had found the weapon to conquer this tough, venomous microbe. Joyfully they canceled their holiday plans and hurried back to their laboratory. Good research workers are just that kind of idiots.

Publication of Dr. Colebrook's historic paper in the *Lancet* was the formal introduction of the sulfanilamide family to English-speaking scientific circles. Brief clinical notes in obscure Continental medical journals might escape attention. Dr. Domagk's laboratory report of hundred-per-cent results with streptococcus-infected mice might lift a credulous eyebrow. But an article in the *Lancet* is something quite different. It demands attention and commands respect.

Copies of this most authoritative of all medical journals containing this now famous paper reached America about the 20th of June 1936. As a matter of regular routine one was placed on the desk of the research director of the Calco

Chemical Division of the American Cyanamid Company. To Dr. M. L. Crossley years of fact-thirsty habit have made the *Lancet* must reading.

Twenty years previously he had been that same young chemistry instructor who had worked on the sorely needed biological stains and uncovered the unsavory secret of the excess starch in gentian violet. Day after day since that early work he had searched among the coal-tar derivatives — synthesizing, manufacturing, applying — growing as the company grew, till now he is captain of the alert and aggressive research team of one of our greatest chemical corporations. As his experienced eye swiftly scanned the *Lancet's* closely printed pages, it was stopped short by the Colebrook article. He skimmed through it. Then he read it again. For several moments he sat quite still piecing together a score of related facts stored in his memory. Within ten minutes he was eagerly discussing the article with the head of the Calco Pharmaceutical Division, Dr. Elmer Northey.

That big, husky, self-contained Westerner is a resourceful chemist. He caught immediately the idea that had flashed before Dr. Crossley. Here was something important. They must get to work at once upon sulfanilamide and its derivatives. It would be a shrewd stroke to be in commercial production so as to anticipate demand, for since it was unpatentable, there would be a scramble among the manufacturers for the market. Dr. Crossley was due to leave for a scientific junket to Europe; but before he sailed early in November, Calco was making sulfanilamide in a pilot plant, and when he returned in February, an industrial operation had already turned out several thousand pounds, the earliest large-scale production in America.

Having determined upon a bold plunge into sulfanilamide manufacture, these two keen chemical brains spent the balance of that June afternoon planning a research of the drug's chemical kin. They had immediately twigged the fact that other derivatives of this sulfa-group might have unexpected therapeutic potencies. They planned to explore various nitrogen compounds and to try linking it also with groups of known anti-malarial properties such as quinoline, isoquinoline, acridine, and others.

Soon samples of various sulfa-drugs were being shipped out of the Bound Brook laboratories for testing at the biological laboratory at Cold Spring, New York, for at this famous scientific center a chemotherapeutic laboratory was maintained by the company as an outside check-up on results. Shortly thereafter Dr. Perrin Long, who had got wind of these pioneering American researches, eagerly offered to cooperate in further testing drugs that seemed promising from the preliminary work upon animals.

During 1937 the resourceful Dr. Northey and his team of fourteen chemists had synthesized over a hundred different likely sulfa-compounds. Meanwhile at the Stamford, Connecticut, laboratory, research headquarters of the parent Cyanamid Company, Dr. Richard Roblin and his team of researchers began their own hunt for good new sulfa-compounds. The pleasant-spoken Dr. Roblin with his inevitable cigarette and his dozen associates matched, independently of their friendly rivals at Calco, their synthesis of sulfapyridine and sulfathiazole. Stamford scored in their original synthesis of sulfaguanadine and sulfadiazine.

The new products made by Dr. Roblin's group were sent to the company's Lederle laboratories for testing; but in 1939 a new chemotherapy division was installed at Stamford. Dr. W. H. Feinstone was brought from Dr. Long's laboratory in Baltimore and put in charge of the testing of all new synthetic products developed by both the Calco and the Stamford teams, which were now both brought under Dr. Crossley's general supervision.

This check-up is no slapdash procedure. The capable, self-confident Harry Feinstone drives himself and his ten-man team through all the meticulous technique of biological testing. They take fifty white mice divided into five groups of ten each, one of which is kept and observed as a control. Each of the other groups is infected, with staphylococcus (boils), with pneumococcus type I, with streptococcus, and with Porto Rico influenza, Francis type. The germs are injected by hypodermic needle into the belly and the drug to be tested is administered through a tube into the stomach.

For a month the test animals are observed as carefully as a mother watches her first-born, and any drug that shows promise is elaborately tested to determine its toxicity by establishing the accurate lethal dose. Next comes an examination of the effect of repeated doses, on both rabbits and dogs; and after three months of such treatment a complete microscopic examination is made of the brain, spinal cord, muscles, the various organs, even the marrow of the bones. Thin sections of stained tissues are compared with specimens from undosed animals. If no histological changes are noted, then the drug is recommended for clinical testing. All this has taken from fifteen to eighteen months.

During the first year of the sulfa-search at Calco and Stamford several new compounds came through these grueling tests. Among these sulfapyridine was produced months before Dr. L. E. H. Whitby in England made public his work with this compound in treating pneumonia. From the American point of view this story has a double twist of irony. On November 7, 1937, that inveterate enemy of the germs, Francis P. Garvan, died of pneumonia. At the time, Dr. Whitby had carried sulfapyridine through its tests with mice and was proving its effectiveness in the Dudley Road Hospital in Birmingham. Another six months and this drug would have been ready to save Garvan's life.

Credit for sulfapyridine is widely given to the English pharmaceutical house of May & Baker, but it is said to have been discovered by their friends Poulnec Frères of Paris. At least the British and U.S. patents on sulfapyridine are in the name of the English firm, but those on the Continent and in South American countries are taken out by Poulnec. Certainly the research teams of the American Cyanamid Company had quite independently discovered this drug. The sulfapyridine patents all are beautifully tangled — there are other claimants and some makers who are ignoring all patents — but obviously all the pioneering was not done abroad.

A similar situation has arisen with sulfathiazole, synthesized in both the Stamford and the Bound Brook laboratories. A clean-cut discovery in this field is credited to Dr. Roblin's company of Dr. Crossley's battalion of researchers in the synthesis and proving of sulfaguanadine. This drug is winning its spurs as conqueror of germs that infect the lower digestive tract causing dysentery, cholera, typhus, and typhoid. Too new yet to be thoroughly tested in clinics are butyryl-sulfanilamide and sulfadiazine. The former is interesting because its sodium compound can be introduced directly into the blood stream, where the alkalinity of other sulfa-compounds is very toxic: the latter because it contains two nitrogen groups and appears to be equally effective against streptococcus and pneumococcus with fewer, or certainly different, toxic effects on the human system.

More than two thousand sulfonamide derivatives have been put together. Thousands of others are possible. Many will be synthesized. Some obviously will be valuable chemotherapeutic agents. What is needed to lift chemotherapy out of hit-and-miss experiments is more definite knowledge of the biochemistry involved. How and why? How do these drugs act *in vivo* and why do they help annihilate the invading micro-organisms? American workers are doing more than their share in discovering bit by bit the facts that will fit together to solve this amazing jig-saw puzzle. Ehrlich's great hope of a wholesale slaughter of germs again shines brightly before us.

CHAPTER IX

TWO MONOPOLIES:
JAPANESE AND AMERICAN

◇◇

DURING the winter of 1918–19 a star salesman of industrial explosives made a series of reports to the home office that put his company into a new business and streamlined the oldest chemical industry in the United States.

The World War was over. The Hercules Powder Company, pre-war manufacturers of dynamite and sporting powders, had naturally expanded their plant capacity tremendously and gathered together a strong, loyal staff of technicians, plant operators, and administrators. Paraphrasing the good, old jingoistic jingle:

> We have the plants; we have the men;
> And we have the money too.

But, by jingo, what to do? That was the problem that kept the Hercules executives awake nights.

Suggestions of all sorts flooded into President Dunham's office. He had always encouraged this sort of co-operation among the members of what he proudly called " the Hercules family," and everybody, it seemed, from the senior vice-president to the bottle-boy in the Kenvil laboratory, had ideas. Some looked good. Others seemed bad, but might be better than they appeared. A misstep would be most unwise

— and expensive — so let us, the far-sighted R. H. Dunham reasoned, " make a business of finding a new business." Accordingly, he carried off half a dozen of his family heads to Atlantic City, away from persistent visitors and the more insistent telephone, to sit down quietly and deliberate upon the question: " Where do we go from here? " The immediate result was the organization of an Industrial Development Division headed by alert Vice-President N. P. Rood.

" Let us," said the new chief, " open an office in Philadelphia so as to be as free as possible from the routine and influences of headquarters in Wilmington."

Thus a systematic survey of every business possibility that bobbed up was undertaken. The rayon field was thoroughly scouted, but Viscose was strongly entrenched and the du Ponts were planning to enter the synthetic-fiber industry. At one time transparent film appeared to be very tempting, but the company had no special qualifications for merchandising to the general public, so that idea was dismissed. Then the reports of " Tubby " James began coming in from the South.

Special sales effort had been put behind agricultural explosives, and noting an exceptional number of sizable orders for dynamite from the Deep South, he had been sent down to cash in on what seemed to be a stump-blowing carnival. Friendly as a Newfoundland puppy, this jovial, resourceful salesman was as sharp as a red fox in picking up sales leads, and he had not been down in Mississippi a day before he had learned the secret of this boom in the stump-blasting business.

" Clearin' land fer more cotton? Shucks, no! They're gettin' out old, dead pine stumps fer th' wood-rosin folks."

" And who the devil are the wood-rosin folks? " he asked.

" Wal, first of all there's Yaryan — Homer T. Yaryan, come from Toledo, Ohio. He's a ripsnortin' critter; smokes fifty black cigars a day; swears worser'n a gray-eyed nigger beating up a balky mule. But is he an inventor? They do say he's invented mighty nigh onto a hundred gadgets, all the way from them swell sectional bookcases Lawyer Jones just bought fer his office down to this scheme fer gettin' rosin and turpentine outter old stumps. He begun at Gulfport back about 1909 and he's got a new plant over near Brunswick, Georgia. Then next, there's the Newport crowd at Bay Minette, Alabama. Newport Industries, Inc., they calls themselves. They don't say much, but they take in a powerful lot o' stumps. Mixed up in the chemical business, dyes outter coal tar, up in Milwaukee, Wisconsin. And last there's the Mackie Pine Products Company, newcomers, just startin' up."

That evening James wrote his first report on wood naval stores. He became an expert on the subject and an enthusiast. He delved into the romantic lore of the ancient pine-products industry and he visited the various plants operating this most modern process.

He learned that it was the Phœnicians who first calked their ships' hulls with pine pitch and tarred their hempen rigging. Those hardy navigators who sailed through the Pillars of Hercules to distant Britain for tin and coasted down the African continent trading for gold and ivory may well have been taught these ship-chandler's arts by the Gauls or even by the bearded Vikings of the frozen North, but they at least deserve credit for introducing them to the classical world. Since their day, till the time of the iron hull and the power-driven propeller, pine pitch and tar were necessary supplies for ships. It was a law of Queen Elizabeth's, commandeering them for her royal frigates, that gave them the general name of " naval stores."

In 1608 the first cargo of American-manufactured wares consisted chiefly of chemical raw materials: pine tar and pitch and pot-ashes. Throughout the colonial period this trade in naval stores and potash continued, and it flourished long after the colonies had won independence. American potashes were driven from a commanding position in world trade after 1860 when the mineral potash salts of the famous Stassfurt deposits began to be seriously exploited. Even to this day American rosin and turpentine continue to dominate world markets. In the more recent development of chemicals prepared from the sap of the Southern pines — that enterprise which Salesman James was urging upon the Hercules Development Committee — we have a virtual monopoly.

The financial backers of that first, ill-fated English colony in Virginia were a group of hard-headed merchants, and while no doubt these stockholders of the London Company did cherish fond hopes of repeating the Spaniards' golden looting of Mexico and Peru, nevertheless they realistically planned to exploit a profitable trade in raw materials. Accordingly, in the autumn of 1608 they sent over eight Polish and German workmen variously skilled in making tar and pitch, glass, and pot-ashes. Captain John Smith vigorously disapproved of these commercial activities and wrote a blunt letter to his worshipful directors pointing out that in Russia and Sweden, where this wood pitch and ashes business was well known, they could " buy as much in a week as will freight you a ship . . . you must not expect from us any such matter, which are but a many of ignorant, miserable souls, that scarce are able to get wherewith to live, and defend ourselves against the inconstant savages; finding but here and there a tree fit for the purpose, and want all things else the Russians have."

He was quite right. For while naval stores, potash, and lumber from the colonies suited perfectly the mercantilist school of economic thought that prompted the motherland to exploit colonial trade for her selfish benefit, nevertheless these industries were ill-fitted to Virginia. They prospered only when transplanted to other localities. Potash moved to the Northern colonies where hardwoods flourished. Naval stores moved southward to the heavier stands of yellow pine.

As the lumberman worked down the coastal plain from the Carolinas, the center of naval stores slipped on ahead of him, from Wilmington to Charleston, to Savannah and Jacksonville. Naturally the richest crops came from tapping the virgin pine forests, and as these vanished into the sawmill, the disappearance of the great American naval-stores industry seemed written plainly in the economic history of our tomorrow. As early as 1900 the experts saw the beginning of the end of our dominance in the world markets.

It had from the first been a wasteful, unorganized business. Literally thousands of individual operators — generally small farmers or sharecroppers — tap the pines on their lands, collecting the resinous, aromatic sap in cups of tin or clay, bringing their crude product to hundreds of little local stills to be separated by primitive distillation into turpentine and rosin. Thence these products move to the big trading centers to be graded and sold by factors. Under such conditions standardization of product has always been unsatisfactory and it has been frequently difficult to keep supply and demand in balance. As a result price fluctuations have been violent. All in all, it has always been an industry as full of economic aches and pains as a rheumatic old darky. It lived on chiefly because it was frequently a side-line, carried on with cheap labor and virtually without overhead.

Besides the tree-tapping method of collecting the oleoresins of the living pines, there has long accompanied it a crude process of destructive distillation of dead wood. This produced no rosin, which till recently was an advantage, since this product has usually been in over-supply. Indeed, at many of the little local stills pits were dug and rosin was run into them. After the World War, when the demand for rosin boomed, many of these old pits were most profitably mined with pick and shovel. Besides producing no rosin, the destructive distillation method has the added advantage of producing pine oil and charcoal. However, it has always remained a sort of " a nigger and a mule" business, scavenger of windfalls and fires, never an important factor because the demand for pine oil was pitifully small and pine charcoal is crumbly stuff.

It was no deep secret that the pine stumps which bristled by the billions on thousands of acres of cut-over land contained some twenty-five per cent by weight of rosin. Uncle Sam's agricultural authorities began to preach the doctrine of a vanishing gum naval-stores supply, and many a bright young man got the notion that there was a fortune in these forgotten wastes of the lumbering operations. The old crude method of piling the dead wood into great pyres, covering them with boughs of live needles, coating the whole with earth, setting fire to the buried wood-pile, and with a slow smoldering flame sweating out the tar would not do. It was wickedly wasteful and it produced no rosin. Scores of other methods were devised. Dozens of companies began to operate. Many pretty stock certificates in sundry wood extraction enterprises were bought by trustful optimists. Still no practical, economical method was found, and still the Department of Agriculture kept on urging inventors and capitalists to save our oldest industry from death by depletion.

Most of these new processes to recover the oleoresinous wealth of the dead wood depended on dry distillation or steam extraction and none produced rosin. Accordingly, the 1909 collapse of turpentine prices, combined with the growing demand for rosin, closed up all these new enterprises as quickly and finally as the first killing frost blackens the lingering zinnias and calendulas. In fact, about this time the rosin tail began to wag the turpentine dog: a fundamental change in the naval-stores industry that upset a lot of people.

Just at this time, 1909, the inventive Homer Yaryan was experimenting in a tiny plant at Cadillac in upper Michigan with a novel extraction process that combined steam and solvents. It got out the rosin as well as turpentine and also the pine oils. He organized the Yaryan Rosin and Turpentine Company, moved his operations to a large-scale plant at

Gulfport, Mississippi, and in his first operating season produced 14,307 barrels of rosin, 1,790 barrels of turpentine, and 700 barrels of pine oil. Here was a tangible start. It was followed in 1911 by another, bigger plant at Brunswick. Next year the two operations turned out 98,000 barrels of turpentine, and so much pine oil that, there being few outlets, they did not half try to recover it.

These two plants were now the sole survivors of all the brave attempts to rescue our gum-rosin and turpentine industry from extinction. In 1913 turpentine prices again weakened. Even this hardy pioneer drew his boilers, let his working crews out, and locked the doors. Yaryan reopened both plants next year after the outbreak of the war.

In two directions the war in Europe exerted a steadily increasing pressure upon the American naval-stores situation. It created a markedly greater demand, notably insistent in its call for more and ever more rosin. It stimulated abnormally lumbering activities throughout the entire area of the Southern pine forests.

The story is vividly told in dollars and cents. When the Kaiser's armies moved suddenly into Belgium in August 1914, gum turpentine was selling for 47½ cents a gallon and turpentine from steam-distilled wood for 5 cents less. Rosin was quoted, according to grade, from $4 to $6.75 per barrel. Four years later, when the Armistice was signed, the prices were: gum turpentine, 71 cents; wood turpentine, 65 cents; rosin, from $14.20 to $18. The price of turpentine had not quite doubled. The price of rosin had quadrupled.

Observing these price fluctuations with an eye trained to watch out for the farmers' interests and as an old champion of conservation of our natural resources, Senator Arthur Capper was seriously concerned over the rapid cutting of Southern pine. He demanded, and obtained, federal funds for an exhaustive study of the naval-stores industry. The findings were as dismal as a cyprus swamp on a leaden November afternoon. Spurred on by the crusading Senator from Kansas, the Department of Agriculture began with renewed energy to campaign for the salvation of this old industry with world-wide markets.

It was just at this time that the new-born Industrial Development Division was hunting business opportunities for the Hercules company. The coincidence clicked. Half a dozen hustling young men, who in out-of-the-way towns signed the hotel registers as coming from " Wilmington, Del.," began traveling through the territory from Charleston to New Orleans. They were exploring the possibilities of the wood-rosin and turpentine business.

" You could see for yourself," says L. N. Bent, who captained that scouting expedition, " that literally billions of old stumps were available. Furthermore, it was equally clear not only that the gum yield from the second-growth saplings was small, but also that these slender trees, already weakened by tapping, toppled over like tenpins in the winter windstorms. The set-up — abundant supplies of raw materials and diminishing competition from gum products — appeared to be just about perfection. Nobody could see but that the fancy war prices were going to last forever. Demand for rosin in both soap and paper was growing. Certainly the ridiculously low prices of 1914 would never again be quoted. Everybody agreed on that point and the Government men had bushels of statistics to prove it."

The Hercules men did a little figuring of their own. From a ton of stumpwood: 185 pounds of rosin; 22 pounds of turpentine; 15 pounds of pine oil. At current prices very simple arithmetic added up a total dollars that left a tempting remainder for profits after all possible expenses of extraction had been subtracted.

The Industrial Development Division reported the wood naval-stores business favorably. The board of directors approved their recommendations. The Hercules Powder Company launched forth into a new business. Every single one of the immediate, supporting reasons that prompted this decision was to prove wrong.

The decision having been made, action followed swiftly. Negotiations were opened with Homer Yaryan for the purchase of his two plants, and at Hattiesburg, Mississippi, a new plant was built. This was completed in 1920, but as the two Yaryan plants had been acquired in the meanwhile, the Hattiesburg operation was postponed several years.

Almost from the first some of the good reasons for this venture were proved invalid. Naval-stores prices began sagging. With the return of President Harding's famous " normalcy," consumers who during the war emergency had been glad to take any kind of rosin became fussy. They found the dark-colored product of wood distillation quite unacceptable. Hercules must tackle the double-edged research job of lowering costs and raising quality.

Then, just to make a hard task harder, all forecasts of the extinction of gum production within the next decade went askew. The second growth of easy-seeding, quick-growing slash pine came along at a rate that dumbfounded everyone. By 1923 anyone could tell that it would provide an abundance of young trees to ensure ample production of naval stores for years and years. Naturally naval-stores prices sagged still lower. To cap the climax, chemical substitutes were successfully invading markets long served exclusively by rosin and turpentine. Lacquers and synthetic resins, for example, cut into the sale of turpentine as a paint solvent and of rosin as a varnish ingredient. These and other chemical developments certainly did nothing to bolster up naval-stores demand.

They had a bull by the tail. One of those same Government authorities who had strongly advocated wood naval-stores production now confessed that " the establishment of the industry will require very large capital expenditures, certainly without immediate return, and with little chance of a fair return unless investment in physical properties is followed by chemical research on a scale few companies are equipped to undertake." One might have developed a bit of skepticism about official forecasts, but here at least were some thoughts for the directors to mull over. They did, and they decided to go ahead. In the next decade they were to dot every "i" and cross the last "t" in that gloomy prophecy. They were to back up their plant investment with over three million dollars in research expenditures. It was ten years before the naval-stores enterprise showed even a current book profit, and in one year alone the actual operating losses exceeded half a million dollars.

A great many men of the Hercules family helped tie this roaring bull and break him to the industrial yoke; but two stand out as inspired and persistent leaders. In the company's inner councils the abiding faith of C. A. Higgins, now president, that the Hercules future lay in chemical diversification persuaded his associates again and again that such a research job demands plenty of patient money and persevering effort. Out on the firing line L. N. Bent planned the campaign so thoroughly and led his men in the attack so courageously that there could be no thought of defeat.

What must be done was self-evident. Their costs were higher than those of the individual farmer tapping saplings with cheap labor and virtually no overhead. Their products were not so acceptable to the consumers. The wiry little New Englander in charge tackled both problems at once and grabbed each with several holds.

Every element of cost, from the collection of stumps to the selection of shipping containers for their finished products, was scrutinized. A powder-making company was naturally predisposed to the old method of blasting out stumps, but yanking them out saved time and doubled the wood salvaged from the same area. So A. A. Shimer, a lanky, likable, Lehigh engineer headed up a mechanical development crew that perfected a whole series of stump-pullers, each new one an improvement over its predecessor. The latest, the design of which was sparked by Phil Powelson, once head of the woods organization of Hercules and now their resident engineer at the new Government explosives plant at Radford, Virginia, is a forty-thousand-pound bulldozer. It can nuzzle a ton of gnarled and rooty pine stump out of swampy ground without bemiring itself or daintily pick a little five-hundred-pounder from the midst of a thicket of underbrush and saplings. This flexible mastodon is a true conservationist. When it is turned loose in a field, it plucks out every last pine stump with a minimum of wasted wood, and by the same token it clears the land beautifully for the plow.

This double reclaimer of waste stumps and waste land was not, however, the sole cost-cutting machine developed. New loading and handling devices were invented and improvements were made in Yaryan's excellent hogging machine, which shreds the wood before it is fed into the stills. Thus a threefold gain was chalked up before the extraction process begins: the costs of collecting the wood are reduced; the supply of raw material from the same area is increased; the yield of finished product from the better-shredded wood is stepped up.

At the other end of the production line that historic relic the rosin barrel of 75 pounds was replaced by light steel drums weighing only 15 pounds: a saving in shipping cost and a convenience to customers.

Commercially all this was helpful; but the real triumph was not mechanical. It was chemical. In the original Yaryan process the pine-stump chips were treated first with live steam and then with a petroleum solvent. The products were a ruby-red rosin, quite unacceptable to the soap and paper trades; a crude turpentine with a lasting, evil odor; pine oil, for which there was a limited use as a flotation agent for separating minerals from ores. Again the attack, quite in the fashion of the modern *Blitzkrieg,* was driven at different points with a common objective.

Initially great effort was concentrated upon improving the product. Along with this went a lot of scientific snooping into the obscure chemistry of the pine-tree oleoresins. At both Brunswick and Hattiesburg the two hard-working plant superintendents, A. S. Kloss and Charles Lambert, overhauled the process time and again to increase yields. Finally the products were considered from the point of view of the customer, modified and specialized better to serve his needs. In all this long battle to win worth from waste the firm hand and untiring mind of Arthur Langmeier, in charge of product development and sales, held true to the course charted by Bent and by his later successor A. B. Nixon.

Faced with the same conditions and producing similar, unsatisfactory products, their rival pioneer in the wood-rosin business, the Newport Industries at Pensacola and Bay Minette, wrestled independently with these problems. By different means and processes both reached the same goal. Hercules, for example, purified the crude red rosin by means of the solvent furfuraldehyde, that war-baby chemical prepared first from corncobs and now made commercially by the Quaker Oats Company out of waste oat hulls. Newport, on the other hand, purifies its rosin by filtering it through activated fuller's earth.

In the end the old cup and kettle processes, which had remained practically unchanged since the Phœnicians first calked their galleys on the shores of the stormy Baltic, were replaced by continuous, automatic, chemically controlled operations. Rosins of every grade from water-white downwards are now produced and classified not only by the ancient, rule-of-thumb colors, but also according to their definite chemical composition. Rosin's faults have even been corrected. Its use has always been handicapped by its tendencies to crack and darken. These are the result of oxidation, a

Plucking wealth from waste, collecting pine stumps to make rosin and turpentine and salvaging cut-over timber land for good use in agriculture.   — Courtesy Hercules Powder Company, Incorporated

similar reaction with the oxygen of the air to that which rusts iron and causes the well-known deterioration of rubber. Knowing more about rosin chemistry, the Hercules researchers figured out that hydrogen atoms put into the rosin molecule would keep the oxygen atoms out. It was a good chemical trick if they could make it work; and they did. To raise the melting-point, which makes rosin's physical characteristics more like the scarce and costly fossil gums used in varnish, they have polymerized the rosin molecules, linking them as the molecules of nylon and the synthetic rubbers are strung together.

It seems curious indeed that during all the centuries man has been using rosin no smart molecule-maker ever conceived of two obvious chemical possibilities. Practically no chemical revision had ever been made of its natural form. Very little effort had been made to explore its opportunities as a storehouse of new synthetic products. Once this locked door is thrown open, rosin is found to be the cheapest of the complex organic acids available for modification or synthesis; all the latent chemical possibilities of coal or cellulose lie just across the threshold. Already some amazing new products have been created.

At the tail end of the rosin-purification processes, for example, a powdery resin-like residue is left for which most unexpected uses have been discovered. The chemists of the packing house of Swift found that a dip in a bath of this resin mixed with a softener is a quick and easy way of removing the bristles from fresh-killed hogs, thus making quite obsolete the nursery rhyme: " Barber, barber, shave a pig." Mixed with paraffin, this same preparation plucks poultry.

The packing houses are credited with using every part of the porker except the squeal. The wood-rosin people do quite as well. From the extracted pine chips Hercules is preparing Vinsol, a dark, high-melting resin, which does not lump in powdered form, as rosin is apt to do, and which forms stable emulsions with asphalt in water. It stabilizes the surface of dirt roads and airplane landing fields against both mud and dust; but most remarkable of all, Vinsol added to cement at the clinker stage, a teaspoonful to the bag, makes it possible to get a good, free-flowing mix with much less water, resulting in a smoother, more buttery, homogeneous mass, eliminating air holes and speeding up the time of setting: capital first aids to better and faster road-building. Vinsol-treated concrete checkmates the ravages of the destructive freezing-thawing cycle and resists the attacks of the ice-removal chemicals applied to road surfaces. Thus this new product of the waste stumps makes the contribution of added life, improved driving surface, and lower upkeep to our highway systems. After this ultimate product, Vinsol, has been extracted, the completely exhausted chips are burned under the boilers, the ultimate of waste-utilization of what was originally itself a waste.

The other side of the picture is that, thanks to chemical engineering principles and methods and apparatus, the yields have also been raised. In 1918 a ton of pine stumps produced about 185 pounds of rosin and 6 gallons of crude oils. The Hercules average for 1938 was 370 pounds of rosin and 14 gallons of oils. The amount of finished product from the same amount of raw material has thus doubled in twenty years.

Pine oil is one of the obligatory products of the wood naval-stores industry, and new uses for it had to be found. They were worked out in the laboratory and then sold to the people who could employ them. This is tough selling as the super-charged B. H. Little found out; but by 1930 pine oil's use as a mining flotation agent had become less important than its uses in processing textile fabrics, as an auxiliary cleansing agent in laundering greasy overalls, as a disinfectant, and in medicine.

Those same clever and exact chemical methods have changed the single grade of very crude, bad-smelling turpentine into ten different, definite chemical products. The fine rectifying stills perfected for the fractional distillation of alcohol and the coal-tar light oils could not handle the terpenes from pine; accordingly entirely new equipment had to be devised. The first attempt in 1924 was a big bundle of operating troubles; the apparatus used today runs continuously and under completely automatic controls. It is now possible to extract the chief chemical constituents of turpentine and pine oil as the coal-tar crudes are recovered at the coking plants, and as a result our oldest industry has switched from a " naval stores " basis to one where its products have become raw materials for chemical synthesis. The pine stump has joined coal and petroleum as purveyors of chemical raw materials.

It is a unique chemical storehouse. From the chemists' point of view absolutely pure rosin is abietic acid, an exceedingly complex, organic acid — its formula is $C_{20}H_{30}O_2$ — selling for about three cents a pound. It is claimed that, judged by chemical values, this is the cheapest organic-acid molecule. The molecule-makers have a bit of useful economic wisdom packed into their saying: " You cannot synthesize very much of a molecule for a nickel." Or as a businessman might phrase the same thing, " You will have to pay at least five cents a pound for any complex organic material." Abietic acid — pure rosin — is plainly an economical starting-point for molecule-making.

Turpentine is made up of hydrocarbons — 70 per cent pinene, 25 per cent dipentene, 2 per cent para-menthane — known as a group as terpenes. Pine-oil constituents are alcohols — 55 per cent alpha terpineol, 12 per cent borneol. Terpineol, as you remember, is itself used in many perfume formulas and as the starting-point in synthesis of artificial lavender, bergamot, eucalyptus, jasmine, orange blossom, and many other scents. Borneol is found not only in pine oil but also in oils of thyme and valerian. Dipentene, a first-class solvent for synthetic resins, is an isomer of limonene, found in lemon oil. Pinene, which is a constituent of many essential oils, is the primary source of synthetic camphor.

Camphor is one of the few inanimate things that truly deserve the abused adjective " romantic." In the interior of the island of Formosa, amid a jungle of gigantic ferns, grows a stately laurel tree. Its crisp, clean scent fills the air, and the aborigines learned long ago to extract from the wood by a primitive distillation process the white glistening crystals we know as camphor. In 1421 an adventurous band of Chinese freebooters took over this beautiful island, and thereafter camphor pressed into little cakes became an article of world commerce.

Originally cherished as a charm against evil spirits, it became a utilitarian moth-repellent, and half a century ago John Hyatt's invention turned it into an important industrial raw material.

For five centuries the Chinese merchants in their own cunning ways made the most of the Formosan monopoly of this aromatic gum. They endowed it with esoteric virtues that made it precious and greatly desired. By pressing it into forms that had significant meanings they sold it for fancy prices as symbols pleasing to the gods, as charms to win the most obstinate mistress, as amulets to ward off disease. In Western lands they sold it as a medicinal. Some of its Oriental properties must have come along with its pleasant, persistent fragrance, for it enjoys a fictitious reputation as a disinfectant and guard against the common cold. Then in 1895 these beguiling methods of snatching extra profits from camphor were replaced by a thoroughly up-to-date development of the monopoly. In that year Formosa, a prize of the Sino-Japanese war, passed to the control of the Nipponese. Industrially, intelligently, realistically, the Japs exploited the island's chief resource. Methods of preparing the gum were modernized to increase the yield and, to the same end, the methods of marketing were systematized.

In 1904 by decree of the Japanese Government the camphor monopoly became an official, legal reality. Since then, with perfect control over supply, the price has been moved up and down arbitrarily to suit the ends of the monopoly. Thus the stage was perfectly set for a thrilling chemico-economic melodrama, the foiling of a natural villain by a synthetic hero, one of the historic struggles between land and laboratory, especially interesting because it developed a deliberate, merciless commercial battle.

As the demand for camphor grew, on account of its use in motion-picture films and pyroxylin plastics made from nitro-cellulose plasticized with the gum, the price was gradually edged up until during the World War period it reached $2.35 a pound.

The chemist's instinctive curiosity about such a product as camphor had been satisfied by the French analyst Dumas, who in 1832 determined its molecular formula, $C_{10}H_{16}O$, and in 1893 by the German synthesist J. C. Bredt, who worked out the structure of that elaborate combination of atoms. Soon afterwards it was synthesized in Germany. Thereafter, whenever the price of natural camphor passed 50 cents a pound, some molecule-maker somewhere was sure to start manufacturing the synthetic product. Japanese retaliation was swift. The price would drop till prospective competitors became discouraged.

Each abortive attempt taught valuable lessons. The synthesis is apparently quite simple. Starting with pinene, the process consists of two fundamental steps: first to camphene, second to camphor. Both steps can be taken in several ways, and by all methods practical " know how " must be acquired before the reactions, so simple on paper, so easy in the test tube, can be carried on in large apparatus.

The British blockade forced the Germans into synthetic-camphor production and they never subsequently abandoned it. In fact, by 1931, European manufacturers produced some

CHAPTER X

THE GREAT CAOUTCHOUC
MYSTERIES

◇◆◇

AT daybreak, July 16, 1916, the super-submarine *Deutsch-land* thrust her ugly, gray nose up through the choppy waters of lower Chesapeake Bay. That evening she docked at Baltimore with a million-dollar cargo of coal-tar medicines and dyes.

It was a sensational feat, boldly conceived and pluckily executed, thus to evade the tight British blockade, cross the Atlantic, and land here vital chemical supplies for which this country was clamoring. It was no lucky fluke, for it was repeated when on November 6 she slipped unannounced into New London with a similar cargo.

This salty bit of bravado appealed to us warmly. While the British fussed over the legal status of this peculiar merchant ship, the whole of America rose up and cheered. These transatlantic voyages were an impressive curtain-raiser to the coming submarine campaign of frightfulness, a warning that this new weapon was capable of unexpected accomplishments. The feat was, moreover, a slap at our infant coal-tar chemical industry. The medicines and dyes brought over were but a drop in the bucket of our enormous demands; but like the mailed fist within the velvet glove, these daring exportations served notice to struggling American dye-makers

168]

that the Germans, once the war was off their hands, would be resourceful, determined competitors.

However, the exploit was something more than a smart publicity stunt. Two million dollars in gold, even in the Kaiser's day, was a sizable block of international credit. Much more important, Germany secured a thousand tons of two commodities she needed sorely. On both return trips the *Deutschland* stowed away nickel ingots and five hundred tons of rubber — the key metal then supplied virtually from a single mine in Ontario; but mostly rubber.

The realistic calculations of the German General Staff, usually accurate to the tenth decimal place, had gone woefully wrong on their rubber requirements. Maybe they were misled by their own chemical people, who, with all the usual fanfare, had announced in 1909 the discovery of synthetic rubber. Instead of underestimating their needs, the High Command may easily have overestimated the value of the substitute material. For all the boasting, it turned out to be pretty poor stuff, though at the close of the war Germany was producing about 150 tons a month and two additional plants were building that would have raised the output to over 8,000 tons a year.

But in 1916, with all the storehouse of America to choose from, the *Deutschland* loaded ton upon ton of caoutchouc, raw rubber, for the main part of both her return cargoes. How dire the German need for rubber must have been could not have been made more tellingly plain.

In our becushioned age it is difficult to picture a rubberless existence. Because it stretches and snaps back, because it bounces, rubber is a unique material with the exceedingly useful characteristics of elasticity and resiliency, stretch and bounce. Rubber also possesses an astonishing versatility of form: " as hard as a fountain-pen barrel, as soft as the putty-like art eraser." And the first great mystery of rubber is not what man did without it — he just did without — but that with

his proverbial luck and innate curiosity he should have failed
for some five thousand years to have hit upon over two
hundred varieties of trees and vines that yield a more or less
rubbery sap.

It is not as if the rubber-bearing plants were confined to a
few rare species growing high on the rocky crags of inaccessible mountain peaks. They are legion and they flourish luxuriantly throughout the great warm belt around the globe's
middle where the human race, struggling up from savagery,
first learned to tan leather, to mold and bake pottery, to make
glass, weld the metals, to weave, bleach, and dye textiles —
in a word, in that very hotbed where the seeds of civilization
first sprouted. The ingenious Chinese, the Hindus, the Persians, even those consummate craftsmen the Egyptians, all
lived with rubber trees about them. The Greeks and the
Romans, those shrewd traders the Phœnicians, the Arabians,
first of our chemists, the inquisitive, acquisitive Italian merchants who scoured the Eastern lands, all missed the many
varieties of gutta-percha. The peoples of Ceylon, Malay,
Indo-China, and all the Spice Islands did no better, yet the
mysterious ruins of the great city and temple of Angkor in
Cambodia are overrun by what is literally a rubber-bearing
jungle, and these lands are today the world's chief source of
plantation rubber. None of those high and ancient civiliza-
tions discovered rubber.

It was found in the New World by Indian tribes living in
the chipped-stone era of savagery, people armed with bows,
who knew fire, but who worked no metals, and who had never
discovered the wheel. This was a notable accomplishment
for the simple races of the Amazon River basin. Admit that
they luckily lived right where the best rubber-bearing tree
in all the world grew; nevertheless, they had learned deliberately to collect the white, smelly sap and to coagulate
it quickly over smoky fires to make it more useful. These re-

peated acts are not happenstance: they show intelligent intent.

Their notable discovery was known in Spain possibly three years after Columbus discovered their New World, certainly within twenty-five years; and it is the second great mystery of rubber that it took the European, for all his arts and sciences, three centuries to make any use of this stretching, bouncing material.

Christopher Columbus is popularly credited with the first, official, white man's discovery of rubber. The bounding play balls he brought back from Hispaniola to Queen Isabella are almost as familiar accessories of our folklore as the cherry tree of George Washington. Probably they are about as historically correct. The story was first told, not in the discoverer's own writings, but in 1615, a century after his death, in a grandiloquent account of the Spanish discoveries and conquests in the Western Hemisphere, written to order for Philip II by the court historian. By this time American rubberwares were familiar objects in Spain and Portugal. They had been brought back by explorers, soldiers, priests, from all the lands of Central and northern South America, for, remarkably, the knowledge of rubber had spread throughout these regions even among tribes who had no knowledge of one another's existence. Each used the rubber gum of the trees native to their territory, and all fashioned it into play balls.

For a century and a quarter Europeans marveled at elastic novelties from the New World, but did nothing about making any use of this unusual material. Besides the balls, bowls and bottles, rainproof hats and capes (forefathers of the sailorman's sou'-wester and the poncho of the cowpuncher), primitive galoshes and galluses were described by travelers, and samples found their way across the Atlantic, plain enough hints surely of what might be done with rubber. Nor was precise information lacking on the simple processes by which these utilitarian gadgets were produced. Indeed, in 1745, at a crowded meeting of the Paris Academy of Sciences, all the secrets of rubber-collecting and manipulating were laid bare. The speaker was an able protagonist, splendidly equipped with accurate information, the knack of keeping his audience on the edge of their chairs, and sufficient position to ballast his marvelous tales. In Charles Marie de la Condamine rubber found its first sponsor.

Seven years before, under the auspices of that same Academy, he had fared forth to the jungles of South America, commissioned to settle a good old scientific argument that had all the astronomers clawing at one another's throats. Was this terrestrial globe of ours a perfect sphere, or was it flattened or elongated at the poles? Tiring of this debate, they could always work up a pother over the question of just how large the earth is anyway. To end all this professorial bickering one need only measure an arc of the meridian at the equator and another as far north as possible. With perfect French logic the Academy sent out two expeditions, one to Peru, the other to Lapland.

Condamine was just the stout fellow for such an adventure. He had been living the gay life of a Parisian playboy, a lady-killer and writer of naughty verses that scanned badly; but with the versatility of a Leonardo he was also a student of astronomy and chemistry, and between flirtations he cultivated the society of savants. As a youngster he had traveled off the beaten path in the Orient and served a term of soldiering. Thus he was an experienced campaigner, and the quality of his courage offset the quantity of his mathematics. Once the main task was completed, he determined to see a bit of the country by crossing the continent from Quito to Para, over the Andes and down the Amazon. It was a hard trip, full of dangers, but he came through safely in three and a half months; and then, still hungering for adventures, he worked his way through the tropic jungles of the coast to Cayenne in

French Guiana. Thence he sailed back to France with material for six ripsnorting volumes of travels, a great collection of poisoned arrows, and half a dozen oval chunks of caoutchouc.

Condamine's lively tales roused the first real interest in rubber. His descriptions of how the natives made raincoats and overshoes by dipping fabrics or molds into the sap of the hevea tree and curing successive thin layers of the rubbery juice over smoky fire was as suggestive as it was vivid. Europeans came to think about making some use of rubber. The difficulty was that the balls of coagulated gum brought from South America would not melt for either dipping or molding, and when they sought to ship the raw sap it fermented to a stinking mess. Obviously what was needed was a solvent that would evaporate and leave the gum in place.

So the chemists went to work on rubber. A French research pair, the physician Herissant and the chemist Macquer, were the first to report results. In 1763 they found that turpentine was a capital rubber-solvent, but the rubber film left when the turpentine evaporated unpleasantly resembled flypaper in warm weather, while in cold it became as hard and brittle as a pane of window glass. Thus at the very outset the primary problem of rubber was emphatically put up to the chemists: how could it be rendered permanently useful?

Naturally the first attack was an exhaustive search for the ideal solvent. One of the best of many tried and found wanting was ether, and Frederick the Great had a fine pair of rubber riding boots made by this process. Ether was then a fabulously costly laboratory reagent, quite out of the question for the commercial production of everyday wares for the ordinary citizen.

One of the peculiarities of chemical progress is that a new product or a new process frequently brings unexpected results in wholly unrelated fields. Such a fortuitous advance was now scored in rubber technology. In Glasgow a talented young chemist, Charles Macintosh by name, had cannily gone into the business of supplying the woolen mills with various and sundry chemical specialties, all sorts of rare and hard-to-make products. In this way he dodged direct competition with older chemical dealers, and as he was alert to new ideas and clever in adapting them to the needs of the Scotch textile trade, he prospered. One of his stand-bys was cudbear, a purple dye prepared by macerating certain lichens in ammonia water, evaporating the liquors, and grinding the residue to a coarse reddish powder. Illuminating gas was an innovation that naturally interested him, and when he observed that the recently organized Glasgow Gas Works produced quantities of crude ammonia liquor as a by-product, he saw a likely chemical opportunity. Being Scotch, he let the waste accumulate, and one day when he chanced to meet the president in the Saltmarket, he said to him:

" 'Tis weak and will need a deal of purifying, but if it could be had cheap enough, I might take some ammonia liquor off your hands."

The gas-maker was a Scot too, and he sensed the chance of disposing of all his troublesome by-products, so he replied: " 'Twould be costly for us to separate the ammonia from the tar, but 'tis child's play for a real chemist like yourself."

After protracted bargaining Macintosh contracted to take all the by-products of the gas works. Thriftily he cast about for ways to turn his coal tar into profits. He found a buyer for pitch, and, producing this, had to distill off the light and heavy oils. He sold the heavy oils to a wood-preserver, but he could unearth no buyer for the lighter distillate. Well, he must find some use for it himself. This crude coal-tar naphtha might be, he thought, the good, cheap solvent for rubber that so many chemists had been seeking. He secured a bit of caoutchouc, dropped it into a test tube filled with his volatile, oily, white naphtha, and made a viscid fluid like transparent honey. On evaporation this left a comparatively thick film of rubber.

Macintosh then had a real inventive inspiration. He smeared his naphtha-rubber dope over woolen cloth, spread over it another piece of cloth, pressed the two together, and created the original Macintosh waterproof fabric. It was still sticky in summer and brittle in winter; but he had found how these obstacles, if not eliminated, might be overcome. He applied for a patent, which was issued on June 17, 1823, and then his troubles began.

In the first place, having failed to solve the basic problem, his waterproof cloth became stiff and crinkly in cold weather, while in warm it smelled most offensively. The natural wool fats speeded the deterioration of his rubber sandwich so that the two layers of cloth peeled apart. The tailors sewed the waterproofed fabric into garments and the seams leaked like a sieve. He was therefore forced to invent a cement to fasten the seams together. This new technique was naturally resented and opposed by the good master tailors. " The medical faculty," so he wrote in his diary, "having lent their aid to run down the use of waterproof (apparently from having found it a decided enemy to their best friends — colds and catarrhs) the use of the article in the form of cloaks, etc., has of late become comparatively extinct."

Macintosh was saved by the British Army. In fact, the Government placed such substantial orders for his waterproofs that he sold his chemical business and, to provide capital for expansion, took into partnership two Manchester cotton-spinners, the brothers Hugh and Joseph Birley. Having survived teething troubles, the infant firm of Charles Macintosh and Company grew lustily.

Still the great rubber problem was unsolved. Caoutchouc baffled the chemists. They could not analyze it by any accustomed methods. It did not dissolve and recrystallize. It could not be treated with acids and the resulting salts identified. Combustion did not break it down into its component parts. It remained a chemical mystery. Not only did it become sticky or hard, but it also lost its stretch and bounce. No real progress had yet been made in retaining its desirable characteristics unchanged.

About this time a London coach-maker became interested in Macintosh waterproofs as a material for carriage tops and curtains. They served his purpose so admirably that he began experimenting to see if he might not circumvent the patents. He failed to find a better solvent than naphtha, but he hit upon the first way of employing the elastic property of rubber. He cut crude caoutchouc into long, thin strips and patented the idea of sewing these elastic bands to glove wrists, waistcoat backs, pocket edges "to prevent their being picked," to shoes "when the object is to put them on and off without lacing." His idea proved so popular that Thomas Hancock, like Macintosh, forsook his original business and became the first rubber manufacturer in England.

In his slicing operations Hancock observed that freshly cut pieces of rubber could be reunited by pressure, and as his stack of scrap cuttings mounted he conceived of shredding them, pressing them together into a block, and cutting them into more bands. He constructed a wooden drum, armed with teeth fitted so as to revolve inside a wooden barrel equipped with knives. Charging this apparatus with scrap, he began to turn the crank. As the rubber was shredded he naturally expected that his rotating drum would turn more and more easily, but instead it required greater and greater strength to move the handle. He opened up the machine and found inside, not a great pile of shredded rubber, but one solid, dough-like mass almost too hot to touch, soft and pliable, so that it was easily molded into a block. No longer did that growing scrap-pile haunt his dreams.

He did not know it, but he had devised the first rubber masticator. He soon discovered that his revolving drum did more to the rubber than appeared on the surface. It increased its solubility. He found also that it was now possible to incorporate into rubber many dry materials, some of which improved it markedly. Unwittingly he had discovered the art of rubber compounding. He was now able to make better macintoshes than Macintosh and in half the time. Sensibly they came to terms and joined forces.

Up to this time in the United States we had simply ignored rubber, but news of these developments plunged a score of hardy pioneers headlong into the business. They succeeded only in losing a lot of good money, most of it borrowed, and in thoroughly disgusting the public with this odoriferous stuff that alternately changed from stone to syrup. All these bold enterprisers used turpentine as their solvent, accomplishing thereby the notable feat of increasing stickiness and hastening deterioration. Only one company succeeded. This lonely triumph was due to the inventive genius of a neglected hero of American industry, Edwin M. Chaffee.

Chaffee made two great contributions to rubber technology: the mixing mill and the coating machine. For these he never received the credit due though he did have the solid satisfaction of success in a field littered with failing competitors. When foreman of a patent-leather factory, he became obsessed with the idea of a rubber coating applied to fabric or leather to give a permanent, shiny, waterproof finish. Working nights in his own kitchen he evolved a mixture of rubber, lampblack, and turpentine so definitely an improvement over existing rubber dopes that he got together $30,000 and on February 11, 1833 incorporated the Roxbury India Rubber Company.

With no knowledge of Hancock's masticator Chaffee now proceeded to invent a mixing mill to assist in the assimilation of the lampblack by the rubber. Like Hancock he was astonished at the results. Instead of spiked, revolving drums, however, he forced the rubber mass between two steam-heated rollers that turned at different speeds. The squeezing-rolling-slipping action ground and kneaded the caoutchouc so that it formed a thin, hot, plastic sheet on the cylinders. Hancock's spiked drums have long since been discarded, but the mixing machines just installed in the latest rubber factory embody this principle evolved by Chaffee. His coating machine employed this same principle of the revolving, heated rollers which made it possible to coat or impregnate from a dry mix of rubber. This improvement saved him thirty-five barrels of turpentine a week, cut the labor in half, and simply eliminated space devoted to drying-rooms. Aided by these Chaffee inventions, his Roxbury company survived. But it did not flourish. It could not prosper so long as the riddle of rubber was still unsolved.

The Roxbury company was drifting towards bankruptcy when the man destined to answer that riddle strolled casually into their retail store in New York to buy a life-preserver. It was a symbolic purchase.

Three weeks later this tall, thin stranger, with the generous mouth and bushy eyebrows, returned and showed the store manager a new valve. It was, so he said, a great improvement for inflating any rubber ring or ball, and would the company be interested in buying it?

The storekeeper shook his head emphatically and was about to dismiss his shabby visitor when he noted the pain of disappointment leap into his dark eyes. He was drawn to the man, instantly, magnetically, as so many others were, and bottling up his curt answer, he beckoned him into his little back office and began to break the bad news gently.

"You've come to a poor place to sell your invention. We are one jump ahead of the sheriff. All our competitors have failed. There is no future for the rubber business. It is a shame, for it is wonderful stuff. It is impervious to water. It will — " and being a first-rate salesman, the manager swung enthusiastically into praises of this wonderful elastic gum.

"But we cannot make it stay put. Nobody can. It becomes as sticky as molasses in summer and hard as a brick in winter.

Last August we took back twenty thousand dollars' worth of overshoes that had melted to mush. No company can stand that. You're an inventor; well, there's your opportunity. Invent some way of keeping rubber soft and pliable yet firm, regardless of temperature, and we will snap up that invention. Yes, and pay you handsomely for it. What good is a valve if the life-preserver itself is no good?"

To us it may seem a rare bit of good luck that Charles Goodyear thus by chance became interested in the great caoutchouc mystery. He himself believed devoutly that he was but an instrument in the hands of the Creator, who, as he wrote, "directs the operation of the mind to the development of the properties of matter, in his own way, at the time when they are especially needed."

Goodyear became the great rubber fanatic. He loved the miraculous gum passionately and was ready to slave and starve, to pawn the blanket off his bed, to sell his children's school-books, to barter his soul — had the Devil given him half of Faust's opportunity — for the secret of rubber. To the cause he martyred his family, ruined himself, and in the end gave his life. He was cheated out of the just desserts of his great discovery, and what money he did collect was gobbled up by paying debts or squandered promoting rubber articles which others made and sold to their own, not his, profit. Charles Goodyear is one of the great commanding figures in the story of our civilization; a gloriously triumphant and unspeakably pathetic man.

Goodyear came honestly by his fervent zeal, his persistence, his inventiveness. His first American forefather was Stephen, a founder of the New Haven colony, friend and later successor of Governor Theophilus Eaton, associate of John Winthrop, Jr., in the first ironworks in Connecticut. The family was wealthy and well connected, and generation after generation its members played conspicuous parts. His father, Amasa, inherited a profitable trading business with the West

Indies. About the time young Charles (eldest of six children) trudged off to school, Amasa Goodyear sold his dock and warehouses and, moving out to Naugatuck, became the first maker of pearl buttons in America. In this switch from merchant to manufacturer he was blazing a path that, as the clipper-ship era passed, was followed by many a shrewd Yankee. To buttons he added clocks, later scythes, and particularly his patented hayfork made from spring steel.

This practical, prosperous parent was dismayed when his first-born son wanted to enter the Congregational ministry, and to cool Charles's religious zeal the plans for sending him to Yale were canceled and he was packed off to Philadelphia to learn business in the hardware store of the Rogers brothers. On his twenty-first birthday, December 29, 1821, he was recalled to New Haven and taken into partnership. For five years father and son worked together building up an exceedingly profitable business manufacturing miscellaneous hardware, chiefly farm implements. Then Charles went back to Philadelphia to open a wholesale and retail hardware business, which was so successful that he overextended himself and was caught badly in the slump of 1830.

Too scrupulous to go through bankruptcy, he tried to satisfy his creditors with promises and long-term notes. Throughout his life these claims hung around his neck, and time after time experiments with rubber were made in a Philadelphia jail, for he was arrested after his return from his historic visit to the Roxbury store in New York.

He now began his great rubber quest. First he tried kneading into raw rubber every material that he could conceive might preserve its desirable properties. Magnesia seemed to give promising results, and during the winter of 1834–5 he hopefully fashioned some crude overshoes of this mixture, only to find on the coming of hot weather that they melted into a sticky mess. Next he tried boiling rubber with lime. Again results seemed promising, but again the outcome was a bitter disappointment. But day and night he kept on experimenting with this and that. To get a novel decorative effect he painted bronze powder in bold designs on rubber-coated draperies. To remove the bronze he used nitric acid and was delighted to find that it left the surface of the rubber tough and leathery. Enthusiastically he took out a patent on this " acid gas " curing process, which, though it only affected the surface, was nevertheless sufficiently practical to enable him to sell some licenses. With this money he moved his family to Roxbury, the ancient rubber capital, for he had begged the use of the idle machinery in a deserted plant. Here he met Chaffee, the pioneer; John Haskins, formerly the Roxbury factory manager, who took out one of his acid licenses; and Nathaniel Hayward.

Goodyear and Hayward were rubber soulmates. While Goodyear saw visions, Hayward dreamed dreams, and he confided that the Lord had revealed to him that if rubber were dusted with sulphur and exposed to action of the sun, a complete curing would be effected.

Goodyear was delighted with the man and his ideas. He gave him two hundred dollars for his sulphur patent and engaged him as assistant. Together they worked upon modifications of sulphur-acid treatments and turned out sundry rubber goods which, being superficially cured, remained only temporarily satisfactory. Goods sold during the previous months now began to flood back upon their hands. More claims, more debts: the comparative comfort of the past year vanished in an auction of the household goods to pay the butcher and the baker.

But Goodyear was now on the edge of his great discovery. In testing the effect of heat upon a sulphur-rubber compound smeared on cloth, one sample, being carelessly left overnight in contact with a hot stove, charred like leather. If this charring might be stopped at the right point, a perfect rubber curing would be effected. He had ferreted out the secret of vulcanization. The second great mystery of caoutchouc had been unveiled.

With a secret worth millions Goodyear could find no financial backer. With the correct answer to the rubber riddle he suddenly became cautious. Accordingly, it was five years after his discovery before his patent, U.S. No. 3633, was issued on June 15, 1844. This delay was costly to the inventor. It enabled the energetic Hancock, as he himself confessed, to secure English patent rights to the sulphur-heat treatment. It created legal flaws which patent pirates the world over used to their advantage. At best Goodyear was a poor trader and, tightly squeezed as he was for cash, he sold licenses and fixed royalties far below their value. In the end he was legally vindicated, for a group of his wealthy licensees clubbed together to prosecute one of the most daring despoilers. They engaged Daniel Webster to prosecute their case and Rufus Choate defended. It was the legal battle of the century and ended in a sweeping victory for the Goodyear patent. But the decision came too late. The great rubber fanatic had plunged deep into debt in putting on great rubber shows at the expositions in London (1851) and Paris (1855), in defending patents in foreign countries, in long experiments to develop new uses for his beloved gum elastic. He patented over two hundred applications of rubber — some of them bob up again as " new " uses every few years — but he never thought of rubber tires. And he died in a New York hotel, on July 1, 1860, leaving to his widow and six children, not a rich estate, but debts of over $200,000.

Yet Goodyear's discovery made rubber an industrial material. In 1838 all the world used less than 300 tons of caoutchouc; a century later 946,378 tons; today over a million tons. By solving the first rubber problem he created a billion-dollar American industry and that industry promptly began developing a new set of problems.

The first and foremost chronic trouble of the rubber indus-

Charles Goodyear's vulcanization process turned rubber from a sticky mass into the raw material of a million-ton industry and made plane and car practical.   — *Courtesy Goodyear Tire & Rubber Co.*

try has been one that cuts viciously both ways: the supply and the price of the raw material. It became threatening during the Gay Nineties when the bicycle craze furnished a little foretaste of what the automobile tire would do to the rubber requirements of America. Then the whole supply came from wild trees, the illustrious hevea from Brazil and a number of other species yielding rubbery sap which grew in Mexico, in Borneo, Indo-China, and several different parts of Africa. Goodyear's vulcanization process had put a premium on the so-called Fine Para grade from the *Hevea brasiliensis.* Both in the time and cost of vulcanization and in the strength and resiliency of the finished product this gum gave incomparably the best results. Towards the end of the last decade of the past century the united pressure of increasing demand and growing scarcity of hevea trees began shoving up the price of Brazilian rubber.

If the tread of your automobile tire were pure rubber vulcanized simply with heat and sulphur, as Charles Goodyear conceived his own great discovery, it would cost twice as much and stand up for about one hundred miles. You expect at least two hundred times that mileage. The tire-makers tell us that a skillful driver (who does not spin his rear wheels by starting with a rush nor drag them by jamming his brakes to the floorboard) ought to get thirty thousand miles.

That thirty thousand miles of progress is a chemical story. Indeed, the art of rubber compounding is now highly specialized, applied chemistry. In dollars and cents the modern tire is as much chemicals as rubber.

All this is recent rubber history. At the turn of the century the industry was so chemically unconscious that one of its acknowledged leaders stated that he would give more for the guess of his old superintendent than for all the facts proved by the best chemist on earth.

One brilliant young chemist changed all that. Arthur Marks drew a whole flock of chemical rabbits out of the old

rubber mixing machine. He flourished them under the astonished noses of his dismayed, rule-of-thumb competitors and
dropped them neatly in the bag. By means of chemicals he
did things to rubber and with rubber which they had all been
wishing. And it paid him handsomely. In money matters he
was as acute as Charles Goodyear was dull, and his methods
of attacking a rubber problem were also the very antithesis
of those of the great first vulcanizer.

Marks as a trained chemist postulated a chemical theorem
and sought a chemical Q.E.D. This was a new approach. It
got amazing results, and he sold chemistry to the rubber industry by the good old dollars-and-cents argument. Having
himself wielded the test tube, after he left the laboratory for
the carpeted office he had the gift — rare in a technically
trained executive — of allowing other men to search in their
own way for the answers to the problems that he posed. He
was a practical practitioner of Francis Garvan's rule of research: get a good man; give him an honest problem; don't
bother him till he gets results.

Marks had still another uncommon combination of talents.
He was a good chemist with a sound commercial instinct.
Years later one of his good friends said: " He lives with one
eye on rubber and the other on the dollar; and whenever both
eyes come sharply into focus something important happens
to the rubber industry."

In those days one of his eyes scanned critically the mounting total of dollars in the raw-materials columns of the factory
cost sheets. The other, roving about, hit upon the growing
pile of second-hand rubber in discarded bicycle tires. Putting
two and two together, he decided that it was just about time
somebody did something about salvaging this waste.

He found that a weak solution of caustic soda, held at a
high temperature for twenty hours, got maximum results.
Cotton fabric and free sulphur are simultaneously removed.
The rubber itself is again rendered plastic. The yield is over

half the weight of old tires so treated. With slight modifications this process today accounts for about a quarter of a million tons of reclaimed rubber produced in the United States each year.

It is quite a business, this reviving rubber that has outlived its usefulness. In the form of inch-thick blankets, thirty by forty inches, a pound of reclaim is sold for each three pounds of raw new rubber imported.

Tires furnish the bulk of reprocessed rubber, but the reclaimer accepts old shoes and garden hose and cherishes such tidbits as former hot-water bottles, tubing, and gloves. His product is sold on rigid chemical specifications based upon the process of reclamation and the analysis of the reclaim. It is a steady business too, and a growing one, and, all in all, far removed from the junky, fly-by-night enterprise one might expect.

Regenerated scrap rubber seems a perfect example of the cheap, nasty chemical substitute for the fine, pure gum of the noble hevea tree. Cheap it is compared with new rubber; yet in the debacle of 1933, when plantation rubber sold for less than 3 cents a pound, reclaimed rubber sold for 5 cents. But it is also stable, for in the past decade when rubber prices swung up and down wildly between 2½ and 26 cents, reclaim was quoted within the narrow range of 3 to 6 cents. You need not be a Certified Public Accountant to figure out what a nine-hundred-per-cent variation in the cost of his chief raw material would be doing to a tire-builder with a nice yearly contract to supply one of the big motor companies a million casings at a fixed price. You can appreciate his warm, friendly regard for lowly, steady reclaim.

Regenerated rubber is no rascally substitute. For certain uses it is positively superior to raw rubber. For example, it is less absorbent of water. Accordingly, it is a truly desirable ingredient in shoe soles and heels, and machine belting. It has legitimate use where new rubber would be a foolish lux-

ury, as in the mat of the automobile running board, which
need never last longer than the motor. Where elasticity, resiliency, and tensile strength are at a premium, reprocessed
rubber is distinctly inferior; and we see how wisely the rub-
ber-mixer is employing this material in the percentage of reclaim to raw rubber in certain standardized products as published in the trade paper *Rubber Age:*

Tire carcases	up to 60%
Inner tubes	" " 30%
Hard rubber articles	" " 40%
Footwear	10 — 25%
Heels	40 — 50%
Hose, insulating wire	10 — 35%

Cheaper, steadier reclaim acts as an economic gyroscope,
a governor on rubber prices, a check upon speculation. This
is a useful purpose. Rubber manufacturers maintain stoutly
that it is less disturbing to us consumers to modify their
formulas than to change their retail prices with every swing
in raw-material costs. That you might debate; but it is a fact
that if Arthur Marks had not made high-grade regenerated
rubber available, we should have poorer rubber goods in
some instances, better goods in other classes, but for all rubberwares we should certainly pay more.

Marks's reclaiming process was made available in 1899
when Para rubber was selling at over a dollar a pound — this
was before there was any cultivated rubber from the Eastern
plantations — and it was an instantaneous success. It made
him a wealthy man. Fortunately he did not hide away behind
a mahogany desk and a brace of secretaries nor yet slip into
an easy chair by his own hearthstone. He became superintendent of the Diamond Rubber Company in Akron, the first
chemically trained executive in the world's rubber headquarters. He was chief chemist and plant manager, power
engineer and personnel officer, cost-finder and price-fixer,

first-aid doctor, even veterinarian, salesman, and his own laboratory bottle-washer. Diamond later merged with Goodrich, but was then a large producer; and their superintendent seldom found time hanging on his hands.

Para rubber from Brazil was the only wild rubber that vulcanized quickly and had sufficient tensile strength for use in tire fabrics, inner tubes, surgical and many other goods, eked out chiefly by gums from Mexico (guayule), from Africa (Massai and Benguela), and from Borneo (Pontinac). These low-grade materials mixed with Para disproportionately lengthened the time of vulcanization (which meant more sulphur, more heat, more labor) and perversely lowered its strength. Accordingly, despite their cheapness, they could not be used to advantage as diluents. All this played right into the hands of the Brazilian exporters. Being perfectly human, they were not content with a handsome premium for their superior rubber. Like Oliver Twist — and almost everybody else — they wanted more, and as the demand for high-grade Para grew more insistent, they evolved what they euphemistically called a " valorization plan." It was an international squeeze play in rubber. They forced the price of their neatly monopolized material up to $1.60 a pound.

Then Marks bethought him of a tall, nervous, energetic youth, a classmate at Harvard, close-mouthed, hard-working, well grounded in chemistry, with the inquisitive itch that afflicts all born researchers. He himself simply did not have the time to give to $1.60 rubber that this so precious commodity rightly deserved. Why not let George Oenslager do it?

So he wrote to his old classmate in care of the Warren paper mills at Portland, Maine, and offered him a job in Akron. Oenslager replied that he knew a little about pulp and paper, but nothing about rubber. Marks wired back: " Neither does anybody else."

A month later the two sat down in Marks's library after Sunday supper for the first of many rubber powwows. The different qualities and prices of the various gums were first swiftly sketched.

" If," continued Marks, " we could make first-quality goods out of fifty-cent Pontinac gum in our ten-ton daily production we would save a dollar a pound, $2,000 a ton, or $20,000 a day." His eyes were both clearly focused upon the objective.

" Low-grade rubbers must lack some unknown substance that is in the Fine Para. The identical hevea tree in Brazil yields either the Fine or the Coarse grade of Para depending upon the treatment of the gum: Fine if the sap is immediately dried over heat; Coarse if it is allowed to coagulate on the tree trunk. Something happens during that slow coagulation. Either the unknown substance is changed by fermentation or it is carried off in the liquid serum that drains away. I've proved that to my own satisfaction, for when I treated Fine Para with acetone it lost two per cent by weight and acted just like Coarse Para. On the other hand, by adding that acetone extraction to Coarse, it becomes almost as good as Fine. There is some substance which added to Pontinac will make it vulcanize like Para and have Para-like properties after vulcanization."

Oenslager, being a man of few words, nodded assent.

" Let's find that unknown substance."

" I'll do what I can."

" It may take you six weeks. It may take you six years. Maybe you will never be able to do it, but go to it."

CHAPTER XI

THE ELASTIC ELDORADO

◇◇

BRIGHT and early the first Monday morning in January 1906 George Oenslager went to work on rubber. He did not suspect it, but he was taking the first steps along the trail of chemical discovery which has meant 30,000 miles of tire progress. He certainly did not dare to hope that within six months he would make a discovery that has saved American motorists over $100,000,000. Not bad, for a man who confessed he knew nothing about rubber!

He is a logical, methodical workman, this bespectacled Oenslager, and he began by comparing Para and Pontinac gums. He found by analysis that they contain virtually the same proportions of hydrogen and carbon. While proving that the two rubber hydrocarbons are very similar, he was teaching himself rubber chemistry. He is as smart as he is sensible. Next he gave a chunk of Pontinac gum a dreadful mauling in a macerating machine to satisfy himself that in processing it underwent no chemical change. This long-legged chemist is careful and he was taking no chances that some unchecked factor might upset his conclusions. At last he was ready and the real search began.

For years white lead, red lead, lime, magnesia, had been added to the rubber-sulphur mix to facilitate vulcanization. Oenslager began a systematic hunt for other catalysts. He chose a familiar formula: rubber 100 parts, zinc oxide 60

[189

parts, sulphur 6 parts, which with Para produces a tensile strength of 2,800 pounds to the square inch when vulcanized for 90 minutes at 287° F. In this formula he substituted Corinto, a notoriously poor gum, which has a tensile strength of only 1,200 pounds after 2 hours of vulcanization at 290° F. With this as a control or yardstick, he began adding all sorts of metals and inorganic salts. From aluminium powder to zinc dust he tested hundreds and found one that gave promise.

On March 22 he proved that a small amount of mercuric iodide would make the product of inferior Pontinac gum almost as good as vulcanized Para. What was as important, its vulcanization time could be stepped up to synchronize with fast-curing Para. He discovered also that by reducing the sulphur and increasing the catalyst the strengths of both cheap and costly rubbers could be markedly increased.

George Oenslager kept his fingers crossed. He knew chemistry, and he suspected that at the same time it was serving as a stimulator of the sulphur reactions involved in vulcanization, mercuric iodide would also act as an oxidant for rubber. Oxygen is rubber's deadly foe. It causes the surface to become hard and cracked. It kills bounce and strength. Knowing that mercuric iodide is a capital oxygen-carrier, Oenslager wondered apprehensively how rubber vulcanized with this newly found accelerator would stand up. He had no way of guessing. The neat laboratory test for quickly measuring rubber deterioration had not yet been devised by William Geer. To make sure, he had to make up some tires of his new mix and put them into service on the road. The trials confirmed his worst fears. He had proved, however, that at least one chemical, used even in minute quantities, did produce the results they were seeking.

Long before the discouraging reports from the road tests began arriving at his desk, this enthusiast was back in his laboratory seeking better accelerators. Even if the rubber vulcanized with mercuric iodide were excellent he foresaw that the chemical, being highly poisonous, would create a wicked health hazard in the rubber factories.

He had enough data, chiefly negative in result, but positive in suggestion, to be sure that it was not the metal in a compound that counted, and noting that the old accelerators — lime, litharge, etc. — were all alkali bases, he reasoned that it would be worth while to try organic bases, preferably one completely soluble in rubber. The cheapest, most available chemical of this kind was aniline. Naturally he investigated it first and found on June 11 that it gave extraordinarily good results.

Again hundreds of careful tests were made with all sorts of organic chemicals. Scores of complex compounds with jaw-breaking names unknown outside chemical circles, such as phenylhydrazine and hexamethyl-tetramine; also naphthalene (moth balls), iodoform, and carbolic acid, the disinfectants; gallic and tannic acids, were tried. Some were good accelerators, others poor, many indifferent. Nitroso-dimethyl-aniline was excellent, better than aniline; but it stained everything — including the experimenter himself — a brilliant yellow. Because of good results produced, its cheapness and availability, aniline was picked for the first working tests. It met these so successfully that it soon became a regular ingredient in the Diamond mixes.

Spurred on by the hope of discovering an even more efficient accelerator, research continued. Aniline also had the serious drawback of being toxic. Oenslager's expectations were soon met by thiocarbanilide. If but six per cent were added to a standard batch of the despised Pontinac gum, the tensile strength was lifted to 3,000 pounds to the square inch and the time of vulcanization cut to ten minutes. This was out-performing the choice Para. Within six months Oenslager had hit the bull's-eye of Marks's target.

Thiocarbanilide met other specifications for commercial

use. It is a white powder, easily handled and incorporated
into the rubber mix. It was reasonably cheap and made from
available materials, aniline and carbon bisulfide. It is non-
poisonous and non-flammable. The simple process could be
handled by workmen who were not brainy and who knew
nothing about chemicals. Accordingly, off in a corner of the
plant area, a little shack of corrugated iron sheets was pinned
together, and George Oenslager gave over being a chemist
to become a chemical manufacturer.

All these proceedings were deeply secret. No other chemist
had been allowed within smelling distance of the laboratory,
which was a good many feet away. Oenslager's assistant was a
former cheese-factory boss, as ignorant of rubber and chemistry as of the Vedas in their original Sanskrit, but an amiable,
nimble-witted chap who invented delightfully fantastic
stories to misinform the whole factory and all its visitors.
Like a couple of schoolgirls talking hog Latin, Marks and
Oenslager gabbled glibly in chemical formulas, coining fancy
names for their new-found accelerators. Mercuric iodide was
" Chinese vermilion "; aniline, " Residium "; thiocarbanilide,
"Lagos." They purchased laboratory reagents in distant
cities. When they came to buy regular supplies of chemical
raw materials, they went through all the furtive maneuvers
of a leading citizen in a dry state ordering a case of Scotch.
They spared no pains to conceal the source and disguise the
contents of shipments of raw materials.

Diamond began using aniline on June 22, 1906, and before
September 19, when thiocarbanilide became a regular ingredient, word was all over Akron that Marks was putting
chemicals into his batches that enabled him to use cheap
rubbers and get high-quality goods. The tales lost nothing in
the telling. His competitors were thrown into a panic lest he
cut tire prices below their costs and ruin them all. Within a
year his carefully guarded cat had slipped out of the sack.

The rubber industry began buying laboratory equipment

and engaging organic chemists in a frantic endeavor to better Oenslager's achievement. It is said that on January 1, 1906 George Oenslager was the only chemist regularly employed in a rubber factory in Akron. Today — 1941 — the Akron Section of the American Chemical Society has over three hundred members. The man among them who is not " in rubber " is as conspicuous as the distinguished guest at the head table who came to the banquet in his business suit. Beside Charles Goodyear, who made rubber practical, stands George Oenslager, who made it cheaper. The one created an industry; the other revolutionized its thinking and its technique.

If Goodyear made the automobile tire possible, it was Oenslager who, himself and through the chemical work inspired by his success, pulled down the price from $40 to $15 and shoved up the mileage from 5,000 to 30,000. We tire-users, who once had to pay out a cent for " rubber " for every mile we drove the car, can now ride twenty miles on the same penny. That saves $28 for every thousand miles we drive, and if you keep your mileage records for the sake of the gasoline-tax credit on your income tax, you can figure for yourself just what contribution this is to your own more abundant life. At least it is a pleasant little help in paying the taxes levied by the politicians who are forever promising to make life safer and richer for us all. The molecule-makers who bring us better goods for fewer dollars do not promise so much, but perform more handsomely.

We Americans are pathetically modest about our chemical achievements. Some of us still think that before the first World War we never had a chemical industry at all, whereas in 1914 we produced in three months more chemicals — measured in tons or dollars — than both England and Germany added together did in the full year. To hear us talk you might think chemistry is as exclusively a German science as Limburger is a German cheese. The science was born in England and educated in France, and not one of its great fundamental laws was discovered in Germany. None of us boast — and we are generally credited with being overfond of that sort of thing — about American chemical contributions.

Rubber is certainly not the least of these. Yet Hancock almost filched credit for vulcanization. Six years too late, in 1912, the Bayer Company announced with great beating of the scientific tomtoms that their chemists, Hoffman and Gottlob, had discovered organic accelerators. Two years later a British chemist, S. J. Peachey, discovered that nitroso-dimethyl-aniline is a superior product. Not to be outdone by the Germans, he penned the complete misstatement: " It is quite true that the Germans led to the discovery . . . but it is equally true that by far the most satisfactory organic accelerator was discovered in a British laboratory." His vaunted nitroso-dimethyl-aniline was that excellent reagent Oenslager had discarded eight years before because it stained everything, including himself, a pretty canary yellow. All this erudite piracy was possible because Marks, playing foxy, did not patent Oenslager's discoveries and there was no record in the literature.

After leaving his initial research to evolve a manufacturing operation for thiocarbanilide, the silent dean of all our rubber chemists never returned to accelerators. Others developed hundreds of catalysts for the vulcanization process, some of them improvements over his pioneering discoveries; he went on to investigate other problems.

He did not do the first work with carbon black, but it was his knowing skill that did most to establish this pigment as the single most important factor in lengthening the life of tires. This microscopically fine jet-black powder is manufactured by igniting natural gas in faulty burners over which a steel plate oscillates, collecting the soot from the incomplete combustion just as a saucer held over a candle flame provides the black pigment for the merry Hallowe'en prank. It comprises as much as thirty per cent of our tire treads. It tremendously increases rubber's resistance to abrasion, and the discovery of its beneficent action led to the whole development of scientific rubber compounding.

The basic rubber mix is still rubber, zinc oxide, and sulphur. But nearly two thousand other materials are used — some more, some less — in elaborate recipes formulated after long series of experiments to produce the best rubber for a particular purpose. The industry has over thirty thousand working formulas for rubber compounds. They range from almost pure gum, as in toy balloons and elastic bands, to compounds that contain but an infusion of rubber, such as mechanical belting, floor mats, and protective or insulating coatings. " Try anything once " has been the motto of the compounder, often with astonishing results. He finds good use in his recipes for " everything but the kitchen stove ": talcum powder and glue, pine oil and shellac, Vaseline, beeswax, mica, potato starch, sawdust, lime, wheat flour, charcoal — what have you? — a perfect witches' brew. He produces a tire tread ten times as resistant to the rasping rubbing of the road as a steel hoop tire of the stagecoach days, or at the other end of the scale a gossamer thread as fine as a spiderweb that will stretch five times its own length.

Modern " ultra-accelerators " act so quickly that to prevent premature vulcanization in the mills, it is necessary to use retarders or anti-scorching agents. As oxygen causes iron to rust and paint to chalk, so it is the cause of all the different ways that rubber deteriorates with age. Hence chemicals are employed to hold in check the action of this potent element. Other chemicals protect from fatigue (stretching and flexing) and from exposure to heat and to sunlight. Rubber's physical properties are modified by plasticizers, softeners, and stiffeners. The combinations and permutations of rubber compounding are almost unlimited.

But all this chemical progress availed nothing in solving

the problem of the supply of crude rubber — that is quite a different story and it takes us back nearly half a century to the sweltering river port of Sartarem, where two bold rascals stole the entire incoming cargo of the first English liner to steam into the upper Amazon.

The worthy Justus Hasskarl, who at the risk of his life had transplanted quinine trees to the Dutch East Indies, set a fashion in botanical adventure that became popular because it proved to be profitable. Thanks to its ability to handle products that require quite an elaborate processing before they go off to market, the plantation system is a first-class means of cultivating the assets of a tropical colony. Such products demand a large capital investment and knowing supervision of plenty of cheap labor: white man's gold and brains with the sweat and muscles of black, brown, and yellow men — the perfect combination for the plantation economy. Hence sugar whose juices must be extracted and concentrated promptly, vanilla beans that need skilled curing, indigo which must be fermented and manipulated, tea, coffee, cotton, cinchona, all these are typical plantation products. Half a century ago rubber caught the attention of an alert little coterie of Englishmen deeply interested in such international botanical experiments.

James Collins, curator of the famous old Physic Garden of the Apothecaries Company — his predecessor Robert Fortune had resigned to introduce tea into India — became chief propagandist for the idea of transplanting *Hevea brasiliensis* to England's Eastern colonies. He wrote a sprightly little pamphlet which Sir Clements Markham sent broadcast to gentlemen in a position to help. Most of them must have tossed it into the wastebasket, for Collins's report is now a rare collector's item; but at least the Duke of Argyll, Gladstone's Secretary of State for India, was won over and some of the directors of the powerful East India Company caught the idea of potential profits.

Several batches of seed were secured. Even in the expert care of Sir Joseph Hooker at the Kew Gardens and Sir William King at the Royal Gardens in Calcutta, only a pitiful few germinated. Collins was sent to South America, but homeward bound he and his hevea collections were shipwrecked. Hooker had a botanical correspondent at Santarem, where the Tapajos River joins the Amazon, an established rubber-trader in the heart of the richest hevea region, a man with ten years' experience in the Brazilian jungles. Hooker suggested Henry Wickham to the India Office as a likely seed-collector.

When first approached, Wickham, knowing how quickly the big, oily seeds of the hevea tree lose their vitality, suggested sending over young plants. Trouble and expense weighed against this proposal, and in the end he agreed to supply seed at fifty dollars per thousand. He had received official confirmation of this order and the seed-collecting season was just opening when the brand-new steamer *Amazonas*, Captain Murray commanding, hove to off Santarem. With the other personages of the little river town he was invited to a jollification dinner on board. They all downed a good many brandy-and-sodas, toasting the maiden trip of the first regular liner service between Liverpool and the upper Amazon. Next morning long before Wickham awoke, the shiny new steamer puffed upstream for Manaos, her last port of call. A few weeks later the jungle telegraph brought him an amazing story.

Captain Murray discharged his cargo of trade goods at Manaos and, acting on the instructions of his two supercargoes, dropped downstream to the junction of the Negro and the Amazon to await instructions for loading his return cargo of rubber. He waited and waited. Not being overly patient, he landed, to learn the dismaying news that his rascally supercargoes had indeed disposed of the goods and forthwith decamped into the tropical labyrinth.

Wickham smiled at the picture of the testy little Scotch sea captain left high and dry in the steaming jungle stream, irascibly pacing the decks of his empty vessel, impotent, with no scapegoat for his rage, and without the means of getting a return cargo. An inspiration flashed into Wickham's head. Here was a heaven-sent opportunity to get his hevea seed — thousands upon thousands of hevea seeds, a whole shipload! — to England quickly.

The thirty-year-old adventurer acted with what he later modestly described as "extraordinary initiative, resource, and organizing capacity." He had no money. He had, however, a perfectly good order from Queen Victoria's Indian Government. On the strength of this he wrote Captain Murray chartering the *Amazonas* and setting a rendezvous at the mouth of the Tapajos.

He clambered into a native canoe and with a pair of stout Indian paddlers pushed up the Tapajos fifty miles into the heart of a region rich in fine hevea trees. Gathering a band of fifty aborigines, he scoured the plateau between the two rivers collecting great basketfuls of the heavy, oily nuts, bringing them back to a village on the river bank, drying them carefully in the shade, packing them between banana leaves in improvised openwork crates that he bribed the village women into weaving out of split canes. Working against time, he loaded a dozen big canoes with his precious, perishable freight and set off to meet the *Amazonas* at the river junction as appointed. Not till his crates were safely slung in the hold and the new steamer slipping rapidly down the Amazon did he pause to draw breath.

A new anxiety rose to haunt him. At Para, the port of entry, they would have to stop for clearance papers. With the cinchona experience before them, the Brazilians were not anxious to see their hevea tree taken over by the plantation system. Accordingly, if the authorities had any inkling of the cargo aboard, there would surely be exasperating, intentional delays, snarling his pretty, dappled seeds up in red tape that would not be cut till their delicate vitality had been destroyed.

When they reached Para, Captain Murray lay in midstream with steam up while Wickham ferried ashore. His friend British Consul Green introduced him to the proper authorities as a special commissioner bringing back botanical specimens for Her Majesty's own royal gardens at Kew. They begged for immediate dispatch lest the rare ferns and beautiful orchids perish. Amid a flourish of compliments the papers were signed and the *Amazonas* proceeded down the mightiest of rivers with one of the most important cargoes ever freighted across the oceans.

Wickham's unannounced arrival with 70,000 hevea seeds created just the sensation that delighted this able but conceited man. A special train rushed his loot from Liverpool to Kew. Orchid houses and propagating sheds were all turned inside out to get the seeds into soil as quickly as possible. Of his great haul only 2,397 germinated, but a year later, in August 1876, 1,919 lusty young plants were shipped to Ceylon.

That was the beginning. It was three decades later, however, before cultivated plantation rubber became a factor in the market. The period was one of widespread, haphazard experiment. Half a dozen different vines and trees that exude a gummy milk were tried out in our own Florida, in Fiji, in Haiti and Hawaii, Trinidad and Tobago, the Philippines, all along the coasts of Africa and Indo-China, and on the islands of the South Seas. In the end *Hevea brasiliensis* was established as the rubber-bearer without rival and the Malaya-Sumatra region the section where it grows best under cultivation.

About the middle of the nineties stories began to circulate about the rubber famine that was sure to follow the ruthless destruction of the rubber jungles. King Leopold of Belgium and President William McKinley between them launched the first rubber boom. From the Congo regions, which between

1895 and 1908 produced nearly half the world's rubber, came gory reports of a conscienceless exploitation of men and trees. It was easy to picture the utter exhaustion of this important supply. A frame was put around this picture when the former Congressman from the Akron district in his first presidential message to Congress advocated rubber cultivation in our recently acquired Puerto Rico and the Philippines. Gruesome rubber atrocity stories in the magazines — this was in the muck-raking era of American journalism — backed up by official consular reports on rubber-growing experiments all over the world, furnished splendid propaganda for the promoters who promised millions in Mexican rubber plantations.

Rubber-plantation companies were organized by the score. Some were honest enough in intent. American corporations owned or had options on over a million and a half acres of Mexican and Central American land and actually planted more than 32,000,000 rubber trees. But most of these enterprises were get-rich-quick schemes to scoop in the dollars in exchange for pretty stock certificates. Some reputable citizens were cajoled into lending their names to fraudulent companies, and Thomas Edison, the great inventor, and Frederick Hood, the big rubber manufacturer, both headed up purely fictitious rubber farms. The New York Teachers Plantation Corporation and the Chicago Police and Fireman's Mexican Plantation Company were floated to make a particularly alluring, exclusive appeal to the five- and ten-dollar investor. Florida, which somehow manages to latch on to every boom scheme, was described as having a climate comparable to the pestilential jungles of Amazonia, destined to be a great rubber land, and as a forecast of recent enticing tung-oil projects, a nursery company at Orlando was promoted to earn " 200 per cent dividends " selling young rubber trees to other planters.

Then came the panic of 1907. It realistically swept all these American rubber plantations into the discard and wafted the microbe of rubber speculation across the Atlantic to England. The British rubber boom soared as high and wide as our own, and for the school-teachers and policemen it ended just as ruefully; but its causes and results were quite different.

In 1900 but four tons of rubber were shipped from all the Eastern plantations. By 1905 this had expanded to 145 tons. A little cloud like a man's hand had arisen out of the sea, but there was nothing in these modest figures to warn the blithe Brazilians that the heavens would soon be black with storms. Cocksurely they took advantage of the failing African supply and the strengthening American demand. Up they boosted the price of Para gum to $1.50 a pound.

By doing so they just about trebled the profits of the planters in Malaya and Ceylon and made their 60,000 acres of hevea trees an extraordinarily attractive investment. In a year plantation acreage jumped to 294,000 and by 1910 it reached 1,112,000. Plantation shipments naturally kept pace: in 1906, 510 tons and by 1910 over 8,000 tons.

That year the Brazilians cheerfully ran the price up to the all-time high of $3.06. The plantation output of 1910 almost doubled in 1911. It all but doubled again and yet again the two following seasons. By 1914 the score in tons shipped stood: plantations, 72,000; Brazil, 37,000; all others, 12,000.

Meanwhile the price of rubber had been tobogganing. From the 1910 peak of $3.06 it slid by 1913 back to the old level of 65 cents. It did not stop, but slipped and slithered down, down till towards the close of 1921 it reached a new low of 11½ cents a pound.

The rubber jamboree ended in a headache for the stock gamblers. Millions of paper profits on the shares of rubber estates were wiped out, but the plantations themselves had been enormously extended and out in the field the managers had learned to grow bigger yields and pare down the costs of upkeep. By 1920 they were selling three quarters of the world's 650,000 tons of rubber and in 1940, with a total out-

put over a million tons, they furnished ninety-five per cent
of the supply.

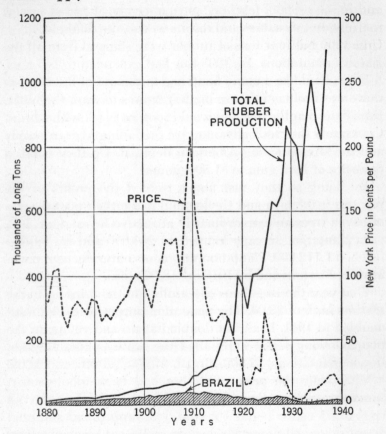

The above chart reveals graphically how quickly and greatly the output of cultivated plantation rubber has grown since 1910, while
Brazilian rubber (shown in the shaded area at the bottom) occupies
a position of steadily decreasing importance in the total world production. The price curve shows plainly that, except for the "booming twenties," the price of raw rubber has been steadily declining.

Rubber prices are as fascinating as a pretty grass widow,
and as dangerous. Also like a merry widow, rubber prices have
received the assiduous attentions of many men, and those at-

tentions have had dynamic results. The Brazilians euchred themselves out of the dealer's seat in the rubber market by raising the price so high that they tempted a flood of capital to expand the estates in Malaya and the Dutch East Indies. Unintentionally, but quite literally, they financed their own deadly competitors.

Their all-time record of $3.06 a pound also set the chemists to work. Admitting the rubber molecule is exceedingly complex — so complex that its exact structure is still debated by the experts — nevertheless you can do a whole lot of fancy molecule-making for $6,120 a ton. The rubber demand is more imperative and many times greater than that for indigo, which had launched a twenty-year research war. Midas' touch was surely in the fingers that would hold up the first test tube filled with synthetic rubber.

As the price slid down, down, interest within the laboratories waned. Out on plantations it became painfully acute. The rubber-growers began courting the fickle prices which had betrayed them into over-planting. For a couple of years they coquetted with gentlemen's agreements to restrict shipments, and when this dalliance got them nowhere the British planters, who produced three quarters of the cultivated rubber, decided to quit fooling and invoke the strong arm of the law for their protection.

A second time two world figures became entangled with rubber prices, and again the results were surprising. Neither Winston Churchill nor Herbert Hoover could have foreseen the outcome when the then Secretary of State for the Colonies backed the Stevenson plan for legally controlling rubber prices for the benefit of British rubber-estate owners and the then Secretary of Commerce protested vigorously in the name of American consumers.

The Stevenson plan did not work out in practice nearly as well as on paper. The Dutch planters would not go along with the scheme of cutting down shipments through export taxes. Indeed, they used — or abused, from the British point of view — it as an umbrella under which they snugly tucked away more than their share of the business. Rubber-smuggling became incredibly profitable, surpassing the wildest exploits and richest loot of our own rum-running. Certainly a Malay pirate with sarong and kris is a worthy rival of the best bootleggers, and a glance at the map shows how admirably his archipelago lends itself to such enterprises. His operations did embarrass the Stevenson plan, but it was defeated, as every legal device to control prices has always been defeated, by perfectly natural economic forces.

The boom in our automobile industry during the Roaring Twenties raised our imports of rubber from 179,647 tons in 1921 to 404,496 in 1928. Not the British planters in the Stevenson strait jacket but the native growers of the Dutch colonies, who are the low-cost producers, profited by this increased sale. So the Stevenson plan, which initially did raise the rubber price, lost control and could not prevent a decline that, once the big depression set in, reached bottom in 1932 at an all-time low of 2½ cents. But the Stevenson plan, which had plenty of vociferous, unfriendly critics, and a rubber price that passed the dollar mark in 1925–6, again caught the attention of the chemists.

Nobody loves a monopolist. Nobody ever has done so. Of course this threat of universal unpopularity has never for a moment deterred anyone who had the slightest chance of establishing a corner in anything from attempting it. King and bootblack, priest and gangster, all have succumbed to the temptation of this very old, highly favored get-rich-quick scheme. No one has ever scrupled to use whatever means, fair or foul, he had at his command to achieve and maintain a monopoly. From salt to diamonds, from the cheapest necessities to the most costly luxuries, there is hardly a commodity that has not at some time or somewhere been garnered into a monopoly of sorts.

Our dislike of monopolies has become almost instinctive. Mankind abhors them as definitely and as vigorously as nature abhors a vacuum. Even the suggestion of an unreasonable control over the supply of anything we really want rouses us to action as a distant bark raises the hair on a dog's neck.

There never was anything approaching a really ironbound monopoly in rubber. Twice, however, sufficient control over supply was established to enable certain humanly selfish groups to boost the price. Both these temporary exploitations started things — the Eastern plantation and synthetic rubber — which very directly affected the profiteers, but did a great deal more to change the rubber industry and the use we all make of rubber products.

Those that live by the sword shall perish by the sword warns the Good Book; and having taken the market from the Brazilian wild rubber by the force of lower prices, will the plantations in turn lose it to the synthetic rubber of the laboratories?

CHAPTER XII

NOT RUBBER, BUT
RUBBERLIKE

◇◇

" How research is shortening one of America's defense lines by 10,000 miles!" So flashes the catchline of Goodyear's double-page advertisement of Chemigum, their new synthetic rubber.

It is a bold statement, thought up by some smart copy-writer to rivet attention and rouse curiosity. Behind it lies a great deal that does not appear on the surface nor in the interesting, informative advertisement beneath it.

First of all, our rubber companies do not intend to share the fate of the Indian indigo-planter, or the Chilean nitrate-miner, or even of the Brazilian rubber-collector. That is good business sense. It is also a tribute to the job of chemical education done by Marks and Oenslager. It is, furthermore, a neat compliment to synthetic rubber.

Amid the munificence of our natural resources we over-look the gaps in the supplies of our essential raw materials. Rubber is one of these. We are as dependent upon outside sources as was Germany when Captain König packed Para gum into the tubelike hold of his *Deutschland*. And we regularly consume two thirds of the rubber produced in the world: six times as much as Great Britain; ten times as much as Japan; twenty times as much as Russia. We have a big stake in rubber.

206]

With eighty per cent of all the motor cars on earth spinning over our highways on rubber tires, and nearly three times as many buses, vans, and farm tractors as all the other countries added together, our transportation has become very dependent upon this resilient material. Pile on top of this our airplanes (soft balloon-type tires alone make landing on uneven ground possible) and the needs of a mobilized American army — at once you get the point of that arresting scarehead.

When the Nazi regime surveyed their essential raw materials, an *ersatz* caoutchouc became a categorical imperative, a Number-One Research for the *Reichsforschungsrat,* that remarkable bureau organized by Artillery-General-Professor-Doktor Karl Becker — a significant hyphenation of titles that! — to co-ordinate all German science to the aims of the state. As General-Professor Becker's chief, Reichsminister Rust, in charge of learning and training, so aptly put it:

> Complete freedom of opinion and judgment are not the marks of a truly free science. Freedom is assured to science neither by its abstractness nor by its independence of current events, so if the Nazi State calls upon German science to co-operate in the Four-Year Plan, it is because the first task of science will be to give us those materials that Nature has denied us. Such a task can only be accomplished by free science, and science is only free if she sovereignly masters those problems that are posed to her by life.

Precisely so, and the long researches into synthetic rubber which the I.G. staff had been carrying forward in a desultory fashion were overhauled and speeded up. The first requirement was that all the raw materials required be cheap, abundant, and available within the Reich. Chemically and commercially the best prospect was butadiene, prepared from acetylene, made in turn from coke and limestone, both ready to hand.

" The problem of synthetic-rubber production in Germany has been solved," declared the Nazi Minister of Economy, Hjalmar Schacht, in a speech delivered in October 1934.

"We have definitely solved the rubber problem! " shouted Adolf Hitler in Nuremberg in September 1935. "Commercial production will commence at once."

" Positively and forever we are free from foreign domination of our necessary supplies of rubber," Der Führer pronounced at the opening of the Berlin Automobile Show in February 1936.

Three times and out! This last announcement was made good by the building of the first synthetic-rubber plant since World War I at Piesteritz. Behind these repeated bolstering boasts lies a story of smart research whose details we can now only guess.

Like all of the Nazi program the quest for synthetic rubber was a race against time. Spurred by patriotic fervor to make their country independent and impregnable, German researchers were lashed to greater efforts by the constant naggings of the military chiefs: " Must all our plans fall down for lack of a suitable rubber substitute? " German feelings were not improved by the knowledge that since 1931 a synthetic rubber made by an American company had been on the market. It was the result of research by American chemists which had started in 1925.

At that time the infant American dye industry was settling down after the rough and disorderly competition that followed the first World War. All sorts of people had leaped into the business, and those that were to survive must perfect operations to increase yields, to raise quality and cut costs, and to extend the range of their colors. These were absorbing, expensive activities. By 1925, however, the more efficient companies began to come to the top. Bound for a meeting in New York, two du Pont executives discussed this situation in the smoking-compartment.

Outwitting nature, synthetic rubbers do things rubber could never do — a porous, transparent, watertight fabric of Koroseal.
— Courtesy The B. F. Goodrich Company

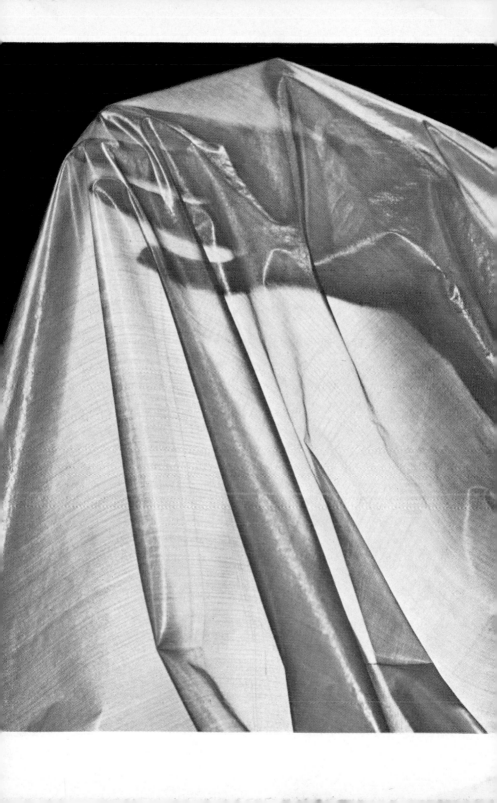

"Our dyestuffs department is straightening out," said Willis Harrington, chief of the chemical division, "so that we can begin thinking about some other projects. Have you any good ideas?"

"It does sound highly speculative," replied Dr. Elmer K. Bolton, who was then in charge of organic research, "but there is a possibility of making butadiene rubbers from acetylene."

This was surely proposing to plow again well-tilled fields. Back in 1860 the Englishman Greville Williams by subjecting rubber to repeated distillations had isolated its parent substance, a hydrocarbon having the formula C_5H_8, which he named isoprene. Twenty-four years later another Englishman, William Tilden, prepared isoprene from turpentine and found that a sample bottle which stood several months on his laboratory shelf had changed from a volatile liquid into a sticky gum — the first synthetic rubber. What had happened was that great numbers of C_5H_8 molecules had linked themselves together, for all the world like a chain of paper clips hooked together end to end.

This change in the weight of a molecule without changing the proportions of its component atoms is called by chemists polymerization. A simple example is the change of acetaldehyde, a white liquid with an aromatic smell and the formula C_2H_4O, into paraldehyde, a heavier, colorless liquid with a quite different, pungent odor which has the formula $C_6H_{12}O_3$. The aldehyde radical is CHO, and so these formulas are also written CH_3CHO for acetaldehyde and $(CH_3CHO)_3$ for paraldehyde. This form expresses more clearly the change wrought by polymerization. These substances have different properties, react differently in chemical combinations, and naturally have different uses. In medicine, for instance, acetaldehyde is an inhalant for catarrh, and paraldehyde is a soporific in sleeping potions.

In like manner what kind of a rubber you have depends

upon how many isoprene molecules are hooked up together. Chemically this is the basis of differences in the quality of various natural gums. Estimates of the number of isoprene molecules that are linked in natural rubber range from 200 to 4,000. The longer the chains, the better the quality of elasticity.

Failure to make commercially a true synthetic rubber lay in the difficulty of inducing the isoprene molecules to hook up into long chains quickly and cheaply. No industrial process can be built upon exposing isoprene to sunlight for a year or so, as in Tilden's sample bottles.

The chemists have ferreted out what happens to the isoprene molecules when they form into long chains and express it quite clearly in a structural formula:

$$\begin{array}{c} H_2CH_3H\ H_2 \\ | \\ C\!=\!C\!-\!C\!=\!C \end{array}$$

If these molecules are to latch on to each other, the double bonds holding the end carbon atoms (C) must be broken. Thus a bond is made available at each extremity as expressed (omitting the upper half of the formula) $-C-C=C-C-$. In the process of polymerization the end C's link up together as follows:

$$\begin{array}{ccc} H_2\ CH_3\ H\ H_2 & H_2\ CH_3\ H\ H_2 & \\ |\qquad\qquad & |\qquad\qquad & \text{etc., } x \text{ times} \\ -C-C\!=\!C-C\!=\!C-C\!=\!C-C- & & \end{array}$$

The most erudite chemist on earth has not the foggiest notion about the hows and whys of this reaction. We know it actually does happen. We have learned how to make it happen. In fact, all this had been discovered before 1914, and more too, for in Germany they had learned to polymerize another hydrocarbon, butadiene, which is simpler, yet remarkably like isoprene in its structure:

$$\begin{array}{cc}
\overset{\text{H}_2}{}\;\overset{\text{H}}{}\;\overset{\text{H}}{}\;\overset{\text{H}_2}{} & \overset{\text{H}_2}{}\;\overset{\text{CH}_3}{}\;\overset{\text{H}}{}\;\overset{\text{H}_2}{} \\
\text{C}=\text{C}-\text{C}=\text{C} & \text{C}=\text{C}-\text{C}=\text{C} \\
\textit{Butadiene} & \textit{Isoprene}
\end{array}$$

It was from dimethyl butadiene they obtained their make-shift rubber of the first World War. It was inadequate and expensive too, since butadiene could then only be prepared by very roundabout chemical reactions.

Production of true synthetic rubber thus appeared to be a stalemate and Harrington was right. But the idea of a rubberlike substitute opened up an entirely new approach to the problem, and the du Pont executive committee agreed to gamble research funds at long odds, no doubt, but certainly for high stakes. So the du Pont research team went to work on the products of acetylene, among which Dr. Bolton hoped to find a substance that would polymerize into a rubberlike compound.

In December 1925 the American Chemical Society held at Rochester, New York, a symposium on organic chemistry. The du Pont director of organic research, Dr. Bolton, naturally attended, and listened with extraordinary interest to a paper on some uncommon reactions of acetylene read by Father Julius Arthur Nieuwland, professor of organic chemistry at Notre Dame University. At such informal meetings a good paper will draw about the speaker a little knot of questioners, and Dr. Bolton stood discreetly on the edge till the crowd had thinned out. Then he asked the retiring little priest-scientist to drive out with him to the afternoon meeting at the Eastman Laboratories. On the way he asked a lot of questions about his reactions.

Back in Wilmington he wrote to South Bend a long letter full of more questions. Father Nieuwland replied that he was a wretched letter-writer; why not send somebody to his laboratory? He would be glad to show whatever he knew.

Dr. Bolton sent Dr. William Stansfield Calcott out to Notre Dame.

It was a happy choice. This retiring Virginian, a man of wide interests, hit it off with the modest Nieuwland, whose graduation essay had been a paper on Keats's poetry, whose hobby was botany, whose avocation was mounting and selling biological microscope slides to raise funds for Notre Dame chemical research. The two found many subjects of common interest. Losing his habitual shyness with this new friend, Nieuwland filled him with the chemical lore of acetylene, whose reactions he had been studying more or less continually for over twenty years. The real nub of all this week's visit, so far as the du Pont search for rubber substitutes went, was the information that sometimes he thought he obtained some monovinyl acetylene along with the divinyl acetylene, and it appeared that this increased the polymerization of the rubberlike product.

This was indefinite but suggestive. Here was a good idea backed by a lot of fine experience with acetylene. Accordingly Dr. Bolton entered into a general agreement on patents with the priest, and du Pont agreed to pay royalties on any that were developed commercially.

These arrangements completed, Dr. Bolton put the divinyl-acetylene problem up to a picked team engaged in studying the giant lineal molecules of which rubber and cellulose are familiar examples. The material Dr. Bolton turned over to this exceptional group was a yellowish drying oil which the Jackson laboratory had produced in a brand-new pilot plant, constructed to try out semi-works scale production. They had found that this divinyl acetylene was not nearly so good a drying vehicle for paints as that which had been prepared in the laboratory's glass apparatus. Painstaking Arnold Collins shortly reported that this divinyl acetylene from the pilot plant was liberally mixed with monovinyl acetylene.

Here by great luck was a source of generous supply of the

illusive mono product Father Nieuwland had been trying to isolate, so the brilliant Wallace Carothers and his associates went to work checking up the reactions of this chemical. They sealed monovinyl acetylene in test tubes with a great number of different reagents to test their effects. One of these reagents was hydrochloric acid, and soon Dr. Ira Williams showed that the best polymer of the group was chloroprene. When chloroprene had polymerized to neoprene, Williams held in his fingers the first bit of successful synthetic rubber. The formulas show how close in its structure chloroprene is to isoprene, the parent substance of natural rubber:

$$\begin{array}{ccc} H_2\ CH_3\ H\ H_2 & \quad & H_2\ Cl\ H\ H_2 \\ \qquad | & & \qquad | \\ C{=}C{-}C{=}C & & C{=}C{-}C{=}C \\ \textit{Isoprene} & & \textit{Chloroprene} \end{array}$$

But what a difference that single atom of chlorine makes! Chloroprene polymerizes more easily and quickly than either isoprene or butadiene, thus lowering production cost. It also contains almost forty per cent by weight of chlorine, which is now a comparatively cheap chemical. The resulting neoprene can be milled like rubber, molded and colored, mixed in all proportions with natural gum. Most important of all, neoprene is, as was hoped, "better than rubber in some respects." Notably it resists the deteriorating action of sunlight and heat, gasoline and lubricating oils, and many chemicals, so that for gas hose and gaskets and many similar uses it gives superior performance.

Fittingly neoprene was introduced at the annual dinner of the Rubber Section of the American Chemical Society at Akron in 1931. Three of its research pioneers, Drs. Carothers, Williams, and Downing, read papers, showed samples, and announced that a du Pont plant was building at Deepwater, New Jersey, for commercial production.

Next year, just when rubber prices sank to the all-time low

of 3½ cents, the new rubber substitute was put on the market at $1.05 per pound. How far a cry from the old hunt for a synthetic cheaper than natural rubber! Who would have dreamed that the first successful chemical rubber substitute would appear when Para gum was selling the cheapest in all its long, vacillating price history and that all the available supply of the synthetic material would be bought up at thirty times the cost of caoutchouc.

That neoprene announcement made before two hundred and fifty of the nation's best rubber chemists was received with polite attention. It did not create a sensation. It did make the front page of the Akron newspaper — it was assuredly front-page news in the rubber industry's world capital — but one suspects that it was the annual dinner and a long list of good local names that inspired the make-up editor.

Among the rubber-plantation crowd this real news was hardly accorded a glance. The bugaboo of a synthetic competitor had bobbed up so often that it no longer frightened even the youngest, most innocent estate assistant out in Malaya or the oldest, most jittery director in London. Besides, the planters had other matters to think about. The three-cent rubber meant ruin to them all. Even the native growers in the Dutch islands could not squeeze enough profit out of three pennies to keep soul and body together. A new restriction program was afoot when the big news of synthetic rubber broke on the opposite side of the globe. If you are negotiating to fix equitable quotas for Malaya, the Dutch East Indies, Ceylon, French Indo-China, Burma, and Borneo, to say nothing of Sarawak and Siam, you need all your wits and tact and patience. To the growers, bedeviled by ruinous prices, the neoprene story seemed a very faint cry of " Wolf! Wolf! "

In America the rubber industry was never less interested in rubber substitutes than right at that moment. Latex rubber was actually selling cheaper than " reclaim." The country was wallowing in the slough of the depression. Who gave a whoop about synthetic rubber?

Nevertheless the new plant at Deepwater was built. Samples were distributed. Well-trained technical salesmen began to turn up in the laboratories and compounding-rooms of the big rubber companies, working alongside their experts, showing how simple it was to use neoprene in regular plant equipment and to work it up by familiar methods. Results of tests for many different uses began to appear in the technical journals. All sorts of check-ups confirmed the salesmen's talk about the positive superiority of the substitute for certain uses. The first year's output was bought completely by eighty different manufacturers, and at $1.00 a pound.

The next year, 1934, the output of that Deepwater plant was doubled. More than one hundred different manufacturers gobbled up every pound. Year after year demand has expanded so quickly that several times it has been necessary to break ground for a new plant addition before the one previously started has been brought into production. The 1941 output of 13,000,000 pounds was three times that of two years before, and at this time neoprene, the first commercially successful synthetic rubber, was still the only one available in the United States in substantial quantities.

First offered at $1.05, the price of neoprene was promptly reduced to an even dollar, and two years later brought down to 75 cents, again in two years to 65 cents; and it is now promised at 50 cents. During the same period quotations for rubber ran up from 3½ cents to 40 cents, back to 15, and up again to 22.

A big price differential still favors caoutchouc against neoprene. But any industrialist buying an essential raw material the price of which controls his entire manufacturing costs derives a heap of solid comfort in steady supply at a staple price. Every gyration of rubber prices is but an argument for the synthetic, and rubber has the unenviable record of a giant price swing from 3½ cents to $3.05, close to a thousand-per-cent variation. The chart of Para gum prices might well serve as working model for the daring young man on the flying trapeze, while the graph of synthetic quotations is a map for a toboggan slide.

While neoprene was forging ahead in this country, German and Russian chemists were at work on other synthetic rubbers. Goaded by the American triumph, the German authorities gave out news of their first Buna rubber before they had properly checked its properties. This earliest of the post-war German synthetics was not a whit more satisfactory than the miserable methyl-rubber that had let them down so badly during the first World War. This first Buna was produced by the polymerization of butadiene, and its name was coined from the first syllable of its parent substance plus Na, chemical symbol for sodium, by which element the reaction was induced.

German chemical research is resourceful and tenacious. In the hope of getting a better polymer researchers began working in emulsions and a little later mixing with butadiene other polymerizable materials. The results were astonishingly hopeful. Find the best of these co-polymers and they would grasp success.

About this time — in September 1935 — salt was rubbed into the American wound by the Russians. The Soviet rubber plight was exactly like the Germans', and how it must have galled to read the official statement of the Director of the People's Commissariat for the Rubber Industry of the U.S.S.R. " Thanks to the Russian synthetic rubber Sovprene," so he said, " while tire output had been increased by a fourth, rubber imports for the first eight months of the year had been cut down 6,907 tons." This meant that some ten million gold rubles would not have to be paid out abroad for gum imports.

You may shrug skeptically at Soviet statistics and wink knowingly at the Russian theft of the neoprene process; but you could not laugh off the fact that some sort of synthetic-rubber production had been achieved while Germany was still experimenting in the laboratory. It was on the strength of those promising co-polymer products of butadiene that Adolf Hitler told the world that Germany, too, had solved her rubber problem.

At the time this was probably almost true. It was soon doubly true. In 1936 Germany had commercial production, not of one, but of two excellent rubber substitutes. Buna S is a mixed polymer of butadiene and styrene; Buna N of butadiene and acrylonitrile. Each type has its own character-istics and so will develop its distinctive uses. Both can be vulcanized — in which respect they differ sharply from neo-prene — and their properties are modified and improved markedly by carbon black and organic accelerators.

Buna S is the answer to the German militarists' prayer for suitable tires for the motorized *Blitzkrieg*, and the Chancellor has bellowed over the short waves that for this greatest, most essential purpose it is twice as good as natural rubber. No-body believes that. Tests in this country are not yet con-clusive, but Buna S is very likely as good as rubber in tire treads and maybe better in some respects. American experi-ence indicates that Buna S is strong in its resistance to both abrasion and heat, but weak in resiliency and elasticity: good for tire treads and machinery belting; poor for surgeon's gloves or elastic bands.

Buna N, on the other hand, possesses qualifications for success similar to those of neoprene. It stubbornly resists deterioration from gas and oil and thus appears destined definitely for use in the so-called mechanical rubber goods. Because its co-polymer, acrylonitrile, is more costly than styrene, it is at present more expensive than Buna S.

Both Bunas are now made in the United States. New Jersey Standard Oil's patent agreements with the German I.G. make them available upon terms that no royalties go to Germany

for any American production. Not only has the petroleum
company itself built a plant at Baton Rouge, Louisiana, with
a capacity of ten thousand pounds of Buna N, but the Fire-
stone Tire and Rubber Company has also taken out licenses
to make both N and S types and is producing both in experimental batches.

But all of our rubbers from butadiene are not going to be
produced by processes " made in Germany." Three others —
each a distinctively American development — are already
here.

When " new business " was reached at the stockholders'
meeting of the Standard Oil Company (New Jersey) held
June 4, 1940, President Farish rose, picked out a single type-
written sheet from the neat stack of papers before him, and
started reading a short announcement. Only a handful of the
thousands of share-owners were present, for we do not have
our British cousins' habit of attending such gatherings; but
those in attendance probably failed to grasp the full meaning
of his words:

> We have discovered in our own research laboratories a syn-
> thetic rubber product, which we call " Butyl Rubber " . . .
> made from petroleum by processes more direct and simple
> than those required for the production of Buna rubber. . . .
> We already have in operation a semi-commercial pilot plant
> at our research center in Bayway.

From a great oilman this was, on several counts, a notable
statement. Its bearing upon national defense and its meaning
to the army of motorists are plain. It hints at a cheaper rubberlike material from petroleum, and it fulfills Father Nieuwland's prophecy that scores of new rubber substitutes would
be discovered. Most remarkable of all, this statement is a
neat lesson in applied chemical economics.

In Germany the hydrogen of water and the carbon of coal
are used to build the hydrocarbon acetylene, C_2H_2, starting-

point for transformation into the hydrocarbon butadiene, C_4H_6, which can be polymerized to the long chain molecules with rubberlike properties. Petroleum, like coal tar, is a complex mixture of hydrocarbons. Its hydrogen and carbon can also be used as basic raw materials for the synthesis of butadiene. Germany is barred from this source material by her well-known, embarrassing lack of domestic oil; but our abundant supplies of low-cost petroleum hydrocarbons are an obvious American starting-point for the manufacture of synthetic rubbers. Accordingly, another research race is on for the most efficient method of preparing butadiene from petroleum gases.

Logically the Phillips Petroleum and the B. F. Goodrich companies have organized the Hydrocarbon Chemical and Rubber Company — Phillips supplying the raw materials and Goodrich taking the finished product, Ameripol, a co-polymer of butadiene of undisclosed composition. They are already selling Ameripol tires at thirty-per-cent premium over ordinary rubber. The third strictly American Buna-type rubber is another co-polymer, Chemigum. Goodyear is in production and using this substitute in mechanical goods. That story of cutting down our defense lines by ten thousand miles is not an empty boast.

When the Defense Program of 1941 was projected, our total synthetic-rubber output had reached about 15 tons a day. Against our daily consumption of some 20,000 tons of rubber this is fantastically insignificant. But the precious " know how " is here. And we have a lavish superabundance of the necessary raw materials.

Our petroleum statistics pile billions on top of millions like a New Deal budget. One who deals knowingly in these enormous quantities is Dr. Gustav Egloff, a compact bunch of energy, the research director of Universal Oil Products, who assures us that the potential supply of butadiene, snatched from our current gasoline production, would provide 80,000,000 tons of synthetic rubbers. That is 125 times our rubber requirements.

So much for butadiene; what about the materials used as co-polymers with it in producing the newer synthetic rubbers?

Styrene, constituent of Buna S, has been made here several years from benzol for the use of the plastics industry. Again we have the "know how" and the raw material. The co-polymer of Buna N, acrylonitrile, is quite a different story.

Driving to Boston from New York on the Post Road, you pass as you reach Stamford, a great glass and concrete building. Formerly it was a silk mill. Today it houses the research laboratories of the American Cyanamid Company. It is the "Stamford" of the sulfa-drug story, the birthplace of the process by which acrylonitrile came first to be commercially available. In this great building all the far-flung chemical activities of the company are co-ordinated. It is equipped with every research tool from an electron microscope to white rats.

Alert research is vigilant not only to prevent surprise but also to grasp opportunities, and as "Calco" sensed the chemical opening in Dr. Colebrook's sulfanilamide paper in the *Lancet,* so "Stamford," watching synthetic-rubber developments, went to work on the ingredient necessary for making Buna N. Sound chemical logic backed this proposal. The primary product in the manufacture of acrylonitrile is calcium cyanamide, which American Cyanamid was organized to make back in 1909.

Much fundamental data had to be uncovered and several commercially feasible processes evolved before the new unit was added to the plant at Warners, New Jersey. The bugaboo was purity. A trace of other substances acts like a broken switch to send the polymerization of acrylonitrile off the right track, and doubling of the initial plant unit within its first year of operations is the best proof that the new process is satisfactory.

While the butadiene rubbers are in the spotlight, a number of other rubberlike substitutes strut about the stage. In fact, one of these is a pioneer American development, antedating neoprene, which has the distinction of having been borrowed bodily, without credit, in both Russia and Germany.

An estimable dowager of Philadelphia, when she mislays her Red Cross knitting, makes it a rule to go hunting for the novel she was reading yesterday. It is a system that has often worked wonders in the chemical laboratory. Perkin was seeking synthetic quinine: he found the first coal-tar dye. Baekeland was hunting a substitute shellac: he discovered the first phenolic plastic. Dr. J. C. Patrick was out to make a better anti-freeze for the motorist's greater winter comfort: he came back with a rubberlike material that is today used in nine out of ten gas stations' delivery hoses.

After several years' active service as chemist for the Armours in South America, Dr. Patrick was supposed to be taking a rest cure in his old home in Kansas City. He could not sit idle, so he fixed up a cubbyhole laboratory and began making the sundry mixtures likely to improve anti-freeze. One morning he mixed ethylene dichloride and sodium polysulfide. He added a bit of acid and suddenly his test tube was clogged with a gummy mess. It was obviously of no use as an anti-freeze, but he began to investigate.

The chemical relationship of his sticky gum to rubber was about as close as Singapore to Pará, nevertheless this wide-awake concocter recognized that it possessed some remarkably rubberlike characteristics. Its stretch was not so good. Its smell was overwhelmingly worse. But its resistance to oil and gasoline was remarkable. Twenty years later no other synthetic rubber has yet been found better in this respect, hence its popularity with the makers of gasoline pumps.

Having decided that his gum was of some use, the ambitious Dr. Patrick christened it Thiokol and began making it on a commercial scale. The stench of the polecat is perfume compared with the smell wafted from his little pilot plant. One of his first tasks, therefore, was to deodorize his discovery. A neighbor was attracted to these experiments — not by the smell; Bevis Longstreth, then president of the Western Salt Company, foresaw a future for this rubber that did not stretch or bounce much, but that did not swell and soften at all in a gasoline bath. So they organized the Thiokol Corporation to manufacture the Adam of all American rubber substitutes.

Being unhandy alike to raw materials and consumers, Kansas City is not ideal for the manufacture of synthetic rubber. Accordingly Mr. Longstreth, as a loyal Princeton alumnus who had learned a bit about Trenton, New Jersey, as a part of his college education, moved the plant to that city. Trenton is second to Akron in its rubber activities and is located close to the hotbed of chemical production in South Jersey, the Philadelphia area, and Delaware. Afterwards he and Willard Dow entered into an alliance: the Dow Chemical Company, producers of the chief ingredients of this rubber substitute, to manufacture; the Thiokol Corporation to concentrate on selling.

Other rubberlike materials are already employed in specialized uses. In some of these applications rubber was never of service. Vistanex, for example, is a polymerization product of isobutylene. It does not vulcanize. However, a fraction of Vistanex incorporated in chloroprene or the Buna mixes, and the compound then polymerized, gives a synthetic rubber of tremendous abrasive resistance properties. Such combinations indicate all sorts of better materials. Vistanex shows also how these synthetics are throwing open new doors of opportunity. It is used with paraffin wax to make a clear, protective coating that is permanently flexible; in plastics to reduce their brittleness; to improve lubricating oils; as an adhesive to fasten metallic labels to glass.

Quite a catalogue of trade-names for rubberlike materials can now be listed. AXF, Flamenol, Igelite, Koroseal, Mepolam, Pliofilm, Resistoflex, each stakes out claims for fields of special use. If you are interested, the manufacturers will be delighted to give all their chemical and physical characteristics and, should you manufacture anything, from tacks to tractors, to instruct you just how you can employ their particular product. A tractor, by the way, has a lot more rubber parts than anyone but a garage mechanic suspects, and probably you did not know that tacks with rubber-coated heads are popular in the upholstery trade, where permanent colors and decorative heads that will not crack or snap off are duly appreciated.

So now in place of one caoutchouc we have many synthetic rubbers. The familiar rubber properties are so made available in applications that the ingenious Goodyear, with all his hundreds of patents, never imagined. Metals are now coated with thick, soft, resilient rubber blankets. Rubber printing rolls are replacing the old ones of glue and glycerin. Rubber in paint makes a coating that really clings to concrete and stone surfaces. Rubber is now incorporated in pottery, in plastics, and in paper. Novel uses for rubber appear every week, most of them quite impractical till these not-rubber-but-rubberlike materials were ready for use.

But most of the rubber still goes into tires. Therefore synthetic rubber is for us a bewildering chemical trick until we find it on the wheels of the family car. This will not happen tomorrow. It would take two years and the investment of $100,000,000 to build plants to supply half our tire demand. Only to escape a rubber famine would so stupendous an effort be made.

In the natural course of events, cost figures will time the invasion of the enormous tire market by the synthetics.

Plantation gum has sold at 3½ cents a pound delivered in New York. Nobody in the rubber world forgets that low record. Such a panicky price would in time force the rubber-planter to join the dinosaur; but nobody knows just how low rubber might go and enable him to survive. Buyers and sellers dispute in a range between 10 and 20 cents. A synthetic rubber which delivered twice the mileage would be a certain winner at thrice the price. Such figures are already within the chemists' calculations.

A plantation to produce 100 tons of rubber a season is said to cost about the same as a 100-ton-a-day rubber factory. The plant can be built in six months: it takes six years for a plantation to come into bearing. All that sounds a lot more gloomy for the grower than it really is.

Once in production, the plantation grows rubber at a fraction of the costs of labor, maintenance, and raw material of a rubber factory. With help rather than hurt to future production, the plantation can be shut down simply by not tapping the trees. A chemical plant out of commission depreciates faster than when operating. Furthermore, the plantation is an efficient producer for thirty or even, with excellent care, for fifty years, perhaps longer. The new rubber-substitute plant is probably obsolete before it can be put into production. So swift is the advance in synthetic-rubber technology nowadays that while the plant is building it will cease to be the last word in efficiency.

Accordingly, nobody seriously thinks the rubber plantations will all be plowed under. But everybody knows the price of natural rubber is never again to be $3.05; no, not even $1 a pound. And the rubber Eldorado, having moved from Amazonia to the Congo, to Malaya, is apparently on the move again to North America.

This prospective migration is, of course, quite different from the former shifts in headquarters. It will certainly increase enormously our use of rubberlike materials. We now consume close to a million tons a year; enthusiasts talk about doubling this.

If that sounds fantastic, think how much rubber it would take to floor all our offices, hospitals, post offices, and other public buildings, to say nothing of our homes. Anyone can picture an ideal flooring of a rubberlike material. If this does not seem impressive enough, we have several million miles of highway that would be vastly improved with a resilient, non-skid paving. With an unlimited supply of rubberlike materials at a low, stable price such wild dreams might be brought down to earth.

CHAPTER XIII

CHEMISTS IN SPITE OF THEMSELVES

◇◇◇

BLASPHEMY is no longer a punishable crime. Today one can invoke the Deity — or the Devil, for that matter — without serious protest. In 1829 it was different.

A hard-bitten, prowling well-driller, punching holes to order for hire, seeking water or brine as his employer elected, was working on the banks of Little Pennox Creek out in the new territory of Kentucky. He sought brine which a local merchant wanted to evaporate to profitable salt. Things had not been going smoothly and the nervous storekeeper was worried about the outcome of his gamble. He fussed and fumed, asking silly questions, bothering the crew, interrupting their work.

" Do you think you'll ever strike salt? "

"By God, mister," boasted the exasperated driller, " I'll drive that there drill till she strikes salt or hell."

Down slammed the plunger — thud!

With a roar a great rush of heavy black oil burst from the well. The little derrick was thrown high above the treetops. Catching fire from the driller's forge, the liquid burst into a vast pillar of flame. He had struck hell, sure enough: the first oil gusher in America.

When the wave of pioneers flooded over the Alleghenies,

salt was one of their first necessities, and following the broad hint of deer licks, they early discovered salty springs and outcrops of the great saline deposits of the Ohio Valley. Along the western slopes of the mountains in Pennsylvania, western Virginia, and Kentucky their efforts to supply themselves with the vital condiment were frequently frustrated by an irritating, useless oil that seeped into springs and contaminated the brine they pumped from wells. To them petroleum was nothing but a damnable nuisance.

Some twenty years after that first burning gusher burst forth in the Kentucky wilds, this same exasperating oil began interfering with the nice little salt business of a canny Scot, Thomas Kier, and his bold American-born son, Samuel. One of their best brine wells, driven four hundred feet deep near Tarentum, Pennsylvania, suddenly began to flow oil. Kier, Junior, who was a frontier capitalist of sorts, resourcefully decided to salvage this waste.

Long before the coming of the white men, the Indians could not fail to notice these oily springs. In the year of grace 1627, when the good Franciscan Father Joseph de la Roche d'Allion came to the Senecas bringing tidings of Christianity, the tawny heathen proudly showed their own sacred shrine. Near what is now Cuba, New York, was a spring that bubbled a precious, healing oil. He wrote back to Paris the first European's account of petroleum in North America, and the Senecas' curative oil became world-famous. In all the intervening years it was a popular household remedy throughout America. Why not, thought Samuel Kier, put this Seneca Oil business over in a big way? So in the *U.S. Commercial Register* for 1850 there appeared a modest little announcement that read:

PETROLEUM, OR, ROCK OIL

" There are more things in heaven and earth,
Than are dreamed of in your philosophy."

The Virtues of this remarkable remedy, and the constant application for it to the proprietor, has induced him to have it put up in bottles, with labels and directions for the benefit of the public.

The PETROLEUM is produced from a well, at a depth of about four hundred feet — is a pure, unadulterated article, without any chemical change, just as it flows from Nature's great Laboratory! There are things in the arcana of Nature which, if known, might be of vast usefulness in alleviating suffering and restoring the bloom of health and vigor to many a sufferer. Long before the proprietor thought of putting it up in bottles, it had a reputation for the cure of disease.

We do not wish to make a long parade of certificates, as we are confident that the medicine can soon work its way into the favor of those who suffer and wish to be healed. While we do not claim for it a universal application to every disease, we unhesitatingly say that in a number of Chronic Diseases, it is unrivalled. Among those may be enumerated all the diseases of the mucuous tissues, such as CHRONIC BRONCHITIS, CONSUMPTION (in its early stage), Asthma, and all other diseases of the air passage, LIVER COMPLAINT, DYSPEPSIA, Diarrhoea, Diseases of the Bladder and Kidneys, Pain in the Back and Side, Nervous Diseases, Neuralgia, Palsy, Rheumatic Pains, Gout, Erysipelas, Tetter, Ringworms, Burns, Scalds, Bruises, Old Sores, etc. In case of debility resulting from exposure or long and protracted cases of disease, this medicine will bring relief.

It will act as a general TONIC and ALTERATIVE in such cases, imparting tone and energy to the whole frame, removing obstructions, opening the sluggish functions which cause disease and a broken constitution, and giving increased and renewed energy to all the organs of life. The proprietor knows of several cases of PILES that resisted every other treatment, got well under the use of the PETROLEUM for a short time. — The proof can be given to any person who desires it. — None genuine without the signature of the proprietor.

Sold by the Proprietor, S. M. KIER, Pittsburgh.

Sales of Kier's Rock Oil grew, and at fifty cents retail for a half-pint bottle it did exceedingly well for the proprietor. But the oil in the salt wells increased more rapidly than Kier's half-dozen traveling medicinal shows could peddle it out even for a full catalogue of human ills. Casting about for larger outlets, he sent samples to James Curtis Booth, the famous consulting chemist of Philadelphia, who eked out his precarious practice by a tutorial school in chemistry. By distillation, so Booth reported, an illuminating oil could be separated quite simply from this petroleum, and he added that this product was in all respects equal to the famous coal oil.

Temperament and timing are important in the affairs of men far beyond the golf swing and the dance step, and these recommendations of Professor Booth were made to just the right man at the right moment. Whale-oil lamps had relegated the candlestick to the attic. The great whaling fleet of New England, scouring the seven seas, was fast driving Leviathan into extinction. As the whales became scarcer, the price of whale oil advanced. Coal oil, sweated out of soft coal by a recently invented Scotch process, had already lighted the way towards brighter, cheaper illuminants, and by 1860 there were fifty-three little manufacturers, operating in this country under patent licenses, doing good missionary work selling not only the new oil but also a new type of lamp. The time was right for the introduction of kerosene.

Acting on Booth's suggestion, Kier built a five-foot brick box in which he installed a coal grate over which he set a closed iron vessel with a long neck where the volatile kerosene, driven off by heat from the crude petroleum with which he charged his five-gallon still, would be condensed and collected. It was the first commercial petroleum refinery in the world. Within a year, in 1858, he had it running so smoothly that he was able to contract with Joseph Coffin in New York to deliver to him "100 barrels weekly of carbon oil that will burn in an ordinary coal-oil lamp" for 62½ cents per gallon.

Thus kerosene was launched on its sensational career. It was the first really decent means of dispelling night's darkness that man had ever found. No wonder that in five years the oilcan became a familiar object from Pittsburgh to St. Petersburg and in ten it was to be found in Peking and La Paz. No wonder, too, that the good old Indian custom of sopping oil up in a blanket from the surface of a spring or the pioneer's habit of carefully skimming off the seepage in a brine well proved very quickly to be horse-and-buggy methods to meet a streamlined demand.

About the time Kier made his first contract, a grown man stood, his nose glued against the window-pane of a Broadway drug-store, like a little boy in front of a toyshop's Christmas display. In his pocket bulged a report on "An Analysis of Pennsylvania Rock Oil with Recommendations for Its Chemical and Commercial Employment," signed by the most distinguished chemist in the United States, Professor Benjamin Silliman, Jr., of Yale. Across the floor of the display window, neatly arranged in foot-high letters spelling out the axiom HEALTH IS WEALTH, were dozens of squatty little bottles with screaming red labels —

KIER'S
Original and Genuine
ROCK OIL

Scattered all about were four-hundred-dollar greenbacks: not good federal currency, but with the smiling countenance of "S. M. Kier, Prop." replacing the benign profile of the immortal Washington and for the view of the new Capitol building was substituted a view of the Kier oil well. It was this bustling industrial scene that hypnotized George Bissell. Stark against a background of billowy clouds stood the angular frames of two well derricks.

"Could Kier possibly be pumping petroleum from real oil wells?" he mused.

An artesian well of oil would surely break the bottleneck of dubious supplies that had handicapped the development of a great business in kerosene. With some banker friends in his native New Haven, Bissell had organized the first oil stock company, but the niggardly quantity of petroleum they had been able to collect on their hundred-acre tract near Titusville had broken the promise of a phenomenally lucrative venture. Bissell's enthusiasm for this drilling idea was infectious and the group agreed to go along with him to the extent of ten thousand dollars in hard cash. They engaged a lanky, raw-boned, joke-loving, resourceful railway conductor whom they dignified with the gratuitous title of " Colonel " and sent out to the wilds of western Pennsylvania to clear up their land titles and drill for oil.

Colonel Edwin Laurencine Drake knew as much as anybody about oil wells, but he knew no more about any other kind of drilling operation. Indeed, his chief qualifications for this epochal job were his ownership of 250 shares of the corporation's stock and a railroad pass that would transport him without company expense to the scene of operations. In the field, however, he proved his mettle. He simply refused to admit defeat. He squirmed his way around insurmountable difficulties. He ignored the jokes and gibes of the whole neighborhood, and though he had far too few dollars to do the job properly, he found and engaged the best brine-well driller in the region, " Uncle Billy " Smith.

They began drilling on June 9, 1859. On August 28, at a depth of 69½ feet, their drill broke through into a petroleum-bearing stratum. Uncle Billy greeted the Colonel next morning with the historic sentence: " You've struck oil, sir."

The simple statement has become a living phrase in our American language, a vivid expression of unexpected success or sudden wealth. Within a few hours after Drake had struck oil, his scoffing neighbors were scurrying about leasing the oil rights of every spring and crevice that seeped a tiny trace of greasy film. Within three months America's first oil boom was on in earnest. With crude petroleum at twenty dollars a barrel, the " Oildorado " was a sober fact. Four years

The combination of all these different hydrocarbons plus such impurities as sulphur, nitrogen, and oxygen, varies greatly in petroleum from different fields. Thus crude oil varies in color from cherry red to amber, to green, to black, and its odor from the rose to the skunk. Texas oil is rich in gasoline. Oil from the mid-continental fields is frequently contaminated with sulphur, imparting an evil smell, so that it must be desulphurized. Pennsylvania oil is famous for the high-quality lubricants it yields. A rough general average of the content of American petroleum would be something like this: 4 per cent of gas, 25 per cent of naphthas and gasoline, 15 per cent of kerosene, 40 per cent of the middle-fraction gas oils, 12 per cent of paraffins, and 4 per cent of pitch.

During the sixties, seventies, and eighties kerosene was the big plum to be drawn out of this oily Jack Horner pie. The gases were piped under the stills for fuel. The naphthas and gasoline were too dangerously explosive to make respectable fuels. Accordingly, they were bothersome wastes to be poured into the brooks and rivers till the good citizens downstream protested and passed laws forbidding this simple method of disposal. One unscrupulous refiner, choking in excess gasoline, offered a smart young employee a new suit of clothes — and no questions asked — for every thousand barrels of the obnoxious liquid that he could whisk away. He was an ingenious destroyer of gasoline, according to legend, but it is not recorded that he became an oil-town Beau Brummel.

When now we are at pains to wring every last drop of gasoline out of petroleum and have even devised cunning chemical means of breaking down higher hydrocarbons and building up those of the lower series into our much-wanted six-to-ten carbon group, all that seems wicked profligacy. It was not. At that time and under those circumstances all those thousands upon thousands of barrels of naphthas and gasoline could not have been used or saved for our use. It was the coming of the automobile that gave gasoline a real economic

" Aviation gas " is a chemical triumph of petroleum refining and you buy at the " ordinary " pump a better fuel than flew Lindbergh across the Atlantic.   *— Courtesy Gulf Oil Corporation*

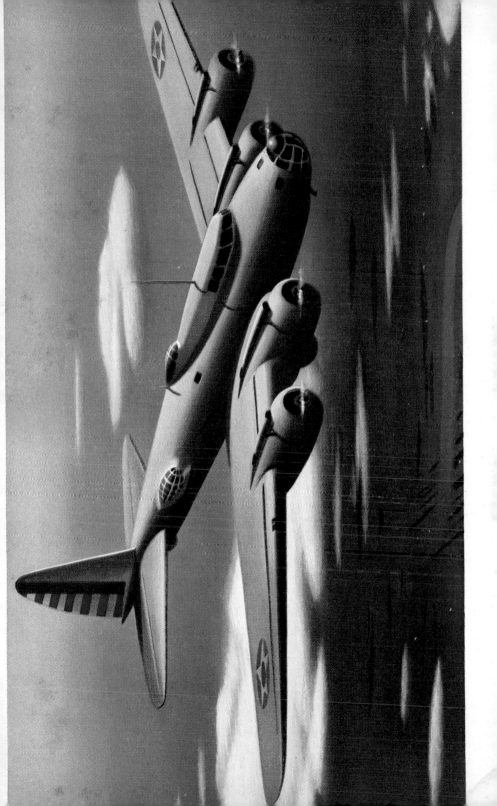

value, while cheap gasoline was in turn an important element in the arrival of the internal-combustion engine. Fuel and engine: egg and chicken — who will flatly declare which came first?

The American motorists' insatiable appetite for gasoline gives even a Rolls-Royce owner an attack of mathematical indigestion. Each year 26,000,000,000 gallons of gasoline! That is sufficient liquid to fill Great Salt Lake twice over. If you are a bit hazy about Utah geography, Great Salt Lake is 80 miles long and 20 to 30 miles wide, and has an average depth of some 13 feet.

Put another way, in terms of crude petroleum, what the automobile demand has done for — or to — the oil industry is graphically told. It took forty-one years, from 1859 to 1900, to produce the first billion barrels of crude oil. The first billion is obviously the hardest, for now we consume a billion and a third barrels in 365 days.

Overwhelmingly the demand for petroleum products presses today upon gasoline, the fraction of hydrocarbons containing from six to ten carbon atoms. This cut runs about twenty-five per cent of the crude. To produce by straight-run distillation the vast gallonage of gasoline we consume — twenty-six billions — means an enormous over-production of the gases and naphthas, lighter than the gasoline fraction, and of the kerosene, gas oils, paraffins, tar and pitch, whose molecules all contain more than ten atoms of carbon. The tail is wagging the head off the dog; the solution of this chemical economic problem has revolutionized the industry.

The petroleum refinery has changed from a simple distillation operation into an organic chemical plant in which the lighter hydrocarbons are built up and the heavier ones are broken down to produce a maximum of that desired gasoline fraction. By thus re-forming the hydrocarbons on both sides of the six-to-ten carbon series, the output of gasoline is materially increased. By the cracking process, for example, the recovery of motor-fuel hydrocarbons from crude is stepped up over a straight-run distillation from 26 to 70 per cent, depending on the type of crude being processed; and some of it contains no gasoline at all to start with. More than half the gasoline we burn in our carburetors is " manufactured."

Long before Sunday driving became a nightmare, back about 1910, when less than a paltry half-million cars were bumping over our rutty dirt roads, the unbalance of the gasoline demand began to disturb the petroleum refiners. Their first move was a simple one. They began stripping the six-to-ten carbon combinations out of natural gas. By 1920 they were in this way eking out the gasoline supply by 9,000,000 barrels; today they recover from this source over 55,000,000 barrels. This was a pleasant lift; but by 1914, when the number of American motor vehicles had risen to 3,750,-000, it was already plain that something more must be done about our gasoline supply.

The first cracking process was an accident. Back in the early sixties, when all the demand was for kerosene, some nameless operator of a little sixteen-gallon still left the job for four hours. According to the teller of the story, his excuse for this lucky neglect of duty varies all the way from the arrival of his first-born son to a convivial glass or two, or more. At all events, when he returned, the apparatus was red-hot and the heavier vapors, recondensing, had flowed back into the still and been redistilled. The result was a twenty-per-cent increase in the yield of the then wanted kerosene. The owner was keen enough to recognize that in this accident he had found something. He began to repeat it deliberately. As the demand for kerosene increased, such rough, elementary cracking operations became quite general. They served as a plain hint, when the demand shifted from illuminant to motor fuel, that such a heat treatment might be worked to crack the heavier hydrocarbons to gasoline.

A few smart oil refiners were beginning to suspect that

there was a good deal of chemistry involved in this booming business of theirs, and some technically trained men began to find places on their payrolls. Among these was a big, nice-looking, well-mannered young man from Cleveland, with a B.A. degree from Western Reserve and a Ph.D. from Johns Hopkins. He went to work in 1889 as a chemist for Mr. Rockefeller's Standard Oil Company.

William Meriam Burton managed somehow to escape from the laboratory out into the plant, and by 1895 he had climbed up to the position of general superintendent of the big refinery at Whiting, Indiana. With all his ability for operating, he had a solid training in chemistry, and out of the combination came the first successful, controlled, large-scale cracking operation. It won for Burton distinguished and deserved honors: both the Willard Gibbs and the Perkin gold medals, and the presidency of the Standard Oil Company of Indiana, the top rung of the executive ladder in the petroleum industry, reached for the first time by a chemist.

Burton's cracking process was neither the earliest nor the latest. Out on the west coast, where the crude oil is extra heavy and where coal for fuel and a demand for petroleum by-products are both conspicuously lacking, much of the petroleum was used as fuel oil in its natural state or run down to asphalt. In 1907 the recently discovered Santa Maria field suddenly "developed water," producing such a beautifully staple emulsion of oil and water that they could not be separated by simple heating in a pipe still as had been done with other ordinary emulsified crudes. To Jesse A. Dubbs, owner of the Sunset Oil & Refining Company, this was a serious matter and he set out to rectify it by inventing a new type of dehydrating still. Unlike all previous "emulsion plants," his did not operate at atmospheric pressure, but the still and condenser were both under pressure generated by its own vapors. The light ends driven off by this pressure dehydrating were quite different from those obtained by ordinary dehydrating or by ordinary refining. They were, in fact, cracked gasoline-like vapors, and when Burton's cracking process attracted wide attention to the possibility of thus increasing the gasoline supply, Dubbs and his son, a brilliant oil technologist named — believe it or not — Carbon Petroleum Dubbs, adapted his process to this new purpose. A laboratory was opened at Independence, Kansas, and the patents were taken over by the Universal Oil Products. Backed by Ogden Armour, six million dollars were invested in making the process adaptable to all types of crudes without clogging the tubes with coke in the heated zone.

In recent years cracking by means of heat has been supplemented by cracking by means of chemicals. By the use of catalysts, those chemicals that promote chemical reactions without themselves entering into the reaction, the higher hydrocarbons are induced to break down into the simpler molecules of the gasoline group with higher octane ratings than can be secured from heat and pressure alone.

Between 1913, when Burton's initial plant went into operation, and 1940, twenty-seven years, cracking saved us 14,500,-000,000 barrels of crude oil. Again the first billion was the hardest, for the operation has become so widespread and been so perfected that in 1940 alone it saved close to two billion barrels. An ultra-modern cracking plant to handle 30,000 barrels of crude daily costs about $3,000,000, but it operates with great economies and will produce 70 per cent (21,000 barrels) of 70 octane gasoline. That "70 octane" is another story to which we are coming in a page or two.

Working from the other end — that is, building simpler hydrocarbons into motor fuels — is a more recent development, but exceedingly important both in gallons and in the high-test quality of gas it produces. From the chemical point of view, the process is one of polymerization, the linking together of similar molecules, the same process by which the long-chain molecules of synthetic rubber are created. The raw materials are those hydrocarbon gases which are in solution in crude petroleum and easily driven off by gentle heat or are separated from the hydrocarbons in natural gas. Some 415 billion cubic feet of these gases, chiefly propane and butane, now burned under stills and boilers could theoretically be converted into some 200 million barrels of polymer gasoline. Polymerization has other advantages. Not only can it utilize the propane and butane from natural gas, but also it can transform low-quality gasolines by cracking and polymerizing into the wanted hydrocarbons.

Still a third chemical method of manufacturing hydrocarbons for motor fuel is available. It is hydrogenation, or the process of adding hydrogen atoms, discovered in Europe and perfected as a large-scale operation in America. It provides great flexibility in the conversion of petroleum hydrocarbons into many new products, and it makes possible, by the addition of hydrogen to the carbon of coal, the creation of liquid out of solid fuels. Lacking in crude petroleum, both England and Germany are manufacturing coal into gasoline by hydrogenation reactions; but until our oil fields begin to fail us, we will not find the process economical for the manufacture of motor fuel.

What with cracking and polymerization and hydrogenation, the production of gasoline has become a real chemical-manufacturing job. The refiners, in spite of themselves, have become chemists. Originally they applied chemistry to squeeze more gallons of gasoline out of every barrel of crude. But now ordinary gasoline is not good enough for the high-compression engines of the modern models and it is practically useless in aviation motors. A post-graduate course in chemistry has become obligatory. The manufacture of high-test gas involves exacting, complex chemical operations beyond the ken of the still operator of the twenties, to say nothing of the synthesis or extraction of such blending agents as isopentane, neohexane, iso-octane, and a score of others whose names even were undreamed of by the petroleum generation of Rockefeller, Archibald, and Rogers.

Ten years ago (so this story was told the other evening at the big, round, open table at the Chemists' Club in New York and it would not be friendly to name names) the director of research of one of our larger petroleum corporations went to his president with a definite proposal. The report that he laid on the big, flat desk was, he was confident, a bullet-proof proposal to manufacture three new chemically allied solvents.

"All the raw materials," he explained, "are our own by-products and the plant is but a unit easily hooked on to the operations at the Southeast Refinery."

The president was interested. "What," he asked, "would the plant investment be?"

"Not to exceed $250,000."

"And what would the profits be?"

"At present prices, items A and B are selling for about a dollar a gallon over our estimated plant costs and C at about eighty cents over costs. But we can expect prices to come down if we go into the field; and it would be more reasonable to figure on a margin of fifty cents a gallon."

The president was more than interested. Compared with those for gasoline and lubricants, such figures seemed a bonanza. But he was cautious by instinct and he had learned through bitter experience that acids and alkalies can chew up costly apparatus with amazing rapidity and that in chemical operations new processes have a disconcerting habit of appearing suddenly and forcing one to scrap perfectly good equipment. So he was curious how much depreciation had been figured into estimated costs. He was comforted and encouraged to learn that it was proposed to write off the entire investment, research and plant, in five years.

"How much can we sell?" he asked.

"In the present market, about 10,000 gallons each of A and B and about 30,000 gallons of C. Demand is growing, and though prices would be lower, sales on all these, especially B, ought to double in the next three years."

The president began studying the green onyx paper-cutter on his desk. His brain was operating as an amazingly quick and accurate calculating machine.

" As a curbstone opinion," he said slowly, " it does not seem to be a particularly interesting proposition."

"But, look here," protested the research man; " on an initial investment of less than a quarter of a million we can show — "

"Yes, I know. But for a quarter of a million dollars we could put in twenty service stations, and you know as well as I do, Jim, that if any one of them didn't sell as many gallons of gas as all these solvents of yours added together we would close it up pronto. That's our business. This chemical stuff is all new to us. It would take a lot of supervision, watching, finding and hiring good men, breaking into a new selling game — oh, a lot of headaches, and there's not enough money in it to pay for the aspirin tablets."

Today, ten years later, that same company manufactures all three of those chemicals, not in twenty and thirty thousand gallon quantities, but up in the higher hundred thousands. Two they use themselves for further chemical processing and blending in high-octane gasoline. All of them they sell to the lacquer, chemical, rubber, and lesser industries.

That is a major industrial revolution, a full change in all the details of management, manufacturing, and merchandising that the president shunned ten years before, a complete overthrow of the established habit of thought. The roots of that revolution have been sprouted in high-octane gasoline.

You need no engineering degree to know that when your motor begins to knock you are not getting its accustomed power. That knock is caused by premature explosion in the cylinders, and although the higher the compression of the explosive mixture, the greater the power, yet high compression induces knocking, which is the evidence of great waste of energy. That vicious circle can be broken, as we all know, by adding anti-knock compounds such as benzol and tetra-ethyl lead. As we do not all appreciate, however, different types of gasoline display very different knocking qualities. Most motorists have a hazy understanding of these facts, but long ago Plato warned us that we do not really know anything until we can express it in numbers. Accordingly, when the engineers began delving into this matter, they needed a scale by which to measure knocks.

From the chemists they secured all sorts of pure hydro-carbons to be used as reagent tests and burned them in a standard engine. They found two, iso-octane, C_8H_{18}, which was the most perfect anti-knock fuel, and heptane, C_7H_{16}, which is a perfectly terrible knocker. The percentage by volume of iso-octane mixed with heptane which causes the mixture to display the same knocking characteristics as the gasoline being tested is called the octane number. If, for example, a gasoline behaves like a mixture of three parts of iso-octane and one part of heptane, it is rated as 75 octane gas. A 100 octane gas corresponds to pure iso-octane with no heptane.

Ten years ago, when this convenient scale was devised, iso-octane was " tops " in motor fuels — aviation-fuel mixtures of 110 octane ratings are now produced commercially — but it was a laboratory chemical which sold for thirty dollars a gallon. Today it is produced in thousands of gallons and sells for thirty cents, so that it is used as a blending agent to raise the octane rating of gas for aviation use.

Lindbergh in 1927 flew the Atlantic on 60 octane gasoline. When you drive up to your friendly neighborhood gasoline dealer — as the radio pluggers always call him — and tell him " to fill 'er up with ordinary," you get gas of about 75 octane rating. If you buy " high test " you get about 85 octane gasoline. Aviation grade rates at least 90 octane and the Army and Navy use 100 octane gasoline.

These are definite measures of the improvement in our gasoline, expressed with the numerical accuracy Plato would commend; but what do they mean to us motorists? Dr. Graham Edgar of General Motors has answered that question.

He operated an automobile over hill and dale at a number of different compression and gear ratios, using in each case the gasoline that was just able to avoid knocking. For the ordinary 5.25 compression engine a 69 octane fuel is required; for the 8.0 compression ration, 95 octane; for the 10.3, 100 octane plus. Driven at 40 miles per hour, the 5.25 engine delivered 12½ miles on a gallon of gas; the 8.0 engine, 18 miles; the 10.3 engine, 21.3 miles. In other words, if we all burned 100 octane gas in 10.3 compression engines, we would just about double our present average of miles per gallon.

If this sounds a bit like the old wisecrack: " If we had some ham, we'd have some ham and eggs, if we had some eggs," remember that we know how to cure the ham and we have plenty of laying hens. The motor industry can certainly build high-compression engines, and the raw materials and the "know how" are both available for all the 100 octane gas we need.

From the blood and wreckage of every great war springs always some material progress, for Mars, the great destroyer, is also the great stimulator of technological advance. Out of World War II with its bombers and its tanks will surely come improved engines and more efficient fuels. Its effect was almost immediately seen in our own production of 100 octane fuel, which was shoved up from 7 to 145 million gallons between 1937 and 1940. One prolific source was at this time first tapped in all seriousness, the natural and refinery gases which by polymerization can be built up into fuels of from 81 to 92 octanes. These high-test gasolines by blending with iso-pentane, neohexane, tetra-ethyl lead, and several others, can be lifted to the 100 octane rating.

Having become chemically minded, this giant among our

industries now proposes to go into the juggling of the hydro-carbon molecules in a big way. Oilmen are accustomed to astronomical figures: $440,000,000 sunk into the ground every year drilling twenty thousand new wells, a third of which are " dry holes "; an investment of nearly four billion dollars in plants and four hundred millions in service stations to produce and distribute twenty-six billion gallons of gaso-line by a million-odd employees, including 35,638 chemists, but excluding the nation's traffic police. Such an industry eagerly embraces the idea of making a million tons of syn-thetic rubbers; and now that they have learned to twist the petroleum hydrocarbons into the coal hydrocarbons, benzol, toluol, and xylol, they assure us that they could supply some 33 billion pounds of picric acid, about 27 billion pounds of TNT, and at least 25 billion pounds of the newest high-power destroyer, trinitro-xylene.

They talk such hyperbolical figures naturally, as one might speak of a dozen eggs or a half-dozen pencils. Somehow or other the record shows that they come through with equally fantastic performances. For example, they are making ten million gallons of perfectly good, drinkable ethyl alcohol a year. Just the other day they started to manufacture syn-thetic glycerin. And, coming back to their main job, they are selling us better gasoline for less money than we could have bought for any price ten years ago, and all this despite a doubling of the gas taxes.

CHAPTER XIV

MANNA BECOMES A CHEMICAL

◇◇

"AND it came to pass that . . . when the dew that lay was gone up, behold, upon the face of the wilderness there lay a small round thing, as small as the hoar frost on the ground.

"And when the children of Israel saw it, they said one to another, It is manna; for they wist not what it was. And Moses said unto them, This is the bread which the Lord hath given you to eat. . . .

"And they gathered it every morning, every man according to his eating; and when the sun waxed hot, it melted. . . .

"And the house of Israel called the name thereof Manna; and it was like coriander seed, white; and the taste of it was like wafers made with honey."

Notwithstanding the miraculous circumstances which distinguish it from anything now known, the manna of the Biblical narrative answers in its description very closely to tamarisk manna. This variety is the sweet white gum exuded by tamarisk trees in the form of small globules, called "tears." These are still collected in the high plateaus of the Sinai Peninsula, the Wilderness of Exodus, by Arabs who in the early morning shake them down onto cloths spread on the ground beneath the branches. It is still sold in the bazaars of the Near East and used to sweeten cakes and cookies.

You can buy manna at the corner drug-store, but you will find its bland, sweetish flavor altogether too mawkish for a steady diet. The druggist still stocks it, however, for it is sometimes an ingredient in old-fashioned cough syrups; more often it is called for in the baby's feeding formula; and it is in demand as a laxative, especially among his customers who have brought Mediterranean traditions with them to this country.

A druggist, the son of a druggist, was the first man to make a thoroughgoing scientific examination of this sugary gum of Biblical fame. Joseph Louis Proust made his careful chemical analysis of manna as a part of his official duties, for he was at the time, in 1806, Royal Chemist to His Catholic Majesty of Spain. His appointment was a rare and juicy plum for any chemist in those days, an honorable, lucrative post where he might have coasted along in a drowsy routine had he been that sort of public servant. With all his good looks and pleasant manners and ambition, it is remarkable that he did not become a typical bureaucratic scientist, for from the day when he finished his studies in the dispensary of the celebrated pharmacist M. Clerambourg, in Paris, until his death, he held some sort of public position. It had been planned that he should return to his father's apothecary shop at Angers to carry on the family business; but the position of chief *pharmacien* at the hospital of La Salpétrière having fallen vacant, young Proust was offered the post. He thus gained at once an honorable place in Parisian scientific circles, a comfortable livelihood, and an opportunity to continue chemical experiments which had for him an irresistible attraction.

He began to analyze all sorts of compounds and materials. He delighted to work on rare and unusual things, minerals from distant lands, gems, drugs, and spices, and he began writing papers about his work that read as well as a dramatic novel, yet were just as sound as the most prosy of the usual scientific reports. Both his experiments and the conclusions he drew from them displayed a bold, independent spirit, and it was largely due to his long continued, scrupulously performed analyses that the fundamental principle of the constant proportions of the elements in chemical compounds — one of the points vital to Dalton's atomic law — was established beyond dispute.

But he was no laboratory mole. He went out nights and he made friends. He was appointed the chemistry tutor at the Palais Royal. He accompanied Pilatre de Rosier in the first balloon ascent, which took place at Versailles in June 1784, in the presence of the French court, the King of Sweden, and a great crowd of scientific notables. Shortly afterwards the Spanish Government, noting the practical progress of chemistry then so conspicuous in France, and hoping to benefit by its application to their own industries, decided to found a perfectly equipped research laboratory at their Artillery School at Segovia and offered the directorship to Proust.

Here he undertook a systematic study of all Spanish natural resources, which led him to examine manna. He found that sixty per cent of this natural gum consists of mannitol, which has since then been found in small quantities in celery, sugar cane, larch, viburnum, syringa, and many other plants. You would not suspect it, but this white crystalline material, slightly sweetish in taste and soluble in water, is an alcohol; chemically it does belong to this large and important family of compounds.

We commonly think of but two alcohols: first, ethyl alcohol, grain alcohol so called, though most of it is made in America by fermentation of by-product molasses from the Cuban sugar plantations, which is the alcohol of medicines and of all the alcoholic beverages; and second, methyl alcohol, wood alcohol, or methanol as it officially is called, distilled from wood, poisonous, unpleasant to the taste, used to denature drinkable alcohol and as a solvent for shellac and varnish, the alcohol of the spirit lamp under the silver teakettle. There are, however, many other alcohols that occur in nature and literally thousands which are theoretically possible, many of which have been synthesized. Glycerin, the sweetish, syrupy liquid that is excellent to rub on chapped knuckles, is an alcohol. So is "Prestone," the anti-freeze whose chemical name is ethylene glycol. These two are familiar examples of members of two other important branches of the alcohol family.

A story is told of a great chemist and a great mathematician that illustrates the many, many possible combinations within the alcohol group of compounds. Ira Remsen, discoverer of saccharin (those little white crystals, five hundred times as sweet as sugar, which sufferers from diabetes drop into their coffee), was a fascinating teacher of organic chemistry. His lectures were better entertainment than most two-reel feature pictures. Among his colleagues on the faculty of the then newly formed Johns Hopkins University was the famous English mathematician James Sylvester, who one morning invited himself to attend one of Remsen's classes.

"We are all honored," said the chemist to his students, "to have with us a most distinguished guest," and he escorted the venerable visitor, an imposing, Jove-like man with a round bald head and a great flowing white beard, to a seat in the front row.

Remsen was lecturing on the alcohols, explaining that they are all made up on the basic formula of a hydrocarbon radical joined to an OH or hydroxyl group. He wrote on the blackboard a long list of formulas beginning:

> Methyl alcohol (wood) CH_3OH
> Ethyl " (grain) C_2H_5OH
> Propyl " C_3H_7OH

and so on up to

> Tarchonyl alcohol $C_{50}H_{101}OH$

He pointed out that the basis of this series was the type formula $C_nH_{2n+1}OH$.

" But," he added quickly, " that is not the half of it, for this is but one series of mono-alcohols containing a single OH group. We have also other series, comparable to the radical with one OH group, but containing more than one hydroxyl group as — "

And he wrote on the board:

$$R \cdot OH \quad \text{mono-hydroxy alcohols}$$
$$R \cdot (OH)_2 \text{ di-} \quad \text{"} \quad \text{"}$$
$$R \cdot (OH)_3 \text{ tri-} \quad \text{"} \quad \text{"}$$

etc., etc., up to

$$R \cdot (OH)_x \text{ called polyhydric alcohols}$$

He stopped short and, laying his finger across his lips, said in a stage whisper:

" Gentlemen, I beg you, when our hour together is over, to tiptoe most quietly out of the room. Our distinguished visitor has fallen fast asleep. I cannot blame him, but it would be most unkind of you to disturb his sweet slumber after I have so successfully administered a soporific."

" Professor Remsen is mistaken so seldom," said Sylvester, rising and facing the class, " that it is a privilege indeed to be able to correct him. I did not slumber, gentlemen: I have calculated that in the polyhydric aliphatic group about which he has just been telling us there are 207,554 possible alcohols."

Glycerin and mannitol both belong in this populous polyhydric family. And thereby hangs this tale, a story that begins with high explosives and ends with turning the children of Israel's manna into two new chemical products, used for a wide variety of purposes that range all the way from an ingredient in cigarettes and macaroons to a medicine for heart disease and the source of synthetic vitamin C. Nor are these new chemicals rare and tricky laboratory reagents. A commercial supply of more than five million pounds annually falls short of the demand.

This Chemical Age

Glycerin and mannitol are chemical kinsfolk. Both are members of the polyhydric alcohol family; that is, they are alcohols containing more than two OH groups. Glycerin has three hydroxyls; mannitol has six of these OH's. Nitroglycerin, which as you would suspect is glycerin treated with nitric acid, is the basis of dynamite. It is also used to treat certain forms of heart disease. The outline of the plot of this chemical detective story begins to make some sense.

In normal times dynamite is the leading industrial explosive, used to blast coal from the mine, and limestone and traprock from the quarry, to burrow tunnels, to level off the hills on our highways, to dig irrigation ditches, and blow stumps out of farm land. Most of us never thought that we use between 400 and 500 million pounds of dynamites and blasting powders for such peaceful purposes every year, and we forget how many hours and how much hard labor they save us.

The aqueduct of the Emperor Claudius brought a supply of water to Imperial Rome a distance of forty-five miles. It was one of the great engineering feats of antiquity, and the most notable part of it was a tunnel right through Mount Salviano. It was built by slave labor, driven by stern taskmasters whose many-thonged whips discouraged any of the leisurely habits of labor that our P.W.A. pensioners so easily acquire, and the construction called for a strenuous technique. The solid rock was heated with big wood fires and suddenly cooled with great douses of cold water. This rapid cooling cracked the granite so that it could then be broken away with pick and shovel and carried out of the shaft in baskets. This tunnel, ten by six feet, 3½ miles long, took 30,000 workers eleven years to complete — and more than 8,000 slaves were driven to death on the job. The Hetch Hetchy aqueduct which brings water to San Francisco has tunnels of roughly the same size, but 29 miles in length, or eight times longer than the Mount Salviano tunnel. The tun-

" Bold as brass " is tribute to the brightness and hardness of one of the very earliest of those synthetic metals we call alloys.
— Courtesy Bridgeport Brass Company

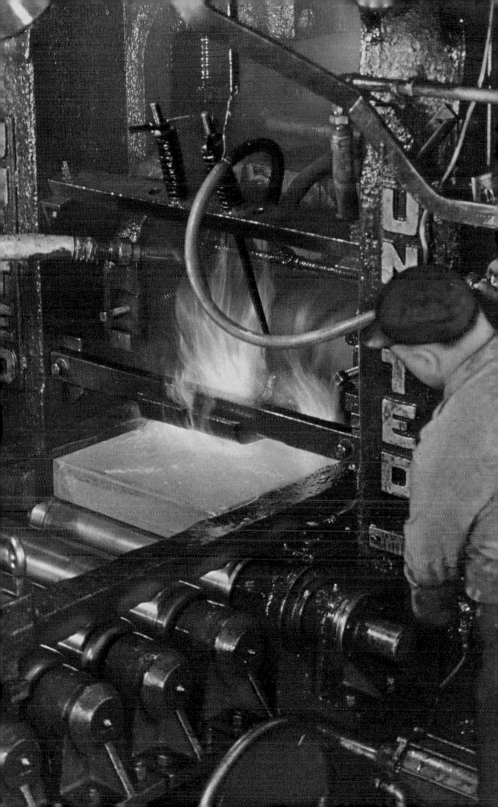

nels in Hetch Hetchy progressed on the average 776 feet a
day and were completed by 100 men in eleven months and
seventeen days.

When the war-god Mars goes to work he commandeers all
these peaceful explosives for his own destructive purposes,
and during the first World War there developed a shortage
of glycerin. It is a by-product produced when fats and oils
are treated with alkalies to make soap. The supply is therefore limited by the amount of soap produced, and there was
some reduction in soap-making due to the extraordinary de-

GLYCERIN DURING WORLD WAR I AND II

[Price range in ¢ per lb.]

Year	Low	High
1914	.13	.14
1915	.12½	.41
1916	.24½	.41½
1917	.35	.51
1918	.11½	.47
1937	.15½	.29
1938	.11¾	.16
1939	.11¾	
1940	.11¾	

The wide differences in the high and low
prices of the first World War period are in
sharp contrast to the steady quotations of 1939
and 1940 — figures from the statistics published
by L. Pasternak & Co., New York.

mand for fats and oils for food in the warring countries of
Europe. And on top of the military demand for explosives
were piled extraordinary requirements for industrial explosives to get out more coal and ore and limestone to provide
more and ever more steel.

Naturally the price of glycerin went soaring. From 12½
cents it rose to 51 cents a pound, and even at this price supplies were woefully inadequate. Glycerin became a chemical
problem that caused bad headaches among the War Indus-

tries Board and the Ordnance Department of the Army. To the dynamite-maker it became a nightmare, and as is the habit in chemical circles, a hunt began for substitutes.

At one time or another all sorts of carbohydrates, which include the sugars, the starches, and the alcohols, had been nitrated and tried out as explosives. As far back as 1840 Sorbero in Italy had treated manna with nitric acid and produced nitromannitol. As mannitol contains six hydroxyl groups to be replaced with nitrogen, and the nitrogen atom is the one that goes off bang! in all explosives, it is a superior disruptant to nitroglycerin, with but three N atoms. At best, however, manna was in limited supply, and it could only be obtained commercially from Italy and North Africa, which immediately involved another war problem — that of ocean shipping. Nevertheless nitromannitol was a possibility not to be neglected.

Late in 1917 half a dozen executives and technicians of the Atlas Powder Company gathered around the big conference table at their headquarters in Wilmington, Delaware, for their regular weekly check-up. The company was considering ammonium perchlorate as a material with which to relieve the shortage of glycerin and hence also nitroglycerin for its commercial high explosives, since perchlorate, pound for pound, gave equal or better explosive strength. Also, military aspects were not overlooked. Since there was no available production of ammonium perchlorate, the first requisite was a practical process for making the material. This study was under way, complications naturally being encountered. R. L. Hill knew that a professor of chemistry at his alma mater, Swarthmore, was highly skilled in electro-chemistry and proposed to consult him.

" The man is Creighton," he reported to his colleagues, " a quiet, unassuming chap, a Nova Scotian trained at Dalhousie University, the scientific type, and we may have to rouse his interest in commercial developments; but he knows his stuff. Being Canadian-born he is especially keen to help us since we are trying to release nitroglycerin from American indus· trial explosives to British cordite. I am sure that he can really do a job for us and that the college would approve our retaining him on a consulting basis."

So it was that Dr. H. Jermain Creighton became advisory consultant to the research staff of the Atlas Powder Company engaged particularly in electrolytic problems. To assist him in this work Professor Creighton took one of his own students, Kenneth R. Brown, a youngster of boundless energy and enthusiasm, who helped in the twenty-four-hour-a-day experiments and yet kept up his regular college work. By the time Brown was graduated, the perchlorate process had been smoothed out, and he was offered and accepted a place on the Atlas research staff.

In July 1918 Hill again went to Swarthmore for a conference with Professor Creighton. Digging about for a substitute for glycerin, the Atlas chemists had come upon a possible available material in vegetable ivory. At that time we imported from Brazil large quantities of the hard white kernels of the ivory nut (*Phytelphas macrocarpia*) to be made into buttons, and the scrap cuttings ground into a paste and treated with dilute sulphuric acid yielded mannose, a sugar corresponding chemically to the alcohol mannitol. This mannitol can be nitrated. Would nitromannitol prove a suitable substitute for nitroglycerin in dynamite? If so, could an adequate supply be produced at a practical cost?

Those of us who lived through the Prohibition era learned that almost any sugar or any starch can be turned by yeast fermentation into alcohol. Chemically speaking, any sugar by the addition of hydrogen can be changed, or reduced as the chemist calls it, to its corresponding alcohol. On paper this is quite simple:

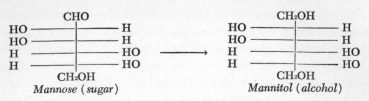

Mannose (sugar)   *Mannitol (alcohol)*

And, theoretically at least, this reduction, or the addition of H atoms, ought to be quite easily accomplished in a water solution through which an electric current is passed, since the H atoms from the dissociation of the H_2O appear at the negative pole. Atlas wanted to turn mannose into mannitol, and this electrolytic reduction of the sugar to the alcohol looked likely. Why not take it to their electro-chemical consultant at Swarthmore and let him evolve a practical process?

Dr. Creighton went to work with small batches of mannose prepared in the company's laboratory. He carried through five experiments, dissolving the sugar, putting it into his laboratory electrolytic cells, and passing through it currents of different densities and using different diaphragms. Then the Armistice came. The price of glycerin tumbled. The mannitol research was abandoned.

Dr. Creighton likes to speculate today upon what would have happened, if in the second of those five original experiments he had not obtained two grams of mannitol. It was not a commercial yield, only a trace from the material used, but it did demonstrate that the reduction of a sugar to an alcohol could actually be achieved by the electrolytic method.

Prompted by very different reasons, he was called back to this work by Atlas six years later. Glycerin was now cheap and plentiful. As a matter of fact, the whole explosives industry had been revolutionized by the Haber process of extracting nitrogen from the air. It was therefore not as a dynamite substitute but as a safer load for blasting caps that the interest in mannitol was revived.

Any material touchy and explosive enough to set off a blast

of dynamite is bound to be dangerous to handle; but there are degrees of this hazard. Accordingly, the industrial explosives industry has for years carried on researches to find detonators that would set off dynamite and yet be as insensitive as possible to impact, to friction, to heat.

Nitromannitol with its six nitrogen atoms had been found to be such a material, and Atlas proposed to load blasting caps with it. Then if they were mishandled they would do less harm. There would be fewer stories in the newspapers of children who have found these beguiling little cylinders of shiny copper and, in experimenting to probe them open with a nail or trying to smash them open with a stone, have lost their fingers. It was a merciful mission quite as important as the purely economic task of substituting a better, cheaper material for a more costly one.

Nevertheless, the economics of the problem could not be ignored and the situation had changed greatly. It was possible, now the war was over, to make nitromannitol from manna imported from Sicily, Greece, Syria, and North Africa. Manna was a comparatively expensive material, however, even for the manufacture of detonators, and, more seriously, it would mean dependence upon far-distant, foreign sources of supply. Since World War I all molecule-makers in every part of the globe have been exceedingly chary about foreign sources of supply of essential raw materials. To drive home this lesson the Atlas executives could see clearly that the possible alternative material, mannose from the scrap cuttings of the vegetable ivory button factories was rapidly disappearing. Synthetic plastics were already beginning to take the place of the hard white nut kernels from Brazil. Today we import none, for the plastics have completely taken over the button business.

These various technical and economic points were all discussed in Dr. Creighton's little office in the ivy-clad, red-brick chemistry building on the Swarthmore campus, sur-

rounded by shelf upon shelf of his technical books, a nautical
chart of the Nova Scotia coast, and photographs of the power
and sail boats that he has navigated through these rocky,
dangerous waters for many long summer vacations. It was
agreed that the electrolytic production of mannitol was possible. The brief, interrupted, war-time experiments had demonstrated this fact. It was further agreed that this material
must be prepared from some American-grown agricultural
product.

"If we can make enough mannitol cheaply enough, we
can find other uses for it."

The speaker was Dr. Creighton's ex-student Kenneth
Brown, whose energetic enthusiasm still surged strong. His
old teacher nodded assent.

"It is everlastingly so," he added. "Give the chemists a
new material in steady supply at a reasonable price, they
will sooner or later find good uses for it."

So Dr. Creighton again began to explore the possibility of
making mannitol from mannose by electro-chemical methods. At the outset he repeated his war-time experiments with
mannose sugar prepared from vegetable ivory. Obviously
the preparation of mannitol alcohol from mannose sugar
would be simplest and the yield would be greatest. Ninety-
one times, varying the different conditions, he ran an electric
current in his small laboratory cells through various solutions
of this raw material. He thus learned to standardize the operation and increase the yield. But it was equally obvious that
ivory nut scrap from the button factories was eliminated as
a source material. Accordingly, he went to work on other
sugars.

He learned after 118 experiments that in an alkali solution
he could produce mannitol from glucose, the sugar from corn.
He found, however, that at the same time he produced
sorbitol, the alcohol derived from glucose itself, and that
while it was possible to vary somewhat the proportions of the

two alcohols, both invariably appeared. In larger cells he began trying out different currents, different temperatures, different materials for the poles and the electrolyte solution. In the end he proved that mannitol and sorbitol could be economically produced from a plentiful, inexpensive raw material from American farms.

A pilot plant was erected at Stamford, Connecticut, and after two years' development work, construction of a million-dollar plant with a capacity of 250,000 pounds monthly of these two polyhydric alcohols was begun near Wilmington. Thus the search which had started ten years before for a substitute for nitroglycerin, and which found a safer detonating material, ended — and yet it had only begun.

Blasting caps loaded with nitromannitol became a reality. Millions are now used each year. But other uses had been found for mannitol and its companion, sorbitol. Nitromannitol itself was promptly discovered to be more effective than nitroglycerin in treating certain heart conditions. Many people suffer because their blood vessels have contracted and stiffened till they no longer easily carry the blood that the heart pumps through them. They must take what is called a vasodilator to relax their arteries and thus relieve the pressure. Both these chemicals act in this way upon the blood vessels, but nitromannitol acts more quickly and its effects are more sustained.

Since sorbitol is the six-hydroxyl alcohol in the same chemical group in which glycerin is the tri-hydric alcohol, it was a reasonable expectation that their uses might well be similar. In normal times — assuming still that war is abnormal — less than a tenth of our glycerin consumption is nitrated to make explosives. This accounts for only some 15,000,000 pounds annually. The 20,000,000 pounds that go into the manufacture of synthetic resins, are growing steadily.

However, by long odds the biggest consumption of glycerin — over 100,000,000 pounds each year — is as a humectant.

A humectant is a chemical that has a sense of moisture.

Mother Nature has provided her children with the ability to absorb or exude moisture. Living plants and animals, according to their needs both of the present and of the future, automatically take on or give off water. In its fleshy leaves and stems the cactus stores water during the rainy season against the dry days that will come in the desert country where it grows. Proverbially the camel can go nine days without a drink. Our own skin is moistened by sweat glands which keep it from drying and cracking.

Man-made products need a similar moisture sense. Unfortunately our mills and factories are not able to bestow upon their wares any ability to keep from drying out in dry weather or from soaking up too much water in damp weather comparable to the automatic moisture-controls that Nature provides. Yet a leather that alternately, according to the whims of the weather, became stiff as a board or soggy as a wet sponge would not make up into a pre-eminently satisfactory pair of gloves. Did you ever bite into a thoroughly dried-out macaroon or try to smoke a super-saturated pipeful of tobacco? One of the early, serious faults of the transparent wrapping sheets was that they became as dry and brittle as a Christmas-tree ornament.

A sense of moisture is indeed important for many inanimate things. It has been supplied by the ingenuity of the chemists. They have developed a whole range of different materials which they call humectants, or humidifying agents, which give the products of the factory an automatic control over their own moisture content that keeps them moist, soft, pliable, fresh. American manufacturers buy over $24,000,000 worth of these humectant chemicals every year.

Among the humectants, the most widely used are the polyhydric alcohols. Glycerin has long been employed in this way. The glycols, and now more recently sorbitol, are other important humidifying agents. Each has its own advantages.

Some of them work more efficiently at low humidities and others at high; one is better for this material and another for that. Several of these alcohols have the advantage of being almost tasteless and quite harmless to the human system. Accordingly, some can be used in bakery goods, candy, salt, meat-packing, and other foodstuffs. The biggest single customer is probably the tobacco industry, but the quantity used in transparent flexible sheeting has increased enormously and is still growing rapidly. Use of a humectant in flexible glues and printer's rollers is obvious since permanent softness and pliability are necessary physical characteristics. Sizing for textiles and dressings for leather are also given this automatic moisture-control with the added advantage of much longer wear for the goods. Cosmetics, insecticides, gelatine capsules, milk-bottle caps, and dolls' heads are among the unexpected uses. As a specific example of the advantages of sorbitol as a softener and humectant: changing only from glycerin to an equal quantity of sorbitol in the same glue formula, the viscosity is increased from 2,120 to 3,500 and the tensile strength from 45 to 71 pounds per square inch.

Detonators from mannitol; sorbitol as humectant; but that is only the start.

Having six different hydroxyls, for any one of which OH radicals the same or different atoms or other radicals may be substituted, the number of chemical derivatives possible is exceedingly large. If but a single element or radical is substituted for from one to six of the hydroxyls, thirty-five different new products are possible. If treated with mixtures of reagents — with two acids, for instance — the number of possible combinations is very much greater. The permutations of such mixed compounds runs close to half a million, or more than all the organic compounds that are at present known in the laboratories of the world. Nobody can guess what prizes may be drawn out of such a well-stuffed grabbag of new chemicals.

Already more than a hundred derivatives of mannitol and sorbitol have been prepared by Atlas and their significant physical and chemical properties determined. It would take many days' hunt through the research reports to find how many others have been prepared in the laboratories of the makers and other chemical firms who have been experimenting with these new alcohols. Only those that show some commercial promise are brought to the market and these offer a bewildering range of possibilities. They are being used as emulsifiers, softeners, plasticizers, stiffeners. Among them are esters, ethers, acetals, ketones — all well-known and important organic chemical groups. Reacted with the fatty acids, some of the resulting long-chain esters are oily substances and others are waxy materials. In these various derivatives greater variety and special properties result from the fact that chemicals or radicals are not substituted for all the six OH groups present. Some are left free, as the chemist says, and some are linked together, to give products that have different degrees of solubility, viscosity, and the like.

When Dr. Creighton first made sorbitol in his electrolytic cells, he bought from a laboratory supply house a working sample of this material in pure form. He wanted to investigate some of its properties in order to devise quick methods of determining quantitatively how much sorbitol was being produced along with the mannitol in his electrolytic cells. He paid $20 for ten grams. The same material can be bought today for 38 cents a pound. In August 1934, when the pilot plant at Stamford was beginning to produce, mannitol was offered in fifty-pound lots at $2.65 a pound; today it is sold in ton lots at 35 cents a pound.

All this is just the kind of story that the newspaper headline-writers enjoy entitling: "Chemists Make Manna." True enough, but more accurately: ten years of research by a brilliant electrochemist resulted in the preparation of mannitol from glucose — the reduction of a sugar to an alcohol by electrolysis. Technically this was a long step into a new field — the synthesis of an organic material by means of electricity — and it won for the studious Creighton the Potts and Longstreth gold medals and a " Modern Pioneer " award. Backed by the resources and the engineering and chemical staffs of a company with molecule-making vision, this Creighton process became a practical, workaday, commercial operation, making ton lots of two useful chemicals that ten years ago were rare and costly reagents sold by the gram. What is important to this country and its people is that these chemicals are made from American farm products and that they have already proved to have an astonishing variety of uses.

CHAPTER XV

THE SKELETON IN THE
VEGETABLE CLOSET

◇◇◇

IF you or I were to step suddenly into a hornets' nest we should not be very apt to delay long enough to start an investigation of the composition of said nest. Gottfried Keller was made of sterner stuff.

In him, of all the poignant human emotions roused by the swift, vicious attack of the yellow jackets, scientific curiosity was the strongest. He noted the tough, pliant strength of the familiar gray " wasp paper " that clung so persistently to his ankles, and even in his frantic agitation to break loose was favorably impressed with these qualities. He determined forthwith to study this curious material under circumstances more favorable to the free play of the disinterested, dispassionate spirit of true science.

As was his custom, he did this as thoroughly as the limited means at his command made possible. He was a poor weaver, operating in his cottage in Hainichen, Saxony, a hand loom, selling his homespun flax to one of those close-bargaining linen merchants from Hamburg and Bremen and the cities of the Low Countries who traveled through Germany collecting a stock of cloth from the peasant handicraft workers. He had had a little schooling — nothing remotely like a scientific training — but he was excessively curious, keenly observant;

and he had the true research worker's ability to fit one observed fact into another.

He had a neighbor, one Heinrich Volter, a handicraft paper-maker, a kindred spirit who liked to play about with new ideas. The pair did a great deal of debating over many a stein of the heavy, heady Saxony beer.

This wasp-nest stuff, Gottfried observed, had some obvious paperlike qualities, and he suggested to friend Heinrich that he might use it in place of the rags which were his sole raw material. If some of the tough and waterproof qualities might be carried over into the finished paper, they would have found something well worth a trial. So they charily collected a stock of wasp-nests and began to experiment. Others before them, and since too, have had the same idea. It was never worked out into a practical process and the labors of Keller and Volker would have had no meaning if the senior partner of this lowly research team had not twisted this failure into success.

Several years later, on a lovely summer evening in 1840, Gottfried Keller was strolling about the village, cooling off after a long day of close work at the loom. He came upon a group of children gathered intently about a big grindstone. One sturdy boy was whirling the crank while the others were taking turns pressing cherry pits against the revolving stone to grind in them a tiny hole. It was a co-operative enterprise for the manufacture of cherry-pit necklaces. Some smart youngster had found that by half burying the pits firmly in a little depression in a board and then holding this against the grindstone, the risk of raw and bloody fingers from contact with the moving abrasive was eliminated. The revolving stone passed in its lowest circuit through a trough of water on the surface of which floated a thick layer of pulverized wood and cherry pits. The insatiably curious Keller scooped up a handful of this yellow, woody scum and pressed it in his hand to squeeze out the water. It became a pulpy mass.

As Keller kneaded this wood pulp softly in his fingers he thought suddenly of the rag pulp that Volter turned into paper. Here was a more likely substitute for the scarce and expensive cloth waste than the wasp-nests had ever been, and off he hurried to his friend. Next morning, to the honest disgust of their good wives, they were at it again, experimenting. Out of these experiments came cheap wood-pulp paper.

This was a discovery of greater import than appeared on the surface. However, this observant weaver, for all his clever curiosity, must have had a dull imagination, since he never sensed even the most obvious usefulness of his process. He sold it for seven hundred dollars. It was the first practical, large-scale chemical use of cellulose, and hidden away behind it lay high-powered explosives, photographic film, rayon, synthetic plastics, and lacquers. What a chemical storehouse! — not to be compared with the rich diversity of products the molecule-makers have wrung and twisted out of coal tar and petroleum, nevertheless in tonnage and as a source of raw materials for big industries surely one of the most important of all the synthetic groups.

This cellulose is the cell-wall material of all plants. It can be found in tree trunks, grass blades, or the soft dome of the mushroom. In almost pure form it is obtained from cotton linters, the soft hairs that grow on the seeds of the cotton plant. Its most economical source for us, however, is the wood of spruce and pine. In commercial quantities it is also recovered from the spent cane, by-product of the sugar factories. This is called bagasse, and pulped and pressed it becomes the familiar wallboard trademarked Celotex.

During the past hundred years many good chemists have done much hard work on this cellulose. It remains a complex mystery. If you want to see what it looks like, absorbent cotton is practically pure cellulose, and so is a common blotter or filter paper, which gives a very good idea of the material felted in sheet form. Under the microscope the long tubelike structure can be seen: in the cotton fiber arranged in parallel chains, in filter paper all hodgepodge like a pile of well-mixed jackstraws.

Structurally cellulose is one of those long-chain, polymerized molecules, like rubber, with the formula $(C_6H_{10}O_5)_x$. That little sub-x is deceptively simple. It represents the number of those $(C_6H_{10}O_5)$ units strung together in some 40 to 60 chains of 15 to 25 pairs each. So x equals somewhere between 1,500 and 2,500. It depends on the source of the cellulose.

Chemically cellulose is a carbohydrate, akin to the sugars and starch, and reacting like an alcohol. It can be converted into either sugar or starch — sugar from sawdust is one of the pet projects of the *ersatz* chemistry of Nazi Germany.

Cellulose is insoluble in water, alcohol, ether, and all the favorite solvents of the laboratory. It can be dissolved, however, in sulphuric acid, in a copper-ammonia reagent, and after treatment with caustic soda in carbon bisulfide. With nitric and acetic acids it forms compounds. And thereby hangs the tale not only of guncotton and collodion, but also of rayon and lacquers.

Just a century ago, the 1840's were a decade of great cellulose discoveries. Besides Keller's wood-pulp paper, John Mercer, a cotton printer of Blackburn, England, found that if he treated cotton goods to a bath in weak caustic soda it shrank, became heavier, took dyes more readily, and acquired a permanent, glossy, silklike sheen. Mercerized cotton became the first of the many modified textile fibers. In 1846 a chubby Swiss chemist, Christian Schönbein, for forty years professor at the University of Basel, treated cotton with nitric acid and produced guncotton, or nitrocellulose. The same year Louis Nicolas Ménard, a French socialist poet and painter who dabbled in chemistry, dissolved this guncotton in a mixture of alcohol and ether and for the first time produced collodion, which we know and use as " Newskin." Both these discoveries were years ahead of their time; but they were the fertile seeds of the explosives, plastics, and lacquer branches of the cellulose group of industries.

It was Gottfried Keller's wood pulp that first flourished industrially. It had, of course, a long head start over dynamite and " Celluloid " and " Duco," for paper had been used since about the beginning of the Christian era, and if we count Egyptian papyrus, since back about 3500 B.C.

Papyrus is, after all, a primitive sort of paper made according to the germ of the same idea, out of the long cellular pith of the stem of the papyrus reed. This was separated by slicing with mussel-shell knives into strips which were laid side by side in a frame, then covered by a similar layer laid at right angles, sprinkled with water, pressed, and dried. The sheets were next rubbed with shells or ivory, which produced a smooth, glossy surface. Well into the Middle Ages this papyrus was the best writing material available. Then true paper, along with gunpowder, was smuggled from China into Europe by the Moors, and this potent pair of inventions overthrew the knight in armor and the mitered bishop and dislodged the deeply entrenched system of feudalism.

The Chinese are proverbially versatile and secretive, and it is said they maintained a close monopoly of the art of papermaking for six centuries. Their most ancient process was to boil the fibrous inner bark of the mulberry tree in a lye leached out of wood ashes. After careful washing it was beaten into a pulp with wooden mallets, suspended in water, dipped up in a bamboo sieve. By gentle shaking the digested pulp was deposited in a thin layer on the sieve as the excess water drained away, leaving a uniform sheet in which the fibers — the long-chain molecules of cellulose — are all interwoven, crisscross, felted in all directions. The sheet was then taken from the frame, pressed between planks, and dried in the sun. Latterly they used bamboo pith and cotton rags. Our ultramodern paper machines, from which roll 1,300 feet every minute continuously mile after mile of sheets six, ten, even

twenty-four feet wide, employ in principle this identical ancient method.

When paper-making was transplanted to Europe neither
bamboo nor mulberry was available and rags became the raw
material. The Moors brought the art to Spain in the tenth
century; thence it spread to France, to Germany, to the Low
Countries, to England. In 1690 William Rittenhouse, a German paper-maker, and William Bradford, an English printer,
entered into a partnership to operate the first paper mill in
North America.

In Europe the scarcity of cotton and linen rags was bad
enough; in the American colonies it was far more acute. The
Boston News Letter in 1769 announced that " the bellcart will
go through Boston before the end of next month to collect
rags for the paper mill at Milton," and this poetic appeal was
added:

> *Rags are as beauties, which concealed lie,*
> *But when in paper how it charms the eye;*
> *Pray save your rags, new beauties to discover,*
> *For paper, truly, every one's a lover:*
> *By the pen and press s'ch knowledge is displayed,*
> *As wouldn't exist if pa; r was not made.*
> *Wisdom of things mysterious, divine,*
> *Illustriously doth on paper shine.*

With a commercial candor not common in 1820, the proprietors of a new paper mill in northern New York State took
the ladies into their confidence and offered them very special
inducements to help solve their serious raw-material problem:

> Save your rags! This exclamation is particularly addressed
> to the ladies, both young, old, and middle aged, throughout
> the northern part of this state, by the subscribers, who have
> erected a paper mill in the town of Moreau near Fort Edward
> — they reflect that without their assistance they cannot be
> supplied with the useful article of paper. If the necessary
> stock is denied paper mills, young maids must languish in

vain for tender epistles from their respective swains; bachelors may be reduced to the necessity of a personal attendance upon the fair, when a written communication would be an excellent substitute. For clean cotton and linen rags of every color and description, matrons can be furnished with Bibles, spectacles, and snuff; mothers with grammars, spelling books, and primers for their children; and young misses may be supplied with bonnets, ribbons, and earrings, for the decoration of their persons (by means of which they may obtain husbands), or by sending them to the said mill they may receive the cash.

Matters had been made worse, rather than better, by the invention of paper-making machinery. In the old handicraft days, when rags were soaked weeks to ferment them before hand shredding and the pulp was laid on the screens also by hand, it required three months to complete this tedious series of operations. By digesting the rags with pot-ashes; shredding them in a Hollander machine, a beater equipped with knives; and making the paper sheets in a machine invented by Nicholas Robert, a French paper-mill worker who sold it to the wealthy Fourdrinier brothers, Henry and Sealy, royal stationers of London by special appointment to the King, the rags could now be turned into paper in forty-eight hours.

The demand for paper was also growing. The newspaper had been invented — weeklies became semi-weeklies, then thrice-weeklies, and finally dailies. Anyone who wanted to keep in the swim simply could not wait his turn to read the latest copy of the *Gazette* or the *News Letter* at the coffee house. Circulation of the news sheets began to mount and Mr. Munsell hoped in 1845 for some cheap mode of converting forests into paper " to feed the all devouring maw of the press." Rags had become, paradoxically speaking, the bottleneck of the paper business, and Gottfried Keller's ground wood-pulp raw material literally created a new industry.

So far practically all the progress in paper-making had been mechanical, but now chemicals began to play their famous, familiar role of time-saver. Muspratt had made cheap alkali available through the Le Blanc process, and Hugh Burgess took advantage of it to make paper pulp by boiling wood chips in caustic soda, bleaching it simultaneously with hypochlorite. Like Keller's ground pulp, his soda pulp is still a minor source of paper-making material.

Two famous chemical brothers of a famous Maryland family perfected one of the chief processes now used for preparing wood pulp. Richard Albert and Benjamin Chew Tilghman were grandsons of Edward Tilghman, attorney, and of Benjamin Chew, merchant, and sixth in direct descent from Richard Tilghman, surgeon, who was granted a thousand acres on the Eastern Shore of Chesapeake Bay in 1661. Both independently and as a team these brothers did many a good job for the infant chemical industries of this country. Richard devised the commercial processes for the production of potassium bichromate and caustic soda upon which the initial operations of two of our great chemical companies, the Mutual Chemical Company and the Pennsylvania Salt Manufacturing Company, were founded. " B. C." worked on ammonia, glycerin, and fertilizers with distinguished practical results. Together they invented the sandblast process for shaping and finishing glass and metal objects. Shortly after the close of the Civil War they started to work on some better method for digesting wood cellulose and they took out the earliest basic patents covering the sulphite process. Their solution of sulphurous acid was not the final answer, but it was the direct hint that led to it.

Always seeking for cheaper and better means of converting materials to man's better use, the chemist kept probing into this pulping problem for the paper-makers. Salt cake (sodium sulphate), the first step in the Le Blanc soda process, was cheaper than caustic soda, and from it the sulphate process was worked out by C. F. Dahl. The first operation was estab-

lished at Danzig in 1885. It is good and cheap, but till recently
it has been chiefly used for the production of the tough,
brown wrapping paper known as " kraft."

The boastful hope of satisfying the devouring maw of the
press with the forest turned to a sickening fear that these hungry machines would gobble up all of the world's wood supplies. Twenty-odd years ago this fear rose to a hysterical
pitch. The circulation of the daily newspapers grew and grew.
A number of popular magazines had each won more than a
million regular readers. Each American citizen who in 1880
consumed some 20 pounds of paper a year was by 1918 using
120 pounds. Two thirds of it went into periodicals and books;
but the Cassandras who foretold the extinction of the forests
viewed with all the proper symptoms of alarm the fast-growing use of paper in the building and packaging fields where
wallboard and paper boxes and shipping cartons were rapidly replacing wood.

" Alackaday," they wailed, " just think of it, seven acres
of virgin spruce forest cut down and thrust into the paper
machines to print a single Sunday issue of any one of half a
dozen of our big metropolitan newspapers! "

Devoted to a study of the world's raw materials and their
political repercussions, the Williamstown Conference of 1926
developed into a gloomy contemplation of a cheerless, com-
fortless, very hungry future for our bedeviled race — after we
had squandered all our irreplaceable raw materials. Petroleum, half a dozen metals, our good farm lands, and most
especially wood were paraded with an imposing array of
statistics. Just as the distinguished audience was about to
dissolve in tears, a tallish man, lean and stoop-shouldered,
rose to his feet.

" Let us," he said quietly, " look the facts of our future wood
supplies straight in the face."

His listeners shivered with apprehension. Surely they
would now know the worst, for here was the great chemical

engineer John Teeple, famous as a builder of new industries, a keen business analyst, an outspoken critic of all blub-dubbery.

" Wood," he began, " is our most ancient and honorable raw material — man's first fuel, his first weapon, his first building material."

Then he proceeded to show how for all of its irreplaceable uses wood has already been largely replaced. As fuel, coal and oil have taken wood's place. Wars are no longer fought with wooden clubs and wooden bows. Wood is no longer the most important material for buildings or bridges or tunnels. In its vital uses as a chemical raw material, wood is no longer necessary for the production of methanol (wood alcohol) or acetic acid or acetone, all of which have been synthesized. Even as a source of cellulose it is not necessary, for the cellulose from annual plants, promptly replaceable, is perfectly acceptable though not yet as cheap and convenient.

" Wood," he went on, " is continually disappearing — in the newspaper headlines — and bringing civilization to an end. Suppose it did disappear, what would happen?

" Just one industry do I find where the disappearance of wood might be a horrible calamity and really change the trend of modern existence. I cannot for the life of me see how without wood the manufacture of antique furniture could continue."

Since Dr. Teeple's wholesome witticism, we have increased our per capita consumption of paper products from 164 to 255 pounds a year: to say nothing of an increase in consumption of rayon (a large part of which is made from wood) from 60,000,000 to 488,000,000 pounds. Yet in 1926 debarked spruce, the most favored material, sold for $25 a cord; in 1940 it could be bought for less than $20.

Judged by the acid test of price, there is plainly no immediately pressing shortage of wood for the cellulose industries. It continues to be the most favored raw material for two

reasons. It can be economically harvested and transported.
This is the great obstacle to a wider use of ton upon ton of
agricultural waste cellulose. Cornstalks, for example, are difficult to collect economically in sufficient quantity at one
point to supply the demands of a reasonably sized pulp plant.
Furthermore, pounds per acre still favor wood. Whereas the
cotton plant yields about 20 pounds of fiber per acre a year,
Southern slash pine has an annual increment of 1,000 pounds
of woody growth and Western hemlock under favorable circumstances will yield more than twice as much. The cotton
fiber is almost pure cellulose in a form susceptible to direct,
economical chemical treatment. Only half the weight of
spruce or hemlock wood is available for commercial cellulose
and this must be not only extracted, but freed from impurities before it becomes a suitable chemical raw material.
Nevertheless, the cost factor is so heavily weighted in favor
of wood cellulose that it overbalances the expense and difficulties of this preliminary processing.

Little Johnny's arithmetic homework presents you with
just such problems:

" If purified, prepared cellulose from wood sells for four
cents a pound, how much will a rayon manufacturer pay for
raw cellulose in cotton? "

Every last boy and girl in the fifth grade, even stupid
Sammy Snooks, ought to solve that one. Therefore it is astonishing indeed how many really brilliant adults can fail to
understand this simple question. Naturally they get the wrong
answer. This is most unfortunate, for this is a practical problem and often these clever grown-ups are seriously endeavoring to solve it. Sometimes they are in positions where their
mistakes are costly to a great many of us.

As we use the man-made molecules more and more, these
plain problems of chemical values are going to be more per-
tinent and more important. Those realistic makers of molecules, the American chemical manufacturers, are adept in

*The color-printer's palette — his inks are now made under chemist's
control as scrupulous as that lavished on vitamin tablets.*
— Courtesy Calco Chemical Division, American Cyanamid Company

seeking out the cheapest, most abundant sources of the atoms that they require in their reactions to build up new materials.

" The more air and water you can get into a new product, the more likely it is to be a commercial success."

So said a witty chemical engineer, and he was not poking fun at the high-pressure salesman nor giving the high financier a sly dig in the ribs. He was expressing vividly a sober principle of his profession. Air and water, the " free goods " of the economist, are important sources of oxygen, hydrogen, and nitrogen, three valuable atoms much used in modern molecule-making. And the molecule-maker is forced by competition to employ the cheapest available elements.

That is what William J. Hale had in mind when he warned the farmers and the politicians that if agricultural products are to be used as industrial raw materials, it can only be upon the basis of their chemical values. The cotton-planters did not understand this A B C of chemical economics, and when the politicians sought to solve the cotton problem, they worked out a wrong answer. By pegging the price of cotton, in order to equalize farm incomes, they separated cotton from the greatest and fastest-growing market for cellulose, which, from the chemical point of view, is what cotton essentially is.

Three years before the first farm-relief law, in 1929, at the peak of the boom, our rayon manufacturers used 25,000 tons of cotton linters, the by-product fuzz, too short to spin into yarn, that clings to the cottonseed, and 44,000 tons of wood pulp. In 1940 they had increased their use of linters to 60,000 tons. Their consumption of wood pulp, however, multiplied by more than four, to a total of 178,000 tons.

The increase in wood pulp used to make rayon in this one year is equivalent to more than 300,000,000 pounds of cotton. For a waste product that is a nice little nibble at our farm surplus; but that is not all the sad story.

The agricultural experts tell us that the world price of

good, spinnable, staple cotton is just about five cents gold a pound. Holding our cotton price above that figure has encouraged cotton-growing in other lands and is costing us our export trade. At five cents for staple, the by-product linters would naturally be selling cheaper and there would be little

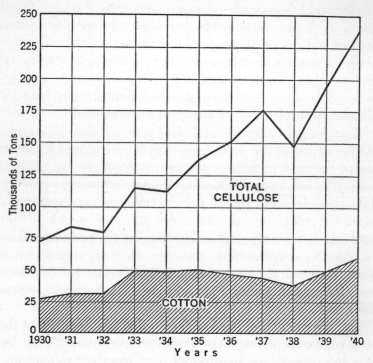

The above chart vividly portrays how the " pegged price " of cotton has encouraged the use of wood pulp as a source of cellulose by the rayon industry. In 1930 cotton supplied 38% (shown in the chart by the shaded area) and in 1940 only 24%, according to the statistics of *The Rayon Organon.*

incentive for the rayon industry to use wood pulp, since at this price the technical advantages of cotton cellulose would encourage them to buy surplus staple. In the wide-open world market the price of cotton has already adjusted itself to the chemical value of cellulose.

A bushel of corn consists of 30 pounds of starch, 23 pounds of gluten, and 1.4 pounds of oil. Starch from cassava is worth a cent a pound; crude gluten cake is worth half a cent a pound; the normal price of several equivalent vegetable oils is five cents a pound. Therefore Dr. Hale points out that corn is chemically worth about forty-three cents a bushel. Your taste for Virginia corn pudding or Rhode Island johnnycake might tempt you to pay at the fancy rate of a dollar a bushel. However, more than three quarters of our corn crop is fed to hogs and cattle or processed into alcohol, starch, and glucose. Either as a meat or a molecule builder the competitive chemical values will in the long run set the price of corn in an open world market.

This dynamic Dr. Hale, provocative advocate of the industrial employment of agricultural raw materials as the solution of the farm problem, tells the politicians bluntly that some day in the not distant future these chemical values will control the prices of all the important crops, and he warns the farmers to forget crop restrictions and by the use of brains and fertilizers to produce cellulose, carbohydrates, and proteins cheaply for industrial processing in chemical factories. For there are definite limits to the capacity of the human stomach. Indeed, our annual food consumption is steadily declining in pounds. No such physical limit restricts other human wants, and some irrepressible statistician has calculated that each of us consumes about nine times as much of the world's raw materials as did the Englishman of Queen Elizabeth's day. Anyone may question such a figure; but nobody can disprove it, which is the cardinal virtue of any mathematical data. That " times nine " is quite correct in that it represents vividly the tremendous lift in the scale of our daily living.

According to all reports, the subjects of good Queen Bess were plucky trenchermen who polished off more foot-pounds of foodstuff energy than the best of us in these concentrated and dyspeptic days. However, their beef and mutton were homegrown, and that adventurous, inquisitive sponsor of tobacco and potatoes, Sir Walter himself, could never have had grapefruit for breakfast. To bring pineapples from Hawaii and to relish fresh peas the year round we have almost annihilated space and time by abolishing the stage-coach and the sailing vessel. In accomplishing such feats we have greatly increased our drafts upon the world's raw materials, since power generated by horse fodder that can be grown in a twelvemonth, or by the winds of heaven, is a very different thing, economically considered, from power generated by coal or petroleum, the supplies of which are fixed and irreplaceable. The great palace at Greenwich where the royal daughter of Henry VIII and Anne Boleyn was born contained far less plumbing than an F.H.A. bungalow. For all his gaudy doublets and hose, the foppish Duke of Buckingham had fewer clothes than a prosperous grocer of La Crosse, Wisconsin. Those worthy booksellers, printers of the first editions of Shakespeare, Spenser, Bacon, and all their brilliant, prolific contemporaries who made the golden Elizabethan age of English literature, actually consumed, all of them in a full year, less paper than goes into a single issue of one of our comic-strip magazines — a horrid thought which we cannot wholly banish by boasting cheerfully that the Elizabethans had nothing whatever to place in comparison with our 45,192 railway locomotives, our 21,698,405 telephones, our 29,468,148 motor vehicles, our 52,500,607 radio sets. Of course they had no corresponding stupendous consumption of metals, rubber, fabrics, coal, petroleum, and lubricants.

Some of these figures of ours are staggering. Omitting all the rest of the world, we use right in this country 444,552,-377 tons of coal, 1,264,200,000 barrels (of 42 gallons each) of petroleum, 31,751,990 tons of steel, 125,056,594 barrels of cement, 6,648,435 tons of asphalt, 148,236,000 pounds of copper, etc., etc., till the digits spin before our eyes like a swarm of gnats on an August afternoon.

Contemplating such figures, a thoughtful man with but a tincture of pessimism can easily calculate himself into a panic over the fate of the human race. The worthy Malthus did so a century and a half ago. Already we have exceeded the two billion human beings on earth which he forecast for A.D. 2000, when he foresaw that poverty and starvation, deterioration and death were to be the inevitable lot of mankind. Nevertheless we are better fed, better housed, better clothed than Malthus's own contemporaries, and we enjoy conveniences and luxuries literally by the hundreds which even his brilliant brain never conceived.

We have performed this economic miracle by making machines to do the work of muscles. Only a hundred and fifty years ago Watt and Newcomen devised the steam engine and Arkwright and Hargreaves set it to spinning yarn and weaving cloth. Then the engineers got busy and began contriving all sorts of tools driven by power. The new machines revolutionized all the old handicraft industries and produced such an abundance of goods at such low prices as man had never had.

Then half a century ago the Count de Chardonnet made the first synthetic fiber, rayon, and John Hyatt in Albany made the first synthetic plastic, Celluloid. Then the chemists went to work creating all sorts of new man-made materials: again more goods and much cheaper, better goods. We have passed out of the economy of scarcity under which man has always sweat and starved, into an economy of abundance.

The more abundant life! We have not yet abolished poverty: thousands of human beings are hungry, starving, dying; but if we have not learned how to live safely and comfortably, we at least have now the means at our command to do so.

The more abundant life — wealth and health — that is what the politicians the world over are promising their people. It

is a grand old promise — a better home, a car in every garage,
leisure time for play, expert medical attendance and scientific
hospitalization, a positive security in old age that drives the
wolf far from the most humble doorstep.

Wealth and health — gold from lead and the elixir of life
— these are what the alchemist of old sought. The same hopes
have lured us onward, upward, through sweat and blood and
tears, since that bitter night æons ago when a naked, grimy,
half-starved, flea-ridden biped brought fire into his damp,
cold den and found that it was good.

These same cherished desires are just what the politicians
have always been promising their people: the Kaiser, " a
place in the sun "; Henry of Navarre, " a chicken in every
peasant's pot each Sunday "; Cæsar, " no Roman citizen shall
ever starve "; Moses, " the Promised Land of milk and honey."
And slowly, bit by bit, that promise has been made good
throughout all the long ages of hard-won triumph over our
material world, not by these voluble politicians, but by a
great army of silent workers — explorers, merchants, herders
and farmers, miners and fishermen, inventors, mechanics and
chemists, industrialists. Set promise against performance: the
record is as simple as the rule of three, the story as plain as a
child's primer.

Because we have at last learned a few of the simple rules of
physics and chemistry and through research are applying
them, we have made more material progress in the past two
hundred years than in the previous two millenniums. Now to
the new machines we have added new materials. The use of
synthetic materials will doubtless revolutionize our industries
as thoroughly as the use of power upset completely the old
handicraft economy.

That was what Dr. Teeple had in mind when he said that it
is indeed fortunate for greedy, unsatisfied humanity that only
comparatively few of the ninety-odd chemical elements are

essential to the processes of life upon this planet, and that all these are widely distributed and fairly abundant. Carbon, hydrogen, nitrogen, oxygen, calcium, sodium, magnesium, potassium, sulphur, phosphorus, and but minute traces of a few others all to be found in sea water: these are the vital atoms, the chemical essentials. All the other seventy-five elements are simply conveniences. Under dire necessity we could do without them or replace them with substitutes.

Among all the animals we are famous for our adaptability. We can change our mode of living almost as quickly as blue litmus paper dipped in acid turns red. We cannot, however, change our method of life any more than we can transform a thistle plant into a fig tree. We can reform our habits, but not our metabolism. We can revolutionize our systems of government, of transportation, of communications; but not our digestive, our respiratory, our nervous systems. Hence there are no substitutes for those fifteen atoms vital to animal existence. The molecule-makers by juggling the commonest elements are stretching out our stores of the scarcer and irreplaceable materials. To its ancient task of modifying materials more to man's liking, chemistry has taken on the new creative job of conserving our raw materials by furnishing us with synthetic materials.

It is upon these premises that our scientists, the most tolerant and optimistic thinkers among us, can quote those appalling statistics of our daily needs, not to blame but in praise of this rapacious, selfish materialism of ours. They ignore the forebodings of Malthus. They despise the wishful thinking of Marx. They know that the more abundant life will be the heritance of all, not as fulfillment of the promises of a Roosevelt, or a Hitler, or a Stalin, but as results of research. If necessity is the mother of invention — so their logic runs — ambition is its father; and with such fecund parents we are assured of a growing host of servants to provide our material wants.

At some distant day it may even come to pass that, having satisfied our material desires, we shall begin to demand mental, even spiritual, satisfactions.

So seen, the synthetic products are much more than substitutes. They have values of their own even beyond their chemical values, and a significance to our industries, our government, our society that surpasses the effect that any living man will have upon the future of mankind on earth. Colors and perfumes, even medicines, however interesting and valuable, are not in quite the same class of importance with the man-made raw materials, fibers and plastics, rubber and fuel. The first, and still in many ways the most valuable, are those products synthesized from cellulose.

CHAPTER XVI

BARGAIN BASEMENT TO
HAUTE COUTURE

◇◇

A MINISTER's son — not the typical roué, but one of those terrifically efficient fellows who irritate the rest of us blundering, happy-go-lucky mortals excessively — was the first to suggest that the chemist should imitate the silkworm and spin artificial threads. Robert Hooke, M.D., was a person notably blessed with talents and singularly lacking in personal charm.

Not only did he write in 1664 a very accurate prophecy of rayon; but he also invented a telegraph two centuries before Samuel Morse was born. He knew everyone in London, as his acquaintance Samuel Pepys confessed a bit enviously; but unlike the gossipy diarist he had no time for either jolly stag dinners or fashionable soirées. He spent his nights hard at work, till three and four, or even till breakfast, writing, making microscopes or watches, performing chemical experiments.

At twenty-nine he built a microscope that was a masterpiece. Scouring the old curiosity shops, the docks, the markets, for specimens, he examined all sorts of strange objects and wrote descriptions of them into a remarkable book that even his enemies read avidly. Somewhere he picked up several lengths of " artificial silk." We cannot guess what these fibers were, but his description is clear enough. It was a single filament — possibly prepared from a spider's web — and he was so enchanted by its possibilities that he wrote quite a little treatise about it.

After all, silk is but the glutinous excrement which the dumb little worm forces through orifices in its body, so he reasoned, and why shouldn't a gum be made and extruded to produce artificial silk? He was so certain all this could be done that he even speculated on the qualities that artificial silk ought to possess in order that it should be even better than the genuine original. He even forecast that those who should produce artificial silk would reap a rich reward. With a typical flourish he added that if nobody else took the hint, he himself might have a go at this silkworm business.

His book *Micrographia* (1664) was full of accurate descriptions of what he saw in his homemade microscope, interspersed with many similar crackpot comments. It stimulated lively arguments over the chocolate cups of Westminster and the ale mugs of the City. His contemporaries would have been dumfounded to know how accurately his preposterous prophecies have been fulfilled, and it would have been a great comfort to many who cordially disliked this skinny, crabbed little medico to know that his artificial-silk ideas had been antedated by the Chinese about 1000 B.C.

We think of rayon as something quite modern. It was first produced by a practical commercial process more than fifty years ago. But back beyond that go years upon years of trials till we come to the Chinese. By macerating dead silkworms and allowing the mess to ripen they were able to draw out from it a continuous thread. It was picked up on a needlepoint, attached to a revolving bobbin, and drawn out till it broke. The process was apparently successful and nobody knows why it was abandoned. The Egyptians spun thread of spider's web, and that art was revived in medieval Italy. It became a business in France about 1750, when Cochot's Spider Silk Works flourished dubiously for a brief period. Another Frenchman, Louis Bon, made gloves and stockings of spider's thread, and many noted that it was finer than silk and much stronger. Thus the product of the silkworm is not after all the last word in luxury and durability.

Then the chemists took a hand. They first mixed up witches' brews of gums, rosins, soap, glue, gelatin, starch, various oils and fats, and what have you, in efforts to imitate, as Dr. Hooke had suggested, "the glutinous excrement." In 1855 George Audemars, a Swiss, shot closer to the mark. He boiled the inner bark of mulberry in soda, added soap, then treated it with lime dissolved in nitric acid, alcohol, and ether, added a rubber solution, and presto change! he picked up on a needle, Chinese fashion, a continuous thread.

High-power explosives and electric lights do not seem to have any very direct connection with artificial silk, yet these discoveries led directly to the first synthetic textile yarn. Nitrocellulose was its chemical father; the filament for the incandescent bulb, its mechanical mother.

Guncotton dissolved in alcohol and ether suggested the line of research that led straight to all the various types of rayon. The tiny holes through which the material for a continuous, homogenous filament for electric lamps was forced and the spinning box for the collection of this thread were devices that by some adaptation became the spinnerets and spinning machinery that produce artificial fibers. During the early eighties twoscore men made discoveries that fell just short of the target. Though many of their inventions were useful later, the honor of producing the first practical rayon goes clearly to the Count Hilaire de Chardonnet.

This chubby French gentlemen had three qualifications that enabled him to make this great discovery. He possessed a wide range of scientific knowledge, a modest competency that enabled him to devote his time wholly to research, and an infinite patience. And the greatest of these was patience.

He was no scintillating genius — either as a chemist or as an engineer or as a businessman — but for twenty-nine years

he worked hard and almost constantly on this single task. In
the end he came forth from his laboratory with something
more than an invention: a whole series of inventions which
created a new thing in the world, a man-made textile fiber.
He knew what he was about, what he wanted, what must be
done to achieve it, and he has left us with one of the clearest
statements of the difficulties that beset the research worker
who translates a scientific fact into a commercial product:

The time employed over this work would appear to be exaggerated if one did not remember that the establishment of so new
and so complex an industry necessitates a whole series of studies,
discoveries, and inventions. . . . Note the difference existing between researches in pure science and those relating to applied
science, especially when it is a question of constructing a work
complete in every part. In the realm of pure science each discovery in itself extends the field of human knowledge; on the
other hand when applied science is in question an isolated discovery is valueless. Every problem which arises must be completely solved. The smallest badly laid stone will bring down the
edifice. Sometimes it is only after months or years of industrial
practice that the best solution of a problem is found.

Chardonnet had been well trained for this long-drawn-out
work. His father, an amateur scientist of note, was his first
tutor; and at fifteen he enrolled at the Faculty of Sciences in
his native town of Besançon. Here he studied chemistry under Professor Loir, Louis Pasteur's brother-in-law, and when
later he went to Paris at the École Polytechnique in 1859 he
came under the great master himself. Pasteur at this time was
deep in his famous study of the mysterious disease of the silkworms which threatened the great French silk city of Lyon
with industrial ruin. Chardonnet assisted in this research.
Therefore he knew the habits and the anatomy of the silkworm as none of the other chemists who were setting up to
rival these lowly caterpillars ever knew them. Two years in
Paris, three spent in travel abroad, then in 1865 a happy mar-

riage and retirement to his private laboratory on the family estate at Besançon.

Chardonnet was interested in photography and late one afternoon was making some collodion-coated plates when the stock bottle slipped from his fingers and broke on his work table. Disgusted, he left the sticky mess and went off to dress for dinner. Next morning it had but partially dried out, and in scooping it up he found that it pulled out into long threads which remarkably resembled silk. That was the beginning. The end came on May 12, 1884 when he was granted French Patent 165,349: " *Sur une matière textile artificielle ressemblant à la soie.*"

Right at Besançon, that very year, Chardonnet opened the first textile-fiber factory. At the Paris Exposition of 1889 he made a beautiful display of his artificial silk, which so far as the feminine visitors were concerned was quite the whole show. It was a sensational début, but unfortunately favorable publicity alone could not ensure success.

His " Chardonnet silk," as it was called, was spun of nitrocellulose. Touched with a flame it ignited — puff! — and it vanished in a brilliant, burning flash. After several disastrous accidents, the fire-insurance companies protested so vigorously that the Government stepped in and closed the factory. Chardonnet hurried over to England, made arrangements to use a denitrating process developed by Sir Joseph Swan, and reopened his Besançon plant, which in a few years was earning large profits.

Today his denitrated-collodion process is almost as obsolete as the dodo. But Chardonnet was the first to produce a multiple-filament yarn by squirting a cellulose solution through a cluster of tiny holes, and the first to make and market a synthetic fiber.

Other methods of dissolving cellulose, forming it into filaments, and regenerating it back into solid cellulose re-formed into long-chain molecules were perfected. Two have been operated and are even now in production, but are not of great commercial importance. A third, similar process, however, accounts for about two thirds of all our rayon. It began with Swan's work on electric-light filaments and was perfected by a famous English research team, Messrs. Cross and Bevan.

Charles F. Cross and Ernest J. Bevan were chums and fellow students under Roscoe in the Owen's College research laboratories. They separated, Cross to go into the textile and Bevan to the paper industry, but two years later, in 1881, they joined forces as consulting chemists with offices in London. Attracted by the success of the mercerizing process, they undertook a systematic study of the reactions of caustic soda upon cellulose and then of all sorts of reagents upon the resulting alkali cellulose. In due course they came to carbon bisulfide and found that in this liquid the white crumbly alkali cellulose makes a definite substance that turns from pale yellow to deep orange and forms into balls. These balls dissolve in caustic soda and an orange syrupy liquid results. After a period of several days' ripening at a temperature that must never go higher than 66 degrees, this syrup, called viscose, can be extruded through spinnerets, the thread being coagulated in an acid bath.

There are tricks in all trades, but few chemical operations are so tricky as the viscose rayon process. Time, temperature, and humidity, all must be scrupulously controlled and they are a difficult trio to keep in hand. The alkali cellulose must be aged, for during this period a mysterious change takes place upon which depends the viscosity of the final spinning solution. If it heats up, all goes askew. Accordingly, it is torn to bits in shredders with cooling jackets in which cold water is circulated, and it is ripened in small batches. If the reaction between this ripened alkali cellulose and the carbon bisulfide proceeds too rapidly, the resulting orange-colored balls will be sticky — and useless. More cold water is circulated around the apparatus. If the final viscose solution is ripened too long, the cellulose tends to separate out. Therefore delicate chemical tests are made to assure that it goes through the spinnerets just at the right point of this critical stage. Variations in ripening mean variations in spinning qualities, and also in the tensile strength and dye acceptance of the finished fiber.

The holes in the spinnerets are 0.08 of a millimeter in diameter, so that ten, twenty, forty of them in the center of the tiny platinum disk appear to be but a dull gray dot on the shining surface. To be seen they must be held up against a bright light. If even an ordinary fly speck of dirt gets into the solution it will clog these microscopic openings, so just before spinning, the solution is sent through filters. Likewise every last microscopic air bubble must be pressed out of the spinning solution.

Each opening in the spinneret forms a filament, each filament hardens separately and immediately in the acid coagulating bath, all the filaments from one spinneret are united to form a single thread. The sulphuric acid in the bath is being continually turned into sodium sulphate by the alkali in the viscose, yet the composition of that bath must constantly remain at eleven per cent acid for the best results. This neat trick is accomplished by circulating the bath through a large correcting tank. The speed of the bobbin must be exactly synchronized both with the flow of the viscose through the spinneret and with the formation of solid thread in the bath. As the thread builds up on the bobbin, its diameter increases, thus increasing both speed and pull. To prevent an uneven thread, the speed of the revolving bobbin is ever so little cut down automatically as it fills with thread.

Out of many such combinations and permutations of chemical niceties and mechanical delicacies come the viscose rayon we know today. No wonder that the coarse, harsh, thick " artificial silk " of twenty-five years ago, with its metallic luster and its distressing habit of losing half its tensile strength on the first trip to the washtub, has been vastly improved.

Experience and larger output combine to raise quality and to lower cost, and, more than that, to make it possible to create desirable varieties of rayon even from the same materials and process.

All these rayons (whether made by the viscose or the Bemberg cuprammonium or the ethyl cellulose process) are cellulose regenerated in form. Even greater variations are possible in the fibers made from such a chemically modified cellulose as cellulose acetate.

This distinctly different fiber we owe to the brothers Dreyfus. They did not discover the chemical compound of cellulose and acetic acid. They were not the first to make fibers out of it. They did, however, put it on the market. One might almost say they forced it on the market.

" Name me three chemical products," said Camille Dreyfus to brother Henri, " that the whole world wants, and cannot get, and will pay well to have."

This was back in 1908. They were youngsters fresh from the University of Basel, where they both had tucked away a lot of hours in the chemistry laboratories. They were out frankly to make their fortunes from chemistry. Their approach was typical of the good research man — set up the ultimate objective at the outset — and it was hereditary too, for their father was a sharp chap who promoted all sorts of little enterprises and lived comfortably by taking a cut of the profits of those that succeeded.

Henri's answer was prophetic: " Synthetic indigo, a chemical substitute for quinine, and a Celluloid that is non-flammable."

Back and forth they debated the merits of the three ideas, tramping the floor together, as is still their habit, the volatile Camille gesticulating to emphasize his pet arguments, the quiet Henri with his hands sunk in his coat pockets.

The great German Dye Trust had already begun to make indigo. A synthetic quinine would be too difficult to make, test, and exploit. So they would make a non-flammable Celluloid. That was their conclusion.

Forthwith they began a year and a half of experiments trying to take the explosive kick out of nitrocellulose. After nearly blowing each other out of the laboratory half a dozen times, they switched tactics and began working on cellulose acetate.

In 1910 they started manufacturing. At this time cellulose-acetate film was just beginning to take the fire hazard out of the infant movie industry, and their first, biggest customer was Pathé Frères. A much bigger customer approached them when the British Government telegraphed Camille to come to London for a conference on acetate dope for the wings of their army airplanes.

Could they make it?

Naturally!

Would they make it in England?

" That depends."

The British offered to build them a factory and buy all the output at a handsome price for the duration of the war, and then take over.

The dapper little Camille bristled all over at such a thought. Even with that fortune he and his brother had set out to make right within his grasp, he had no notion of trading his secrets for some war profits.

Negotiations were long drawn out but never dull. In the end Dreyfus walked out with a big contract for cellulose acetate dope in his pocket. Off he went to raise the money to build the plant to fill his fine order. He quickly found that capital, big capital such as he sought, is very set in two ideas. It wants to know all about the business and it wants to control it. Neither of these ideas appealed to him in the least, and he had quite a time finding bankers sufficiently uninquisitive and trustful to suit him. He succeeded, and ground was broken for an English factory.

After we joined the Allies Newton Baker, Secretary of War, cabled Camille Dreyfus to come to Washington to discuss plans for a similar factory in America. Camille was busy tuning up the English plant for its initial run-through. Besides he had learned the wisdom of a buffer negotiator who could learn much and yet commit his principal to nothing definite. Accordingly, he sent over Major E. E. Boreham, late of the British Army, more lately associated with tight-lipped, gray-eyed Robert Flemming, the Scotsman who had found most of the capital for the British Cellulose and Chemical Company.

The Major was an adept trader and he came back to Dreyfus with a contract for a million and a half pounds of acetate dope and an agreement on the part of the U.S. War Industries Board to build the necessary plant, said plant to be sold to the Dreyfus brothers, if they wanted it, at the end of the war. All this was very much to Camille's liking, and since the War Department insisted that this plant be put back away from the seacoast, a tract of eight hundred acres was bought at Cumberland, Maryland. Here there was abundant water from the Potomac, and they would be located close to their supplies of coal and cotton. The Armistice in November 1918 caught them with a half-built factory building. The Government canceled their contract, but in due time and after a deal of prodding paid all of the out-of-pocket expenses.

The end of the war put Camille and Henri Dreyfus in an exceedingly uncomfortable position. They had a little plant in Switzerland which was obsolete; a big plant — far too big for peace-time demands — in England; a large tract of land and some bare brick walls in western Maryland; and no money. All their war profits had been poured into their expansions.

The viscose-rayon process was well established in England, on the Continent, and in America, and neither they nor anyone else knew how to make acetate fibers either cheap enough or good enough to compete with it. Nevertheless they decided to go after the rapidly growing synthetic-yarn business. Accordingly, they shut down the Swiss plant; abandoned their American building; operated the new English plant at about quarter capacity, and retired to its modern, well-equipped laboratories to learn the tricks of acetate-yarn manufacture.

It took a year to work out a commercially feasible process. Their first shipments were promptly returned with sarcastic comments by their textile customers. Their fine, new fiber would neither spin in the ordinary textile machinery nor dye with the regular textile dyestuffs.

Back to more research. Henri turned himself into an expert mechanic specializing in spinning, knitting, weaving machines, while Camille borrowed from their old Basel neighbors, the textile finishing house of Clavels and Lindenmeyer, thirty chemists and dyers and set himself up as an expert colorist. Another year and the brothers came out of their research séance with a perfected technique of handling acetate yarn and a new set of acetate dyes. Incidentally they had a whole series of patents controlling the spinning and dyeing of cellulose acetate fibers.

In 1920 they were ready to go, but without the funds to go with. This is not the place to tell the harrowing story of their financial troubles, nor of the battle royal between Camille Dreyfus and Alfred Lowenstein for the control of the British Cellulose and Chemical Company. In the end the brothers held on to their own, but it cost them five and a half million dollars plus three-per-cent royalty on all sales up to fifteen millions.

In the meantime they came over to the United States in 1924 and with twenty-three million dollars provided by their old Scotch friend Robert Flemming, and J. P. Morgan, they completed the Cumberland plant and offered their yarn to the American textile trades. Our knitters and weavers were not at all interested. This new fiber needed special handling, different spinning, different dyes, different finishing methods.

Besides it was high-priced, much higher than viscose fibers. So the embattled brothers fared forth to beat down the prejudices of their customers and overcome the lusty competition of makers of synthetic fibers already entrenched in the American market.

The pioneer of the synthetic-yarn industry in this country was Arthur D. Little, an ideal sponsor for any new project of a chemical nature that required courage, imagination, and high financing. Dr. Little was a unique figure in the chemical development of this country. He was himself unique — a chemist who collected Chinese porcelains, an engineer who was an epicure, a technician who belonged to the right clubs, a gentleman and a scholar and a good judge of chemical values. He was equally proficient reading a centigrade thermometer or a balance sheet, as at home in the banker's private office as in his own laboratory. He was our first great salesman of chemical ideas and he made it his business to have a finger in almost every new chemical pie that came out of the research bakeshops.

Little was in touch with Cross and Bevan and they promptly communicated to him details of their viscose discovery. In 1893 he arranged to experiment with the new material and he used it to prepare cellulose acetate sheets. Later he and William H. Walker, the great M.I.T. professor of chemical engineering, teamed up to develop cellulose acetate. With Harry Mork in working charge, they perfected a fine electrical wire insulation which they manufactured in a small plant near Boston. They also made a non-flammable acetate film which they sold to George Eastman of Kodak fame. In October 1902 these three were granted the first U.S. patent for artificial silk from an acetate fiber, a practical process six years before the Dreyfus brothers made their earliest experiments.

This ended the experimental period, and the decade 1900–10 was marked by commercially unsuccessful efforts to manufacture synthetic yarns in this country. With Little as his chemical adviser, Daniel C. Spruance, of the well-known Philadelphia family, took on the American rights to the viscose process. The Cellulose Products Company was organized with a distinguished personnel that included in the laboratory Carleton Ellis, who died in 1940 with more chemical patents issued to him than to any other American, and at the head of sales William C. Spruance, who later became vice-president of E. I. du Pont de Nemours & Co.

Only a few months later T. S. Harrison, grandson of John Harrison (the first American maker of sulphuric acid) and head of the century-old chemical and pigment house of Harrison Brothers, stepped into the synthetic-fiber ring. His General Artificial Silk Company had bought the American rights to the Stern and Topham process for spinning viscose filaments.

Very quickly both companies made a pair of joint discoveries. First, this synthetic-fiber business demanded more capital than either anticipated. Second, neither process separately controlled was worth much. Spruance sold out for $25,000 to Silas Petit, a Philadelphia lawyer who was a big stockholder in the Harrison enterprise, and for a similar sum Petit also acquired the remaining assets of that enterprise. Viscose and spinning rights were now in one basket, but shortly after he formed the combined Genasco Silk Company, Lawyer Petit died, and his son began hunting a buyer.

Hindsight is proverbially acute, but looking backwards one now marvels at the opportunities to get in on the ground floor of the rayon industry in America that went begging. Young Petit hawked the viscose process to half the banks and all the leading chemical, paper, and textile companies. Dr. Little had gathered his various acetate processes into the Lustron Company and with Gustavus Esselen, now a leading chemical consultant of Boston, in charge of the research, had been selling his yarn successfully as a twisting for the pencil stripes in men's suitings and other specialized uses based on its different dyeing affinities from those of wool and cotton. But he, too, was anxious to sell out. He was a consultant rather than a manufacturer. In later years he told gleefully how he offered the acetate process on a silver platter to such shrewd, far-sighted financiers as Frank Vanderlip, Bernard Baruch, and J. P. Morgan. It does not flatter all our boasted Yankee smartness that American rights to both these basic processes were snapped up by foreigners.

Gloomy Samuel Courtauld, head in the third generation of the ancient and profitable firm of Messrs. Courtauld's, Ltd. may well deserve his reputation as the most pessimistic man in the British Empire, but he did foresee the bright future of synthetic yarns and he boldly put his company into this untried business. Furthermore, when his hustling American agent, Samuel Salvage, wrote him that the United States rights to the viscose process were on the market, he sent immediately his trusty lieutenant Henry Greenwood Tetley across armed with a letter of credit for 130,000 pounds sterling or 800,000 American dollars. Young Petit controlled his astonishment at the arrival of a live prospect for his Genasco corpse so successfully that he managed to wangle $113,000 for all the sketchy assets that had cost his father $50,000. He retired jubilant.

The efficient Mr. Tetley organized the American Viscose Company. He took on Dr. Charles Ernst, the Petit chemist; gave him three per cent of the new stock in lieu of a handsome salary; sent him to England to learn the tricks of viscose production; and after his education had been completed, put him in charge of the American plant. Ernst was a real chemist. He tackled his new job from the chemical point of view. He made substantial contributions to better and cheaper yarn.

At the same time Mr. Tetley took on Samuel Salvage, gave him five per cent of the company stock, and sent him out to

sell viscose yarn. Salvage was a real salesman. The product
he had to sell was in those days about as thick and stiff as
horsehair. Accordingly, when the textile trade laughed at this
crude silk substitute, he sold it to the braid-makers; and when
they kicked him out because it would not stand washing, he
sold it to the makers of millinery trimmings. As quality improved, he went back again and again, always selling for better and finer uses. No other single man did more to bring
rayon out of the cheap goods sold in the bargain basement
into the lovely, costly underthings and evening gowns of the
haute couture than did Samuel Salvage.

Again dollars make a convenient and understandable yardstick. The $800,000 invested in 1910 became in 1941, when
the Courtauld interest in the American Viscose Company
was sold to build up British war credits, the neat sum of
$40,000,000. That figures out exactly 500 for 1 in thirty years.

In 1924, when Camille and Henri Dreyfus came across the
Atlantic to invade the American rayon market, they very
sensibly decided to acquire Dr. Little's old Lustron Company. It had some useful patents and some interesting European rights, either of which was a seed that might sprout an
American acetate competitor. There was no hope whatever of
maintaining a monopoly, for the most basic of patents do ex-
pire in seventeen years; but it would be a distinct advantage
to get away to a clean start.

From the beginning Camille Dreyfus decided to go out
after the Fifth Avenue trade. No suspicion of the cheap and
nasty substitute fiber was to attach itself to his beloved acetate. With great care he laid his plans to take every scrap of
advantage that his yarn's distinctive qualities afforded. He
put those plans through with the same audacity that is characterized by his own purple shirts and white spats.

It was to be made clear that Dreyfus's acetate was no ordinary man-made fiber. Hence he scorned the name "rayon,"
which all the other filament-makers had agreed upon as a

generic name that would help the public forget all the unpleasant connotations that clung to " artificial silk." He coined
his own name — Celanese; and he fought tooth and nail to
make that name stick in the textile trade and with the public.

When the textile industry would have none of his yarn, he
wove and knit it into superb fabrics, beautifully dyed, and
brought it straight to their customers. To compete with his
own prospective customers in this fashion was the boldest
kind of frontal attack. It succeeded.

He priced his yarn to begin with at $2.90, nearly twice the
price of rayon. And he made his sales play, not in the textile
mills, but in the department stores. He sold the public, and
consumer demand sold his Celanese. With the passing of the
years the price of acetate has squeezed down closer and
closer to that of rayon. Steadily, too, its share of the market
has expanded. In 1924, when the total synthetic-fiber production of the country was 42,200,000 pounds, Celanese furnished but 0.3 per cent of that total. In 1940 all acetate yarns
supplied 34.1 per cent of the 487,500,000 pounds output. For
today the two pioneers — Viscose and Celanese — both have
plenty of stiff competition. Both, however, still maintain their
leadership in their respective fields.

In the viscose division: Viscose, 120,000,000 pounds per annum; DuPont, 60,000,000; American Enka, 35,000,000; North
American Rayon, 35,000,000; Industrial Rayon, 35,000,000.

In the acetate division: Celanese, 60,000,000 pounds per
annum; Tennessee Eastman, 35,000,000; DuPont, 20,000,000;
Viscose, 16,000,000.

It is too much to hope that these highly confidential figures of the individual companies' output are exact, but they
represent the estimate of one in the trade and may be taken
as roughly indicating how production stands. However, the
array of digits in the table of fiber consumption is really a
good deal more impressive than it appears to be on the surface. What started out as a silk substitute now outsells silk

about fourteen pounds to one. But it is even more remarkable that during the past twenty years, when our consumption of rayon has grown from 10,000,000 to over 400,000,000 pounds, our consumption of silk has dropped from 81,000,000 pounds in 1929 to 35,800,000 in 1940. We now use just as much rayon as we do wool, but there has been virtually no increase in our wool consumption. We regularly use each year in the range of three to four billion pounds of cotton fabrics. That is nearly ten times as much as we use of rayon, but a hundred times as much as the rayon we consumed in 1920. If you doubt that rayon has grown more at the expense of cotton than of silk, just try to find a pair of cotton stockings.

Put another way, our relative consumption of the various textile fibers may be expressed thus: for every pound of rayon consumed in 1940 we used 8 pounds of cotton, 5/6 of a pound of wool, 1/14 of a pound of linen. Twenty years ago for each pound of rayon we consumed 324 pounds of cotton, 36 pounds of wool, 3¼ pounds of silk. Those ratios are an impressive demonstration of rayon's growing importance as a textile fiber.

CHAPTER XVII

NEW FIBERS: NEW FABRICS

◇◇

ONE winter afternoon in 1938 twenty-six distinguished experts sat down around a great oblong table in a pleasant conference room in the Statler Building, Boston, to discuss what synthetic fibers were doing to the New England textile industries, and how, and why, and what, if anything, could be done about it.

They were a hand-picked group selected by the august New England Council. Among them were mill-owners and mill-operators, chemists and dyers, experts in wool and cotton, silk and rayon, a chemical economist, and two college professors: a cross-section of authoritative opinion.

The topic for discussion was live. It involved important financial interests and a big slice of the laboring population of the region. The occasion was serious to the point of solemnity.

In the course of the afternoon the then new Lanital, the so-called synthetic wool, made from casein by the Italians, was brought up and a sample was produced by one of the members of the conference. It was passed around the table. Even among these experienced professionals it called forth expressions of delighted surprise. At last it reached the distinguished chief chemist of one of the country's most important woolen companies. Here was the expert of all the experts on such a material, and all turned to him expectantly.

" I've seen it, of course," he said. " In fact we have just completed some rather exhaustive tests on it."

His audience leaned forward and he continued quietly: " Believe me, gentlemen, when I tell you it is not wool. It does not look like wool nor feel like wool. It does not spin like wool, nor weave like wool, nor dye like wool. It has not the feel of wool, nor the drape of wool, nor the warmth of wool, nor the wearing qualities of wool. It will never be " — and his voice rasped sarcastically — " anything but a cheap and nasty substitute! "

He tossed the little fluff of white fibers contemptuously into the center of the big table. Silence, like a wet blanket, descended upon the group. Till this point the atmosphere had been rather optimistic, the feeling being that synthetic fibers gave New England mills a distinct advantage over their dangerously successful Southern rivals. This pronouncement was therefore distinctly off key. It sounded ominously final. A neat little man with a jutting jaw and twinkling eyes rose at the other end of the table. He was a ranking officer of the corporation that makes Palm Beach cloth.

" I hesitate," he said softly, " to disagree with so distinguished an authority. But, gentlemen, while we must admit that many of the qualities of this material are not very wool-like; nevertheless, I submit to you, it is not cheap; it is not nasty; and it is not a substitute."

A hearty laugh cleared the atmosphere and he continued: " I would be embarrassed if you should misunderstand me, but I must speak out in meeting. My company has put on the market a certain lightweight men's suiting material which the public has been generous enough to tell us looks better, cleans better, holds its shape better, wears better, and is notably cooler and more comfortable than the finest lightweight serges and worsteds. Our fabric is tailor-made out of a combination of natural and synthetic fibers — mostly synthetic. Indeed, it could not be even approximated without the use of at least two different types of rayon. We are merchandising men's suits of this synthetic cloth at $17.50 retail.

" Do not, I beg of you," he added, " take what I say as either a threat or a promise; but we are hard at work to create a heavyweight men's suiting material which will look better and wear better, drape better and hold pressing longer, and in addition be warmer and more comfortable than the best tweeds and heavy worsteds now on the market. That, too, will be a tailor-made cloth, a mixture of natural and man-made yarns. Only by creating new fabrics can we improve on the wearing apparel that Nature has given us for centuries. Our research will all come to naught if, having made this new suiting material, we cannot sell suits of it for $20 retail.

" What the textile industries of New England need," he said, leaning eagerly across the table, " is the vision to see that these new synthetic fibers mean new fabrics, new opportunities; and the courage to welcome them, to experiment with them, to make cheaper, better fabrics out of them. Finally we need to go out to sell two, four, ten times as much dress goods and suitings as the public ever bought before.

" Then we ought to pray, night and morning, that the tailors will be as smart in contriving new styles as the dressmakers have been, so that the men will be ashamed to wear a $20 suit for five years as they now wear your $50 worsteds and homespuns! "

And that, of course, is just what the textile industry has done. We have all sorts of new, made-to-order fabrics — doeskins and sharkskins, wrinkle-proof crepes and crush-proof velvets — and every season other new textile materials are introduced. These veritable creations in cloth and knit goods are the result of a great progressive evolution in the quality and the variety of the man-made filaments. In the meantime there has been a counter-revolution in what m'lady and her consort think of the synthetic fibers.

At the Paris Exposition half a century ago Count Hilaire's explosive nitrocellulose was hailed " Chardonnet silk." He has admitted that he frankly imitated, as well as he was able, the methods of the silkworm. His object was to make an artificial silk. In the early days all the energies and talents of the pioneers were bent upon producing a cheap substitute for silk.

Now, " substitute " — especially " chemical substitute " — has unpleasant connotations. In these days of nationally advertised goods we have all been taught that " just as good " is either a joke or a fraud. So long as man-made fibers were only " artificial silk " they were predestined to the bargain basement. The public recognized this clearly long before the fiber-makers awoke to the fact that although a rose by any other name may smell as sweet, nevertheless, if you give a dog a bad name, you might just as well hang him. " Artificial silk " was a distinctly bad name. So in 1924 they sat down and deliberately coined a better one: " rayon." We have seen how Camille Dreyfus outsmarted the rest by insisting that his fiber was different from the regenerated-cellulose rayons and refusing to call it a rayon at all, and gave it the mellifluous name " Celanese."

The earliest rayons were crude stuffs. Thirty years, however, saw sufficient improvement in quality to enable the synthetic fibers to take real advantage of a whim of fickle Dame Fashion that gave them their first big opportunity. When dresses dusted the ground and women's shoes were almost as high as a hunting boot, it was all very well to wear cotton stockings. But when skirts crept up to the knee-caps, as they did during 1918–20, and pumps with French heels replaced the sturdy Victorian footwear, then sheer, smooth stockings came suddenly out of the luxury class. Stockings of pure, unadulterated, unweighted silk cost five dollars a pair (and it is admitted in the inner sanctums of the hosiery industry cannot be bought for less even to this day) while stockings of silk and rayon, or rayon unmixed, could be sold for a fifth as much. It was on the trim legs of the post-war flappers that rayon stepped out into big business. In 1920 a third of the rayon output, some 3,500,000 pounds, went into hosiery, which in 1940 took about 14,100,000 pounds. But that fourteen millions is not one pound in three of the total rayon used as it was then, but only one pound in twenty.

During the Roaring Twenties rayon, having established itself firmly in the women's underwear and stocking trades, began to edge into dress goods. Its better ability to stand the mauling of the washing machines, the ravages of laundry soaps, and the heat of the pressing iron were widening its usefulness.

Moreover, the operators of that amazing, distinctly American institution the dry-cleaning industry were going through their own chemical revolution. Rayon helped them to realize that chemistry is the basis of their $400,000,000 income, earned by removing dirts and stains. In the early stages their solvents, being quite unsuitable for the new man-made fibers, brought many an irate woman fuming into their stores. In 1926 their National Association organized a co-operative laboratory and engaged a staff of chemists housed in a fine building located at Silver Springs, Maryland, which, as the Englishman says, is a " good address " for any kind of cleaning establishment. Not a soap, not a cleansing fluid, not a single machine or method of operation that was standard in dry-cleaning practice in 1920 is in use today. Even in these times of swift and sweeping technological improvement, so complete a change, all within a single business generation, is a unique record.

It was during the middle twenties that, thanks to one of the earliest modifications in the physical structure of synthetic yarns, the crepe rayons appeared. The ordinary continuous rayon thread, which may be made up of from 14 to 270 distinct filaments twisted so as to hold them together, has but half a dozen turns of this twist to the inch. If a high twist is given — say about fifty turns to the inch — then a creped yarn is produced. Crepe fabrics are made by using this creped yarn for the filling — that is, the crosswise threads in woven goods. A woven fabric is composed of at least two yarns, called the warp and the filling, intertwined, the warp lengthwise (parallel to the selvage), the filling woven in and out, over and under, between the warp. The fabrics known as " sheers " are produced when a creped rayon yarn is employed for both warp and filling.

This highly twisted rayon opened up vast new vistas. It was going to be possible to create all sorts of new effects in fabrics by giving the knitters and weavers a variety of rayon yarns with which to work. A bewildering multitude of chemical and physical combinations were discovered. Because the rayon yarns are man-made it is possible absolutely to control all these factors and to change or modify them definitely.

Already the chemists had been improving rayon materials. One of the serious early faults, the coarse, harsh " feel " of the yarn was corrected. Its tensile strength, due in the case of viscose rayon to just the exactly correct times and temperatures of the tedious, tricky aging operations, was improved greatly. A long series of carefully controlled experiments in which one after another of all the steps in the process were changed, back and forth, up and down, for longer and shorter periods, were carried on until just the maximum of perfection was reached. The hard, metallic luster of the first rayons was softened. By adding mineral oils, similar to those we pour into our motors as lubricants, or inorganic pigments, like the white leads and zinc oxides which the paint-makers employ as the body of their paints, it was found to be possible to dull the shiny sheen. Accordingly, rayon is now made with lusters that range all the way from brilliantly glossy to a dull chalky, and the degree of luster or dullness is permanent. The dulling agents are added to the spinning solution before it is forced through the spinnerets, and, far from impairing the strength of the filaments, often improve their wearing qualities.

Because the viscose and acetate yarns differ chemically, they have distinct chemical characteristics which make possible another set of variations. The former is pure cellulose; the latter, cellulose acetate, a chemical compound of cellulose. Camille Dreyfus is said to have torn his hair in agony when his customers threw back his first samples because they would not dye with the ordinary textile dyes. He might have spared his scalp and his nerves. Arthur Little had already learned that this eccentric dye affinity was a great blessing in disguise.

The different dye affinities of wool and cotton had long been used to effect the great economy of cross-dyeing. A cloth woven of the two fibers is plunged in a vat containing a mixture of two dyes, the one acting on the wool, the other on the cotton. The fabric emerges in two colors. Dr. Little's first acetate customers used his yarn to weave pencil stripes in men's suitings, which remained white when the woolen goods were dyed black or brown or navy blue with wool dyes. The acetate rayons thus made possible many new and original beautiful color effects which at the same time resulted in great economies. Dots, triangles, circles, stripes, geometrical figures, and floral patterns, all sorts of intricate color designs are produced simply and quickly in two, three, even in four colors by cross-dyeing. A familiar example is the upholstery material in which a high-luster figure is embroidered on a dull background — rayon on cotton — colored in contrasting or blending shades.

With the scientist's passion for numbers — accurate weights and exact measurements — the rayon industry borrowed from the silk trade the denier scale of fineness and made it a very exact measure. It is a unit of weight used to express the " number " or " size " of silk and rayon yarns. A one-denier filament is of such a thickness that 9,000 meters — 9,842 yards and 6 inches — weigh one gram, or, put another way, denier is the weight in grams of 9,842½ yards of rayon yarn. Thus a 150-denier yarn is one of 9,842½ yards, weighing 150 grams. Obviously the higher the denier, the coarser the thread, a 200 being twice as coarse, and so twice as heavy, as a 100-denier.

Starting with the individual filament, which may be considerably finer than that spun by the silkworm or as coarse as a horsehair, it is practical to twist together as few as a dozen or as many as three hundred. A fine yarn is one that is light for a given length. A 75-denier yarn would be light even if it contained as few as 30 or 40 filaments; but a 150-denier yarn would be considered fine only if it was made up of very fine filaments, as 150-denier, 150 filaments.

The simplest variations in the rayon yarns are those resulting from changes in the denier of either the filament or the yarn or both. The silkworm produces a thousand yards of thread composed of from two to six filaments of about 1.5 denier each. In 1918 the only size rayon produced was yarn composed of 12 filaments of 12.5 denier, roughly ten times as coarse as natural silk. Today 150-denier yarn is made of 225 filaments of 0.66 denier, twice as fine as the silkworm's product. Yarns are made ranging from as coarse as 900 denier, used for tapestries and upholstery plush, or even 1,100 denier for automobile-tire cords, to as fine as 50 denier made up into tricolettes and milanese knit goods. Yarn as filmy as 35 denier can be produced, and is, for special work. It is 0.0004 of an inch in diameter, a ninth the thickness of the sheet of your morning newspaper, and in a pound of it there are 4,227.5 miles of length. Season after season the textile industries demand finer rayons, so that the average of all yarns spun in 1935 was 140, and in 1940, 123 denier.

One interesting, useful novelty effect is produced by varying the rate of feed of the spinning solution to the spinnerets and the tension of the bobbins. This produces a yarn of varying thickness, thick and thin. In plain weaves this uneven yarn gives a linen-like surface effect. Woven into satins, crepes, taffetas, it creates a fabric with a pleasing irregularity in both surface and texture.

The cellulose acetate yarns have certain molding characteristics of the cellulose acetate plastics. Accordingly, they can be hot-pressed under exacting conditions of moisture and temperature and pressure into permanent forms. Advantage is taken of these properties to produce ciré effects by pressing the fabric between hot rollers. By embossing or engraving the rollers a moiré, watered-silk, or other patterned surface is obtained.

The number of twists given to the filament in an inch of yarn is now carefully controlled, but there have been devised other spinning treatments of the yarn which make possible many novel effects. By various methods of braiding, plaiting, plying, and cross-twisting together two or even more yarns, the " seeded," " nubbed," " pigtail," and ratiné, bouclé, and other unusual and attractive effects are made both in woven and in knitted goods.

Taking advantage of this wide variety of yarns, the textile mills have been quick to create many new fabrics. For example, the popular blistered or quilted effect can be given rayon cloth owing to the fact that acetate shrinks less than viscose rayon. These matelassé goods are woven in both warp and filling of two threads, one a highly twisted creped viscose, the other a standard-twist acetate. The tight twisting increases the shrinkage of the viscose, and the result is a permanent puckering of the surface. Double-faced fabrics are made by throwing the acetate warp to one side of the cloth and the viscose filling to the other. If a high-luster acetate is used with a dull viscose, the resulting fabric may have a dull, ribby face with a smooth, satin back, and these either may be both dyed the same color or, thanks to cross-dyeing, may be had in boldly contrasting or delicately blended duotones. Material of this type is used for aviators' oversuits. The satin inside slips easily over either lightweight summer clothes or the woolens and woolly sheepskin clothing of winter. Very light in weight, but so tightly woven as to be windproof, they afford the greatest possible degree of ease and comfort.

Such novelty fabrics, created by the hundreds out of the novelty rayon yarns, were welcomed joyously by the modistes. During the middle twenties the Worths and the Paquins awoke to the inspiring fact that they had now wonderful new materials with which to work. They found sheers lighter in weight than they had ever had, yet with a good drape, a much better " coverage," and almost wrinkle-proof. At the other end of the scale they had wonderful crush-resistant, transparent velvets. Today in the fashionable shops on Fifth Avenue rayon dresses outnumber silk ten to one and cotton twelve to one. This is the actual count of a buyer checking up in the best and most expensive stores in the nation's style capital.

During the early thirties the rayon manufacturers learned a way of making their filaments at once finer and stronger. It is not exactly a new trick. For the past forty-eight million years it has been practiced by the silkworm. At least the paleo-entomologists, who specialize in fossil insects, set that date as when this ancient species acquired the cocoon-spinning habit.

As the silkworm exudes the filaments from its spinnerets, it stretches them out to make them thin. This stretching gives them added strength. We know now that this physical stretching arranges the long-chain molecules into parallel lines. The same thing happens if the man-made filaments are stretched.

Physically the effect is also produced when steel is rolled, but one would not think offhand that a rayon yarn could be produced with a greater tensile strength than steel wire, yet this is a sober fact. " Cordura," a viscose yarn perfected by du Pont from a carefully cleaned cotton cellulose and stretched, has a tensile strength of 70,000 pounds to the square inch against 48,000 for steel. It is used as the cord fabric in automobile tires. It proves to be more serviceable than cotton, especially because of its absolute uniformity and its greater efficiency under conditions of heat. At 250 degrees " Cordura " loses 12 per cent of its tensile strength, but cotton loses from 30 to 50 per cent. Thus while at 60 degrees the two are substantially equal, at 75 degrees " Cordura " is twice as good and at 100 degrees ten times as good. This is the yarn that flashed into the headlines of the newspapers in 1937 when the sails of the cup-defender, the *Ranger,* were woven of it. Its lack of stretch, its smooth surface, lightness, and disinclination to harbor mildew, have since made it standard equipment for the best racing sails.

Another neat trick — and a very old one — was found out during the late twenties. Nobody seems to know who first thought of cutting the continuous rayon yarn into short lengths and then spinning them as the short natural fibers of wool and cotton have been spun into yarns since the first textile was made. So simple an expedient greatly enhanced the already famous versatility of rayon. The growth of staple fiber, as it is called, rivals Jack's luxuriant beanstalk. Before 1928 it was too insignificant for a place in the elaborate, accurate statistics published in *Rayon Organon.* That year were recorded American production of 165,000 pounds and imports of 200,000 pounds. In 1940 the total was 98,834,000 pounds: 81.8 per cent of it made in America.

Staple rayon performed a textile miracle. It successfully invaded the stable, ultra-conservative men's suitings trade. Almost since rayon first went beyond stockings and " undies," seersuckers and linens for summer wear had been made of it. Its property of remaining permanently white had helped here, but yarns spun of staple fibers had a new rugged strength that carried them into the lightweight dark clothes competing with worsteds and flannels.

Such neat little tricks as stretching and cutting the rayon filaments were thrown into complete eclipse in 1939 when a really new fiber, one that contained no cellulose at all, appeared. In all respects this was an epochal discovery.

It was, in the first place, an absolutely new material. Its creator, the du Pont Company, coined a name for it that is not yet to be found in the dictionaries. Nylon is literally something new under the sun. It is not easy for us to conceive of an entirely new material. A combination of the chemical elements that was never before put together baffles a lively imagination, and while such unique pieces of matter are common enough in the laboratories of the synthetic chemists, the man on the street seldom, if ever, gets his hands on anything so perilously close to a miracle of chemical creation. Nylon is such magic stuff. It may look like a hog bristle in a toothbrush or a silk thread in a pair of stockings, but it is really a quite different material.

Sober-minded scientists who dislike ballyhoo as a hen hates water have hailed this synthesis of a fiber made wholly from inorganic, mineral raw materials " the most important chemical discovery since Fritz Haber's process for taking the nitrogen from the air." That is lavish praise. It places nylon at the pinnacle of achievement for the first third of the present century, a period richly productive in startling chemical progress. But it is not extravagant recognition. Indeed, judged by its ultimate, practical results in more and better goods for everyday living, as well as its highly suggestive technical bearing upon the important subject of the giant molecules, nylon may well prove to be a chemical discovery as pregnant with fresh ideas and new products as was the first coal-tar synthesis a century ago.

In 1931 after the chloroprene research had moved into the semiworks plant to be whipped into a commercial process for the manufacture of Neoprene rubber, Wallace Carothers was encouraged to think of a new type of fiber from the linear polymers he had been studying since 1928 when he first came to du Pont. Inquiry into these giant molecules in the hands of this brilliant genius had unexpectedly borne economic fruits in the hands of Ira Williams. On the groundwork of Carothers, Williams had built the first practical synthetic rubber.

There are no flies on the walls of the private offices of a good research department, and a good research worker is not given to gossipy chatter. It is no secret, however, that Carothers, delving into the mysteries of the big, linear molecules, had created a host of them out of a variety of materials. Dr. Bolton has confessed that he and some other realistic executives cudgeled their brains to find uses for these fascinating products. With the rubber goal in sight, it appeared likely that search for a new type of synthetic fiber was the most promising. Obviously there was a place for such a material. The price was still sufficiently high to furnish a tempting target. For all the improvement in rayon quality, much desired properties were still lacking. If a new fiber possessed some unique desirable characteristics, the textile industry would undoubtedly welcome it. The public, too, had been educated to the point where they would accept such a new material. Since cellulose is itself one of the giant molecules, the work began by attempts to modify chemically a wide variety of cellulose derivatives. They failed to better either the costs or the quality of existing synthetic fibers.

" Your work," Dr. Bolton said to Carothers, " is to continue your fundamental, scientific study; but keep an eye upon any of your polymers that seem to have fibrous possibilities."

And that curious, melancholy enthusiast, who relished a really profound chemical problem as a connoisseur enjoys a vintage wine, went back to his well-equipped laboratory on the outskirts of Wilmington. He returned with a reasonable answer.

Seeking molecules of all sorts that could be polymerized, joined together end to end like paper-clips strung together, similar to the long-chain molecules of rubber and cellulose, Carothers and his associate Julian Hill noted that the molten mass made in one of his many experiments could be drawn out into long threadlike chains. This was not exceptional. It was indeed remarkable, however, that this crude, thickish fiber, even after it had cooled, could still be drawn out several times its original length. Carothers had never found anything like this before. He began to investigate.

His molten mass was a polyester, one member of the big chemical family of the esters, polymerized. It was an exceedingly complex composition which was obviously a new synthetic plastic. Upon cooling, it set into definite shapes and could be extruded in thin sheets or in thick rods. But its stretching was unique. It miraculously changed the properties of that coarse fiber. Instead of setting like the usual plastic material into a stiff, brittle thread, it remained supple and pliable.

Drawing out fine filaments by hand through a hypodermic needle and stretching them, Hill began testing out this new fiber. It was not very promising. Its tensile strength was poor. It had little elasticity. But it was a good start in a new direction.

He began concocting hundreds of chemically allied compounds and investigating their fiber-forming possibilities. The amide group, $CONH_2$, are derivatives of ammonia, NH_3, in which one H atom is replaced by the acyl group CO. There are also secondary and tertiary amides in which the CO radical replaces two and even three of the hydrogens with the formulas $(CO)_2NH$ and $(CO)_3N$. New fiber-forming plastics were found which are a product of an amide with a polybasic acid. Here is another big chemical family, distinguished as being acids with two or more hydrogen atoms which are replaceable by metals or organic radicals. The simplest acid of this group is oxalic acid, the good old straw-hat cleaner of yesteryear, which has the formula $(CO_2H)_2$.

Without getting tangled up in the complexities of higher organic chemistry, one can guess that with many amides and a great group of polybasic acids, either of which reacting with the other can combine by replacing all or part of its H atoms, it would take a mathematician like Professor Sylvester to figure out the staggering total of the possible permutations and combinations. To make a long and complicated chemical research short and simple, Dr. Carothers found certain products of the reactions of diamides and polybasic acids that could be polymerized into giant molecules, and drawn and then stretched into fibers possessing new and much wanted characteristics.

When the first of these stretchable plastics had been discovered, forty chemists had been told off to help investigate the possibilities of other members of this group. After two years' intensive work they selected " Fiber #66 " as the best.

In the du Pont laboratories they are still putting together new products of this class, and it will be remarkable if they do not find other fibers of different, desirable properties. But " #66 " became the nylon we know. We should not forget, however, that " nylon " is a generic term like " glass " or " leather." It refers not only to the yarn knitted into stockings, but to the bristles used in toothbrushes, to fishing leaders, and many other articles. More than this, " nylon " means all of the polyamides of this great group, and we may confidently expect that other nylons will appear.

It is perfectly true that the chemical genealogy of this nylon family starts literally with coal, air, and water. But that is a deceptively simple statement. It pictures to the ladies a great kettle into which coal and water are poured, mixed up with air, cooked together with some chemical hocus-pocus, till from it are drawn the long, beautiful, silken threads that are knitted into their new nylon stocking. Nothing of the sort happens. The coal is the source of coal tar, from which the intermediates such as phenol and benzol are extracted by fractional distillation. The water is a source of hydrogen. From the air comes nitrogen and oxygen, the former fixed in the form of ammonia, NH_3.

Out of these elements are built up the complex diamides and the more complex polybasic acids. The products of their reactions must then be polymerized, itself a tricky chemical operation. Several of the reactions must be carried on in glass-lined vessels to prevent a trace of contamination. Others take place in platinum apparatus to guard against corrosion. At one stage the temperature rises to 275° Centigrade, nearly three times as high as the boiling-point of water. To obtain a light-colored product oxygen must be scrupulously excluded. This necessitates working the spinning solution under a blanket of inert gas such as nitrogen or carbon dioxide. It took three years of active and hearty co-operation among chemists, physicists, and engineers to bring this process from the laboratory workbench to the commercial plant.

That plant is as novel as its product. It is a long, single-story building with a tower at one end, a great capital L laid on its shank with the foot projecting skywards. From the top of that tall tower downwards, with one step in the operation on each floor, the raw materials travel through all the various chemical operations. On the ground level they have become the colorless chips of nylon, which are melted and fed into the spinning machines. After spinning they are stretched, and the X-ray has revealed that seemingly miraculous change in properties is due to the rearrangement of the long molecules. In the chips they are jumbled indiscriminately, like a box of matches piled up in a heap. In the stretched filament they are arranged in perfect order lengthwise of the thread.

From this point the nylon yarn travels the length of the long ground floor. It is twisted, sized, and lubricated. This finishing process is preliminary preparation for the weaving or knitting of the fibers in the textile mills. After a careful inspection, the yarn is packaged in skeins and wound upon cones, packed, and landed in the shipping room at the end of the building where the loading platforms face the railway siding.

Ground was broken for the plant at Seaford, Delaware, on January 20, 1939. It went into operation on December 15, two weeks before its scheduled opening. It cost $8,000,000. It was built to produce 4,000,000 pounds of nylon yarn a year. Before it had been in operation six months plans to double its capacity had been drawn and still another, larger $11,000,000 nylon plant started at Martinsville, Virginia.

One most notable feature of this important chemical development is the amazing consumer acceptance of nylon. Unlike rayon it was not introduced as a cheaper substitute, but offered as a new, man-made fiber of certain superior qualities and at a higher price. This commercial candor, something quite recent in the marketing of synthetic products, was paralleled by a bold selling policy. The du Ponts make nothing but the yarn — indeed, a number of different weights of nylon yarn — and they sell it without any special agreements or exclusive agencies to all textile mills quite as freely and openly as wool or cotton are sold. They began delivering yarn to the hosiery mills in January 1940, and by agreement May 15 was set as the day when nylon stockings would first be sold in the retail stores, a sort of national nylon day.

Something happened as new and remarkable as this new fiber itself. Mrs. Jones told Miss Smith that the stock of nylon stockings at Black's department store was of necessity going to be quite limited. They went down and stood in line before the doors opened to be sure of getting at least a single pair. And that over-demand continued for more than twelve months. Not only had the women of America, who control most of the money in the family budget, been sold nylon, they had been unsold the unpleasant connotations that have so long clung to the idea of a chemical substitute.

While nylon was the first fiber not made from the natural long-chain molecules of cellulose, it is no longer alone in this glory. Vinyon is made by Carbide & Carbon, starting from natural gas. Aralac is being produced from casein by the Aritex Corporation, a subsidiary of the National Dairy Company. The Ford Motor Company is making an upholstery fiber for its own use from soybeans. So it goes — one chemical discovery in a new field almost always is followed by others — and a whole new chapter of chemical history is beginning on non-cellulose fibers.

CHAPTER XVIII

THE HERALD OF
THE PLASTIC AGE

◇◇◇

THE white man's conquest of Africa inspired the first modern synthetic plastic. The sequence of events, if unexpected, is unmistakably clear.

The Europeans brought firearms into the remotest jungles of the Dark Continent. As quickly as the natives overcame their awesome fear of the fire-spitting sticks, they coveted these weapons, so infinitely more deadly than their bows and spears. But rifles were costly, more costly than wives or cattle. In these time-honored symbols of African affluence the white traders displayed little interest: they wanted only gold and ivory.

So began a veritable holocaust of elephants. More ivory to buy more firearms to get more ivory — the vicious circle had its inevitable results. First, as the supply increased, the price of ivory dropped. Then, as the source of that supply was cut down, it began to mount. The utter annihilation of the great herds of wild elephants began to be seriously discussed by sportsmen and naturalists and with ulterior motives by those who traded in ivory.

In New York the largest American makers of billiard balls, Messrs. Phelan and Collander, became thoroughly alarmed. If this essential raw material of theirs should vanish, what

316]

would they do? They offered a handsome prize — ten thousand dollars in gold — for the best substitute material.

The prize-contest habit is almost as fixed a feature of our American Way as firecrackers on the Fourth of July and they were stormed by a host of claimants. Among them was an ingenious printer of Albany, New York, one John Wesley Hyatt. He did not win the award. But he continued to experiment with plastic compositions and in 1868 produced a new material which he christened " Celluloid." He did not realize it, but he had created a new industry. More than that, we today, three quarters of a century later, are only just beginning to realize that Hyatt initiated an entirely new epoch in industry, the Age of Plastics, successor to the Age of Metals.

Hyatt was a prolific inventor and a reasonably astute businessman. It is curious, therefore, that he never properly valued his own invention of Celluloid. No doubt this was because he was a mechanical genius, but no chemist. Having no knowledge of chemical theory, he had no sense of chemical values. Even the award to him of the coveted Perkin Medal by the British Society of Chemical Industry failed to impress him with the importance of his chemical accomplishment. On the other hand, had he been a trained chemist it is quite likely that a properly wholesome respect for the explosive properties of nitrocellulose would have stayed his hand from those very experiments which brought the new plastic into existence. He is a perfect exponent of the proverbial wisdom of blissful ignorance.

Son of the village blacksmith of Starkey, in upper New York State, Hyatt, who was born on November 20, 1837, was a product of the little red schoolhouse. He did get in one supplementary year at the Eddytown Seminary, where he displayed a natural aptitude for mathematics, but at sixteen, like many youths of his time, he went west. In Illinois he learned the printer's trade. For the next ten years he roamed about from one little country newspaper shop to another, quite in the fashion of Mark Twain and many another young man, for those were the days of the real journeyman printers. Eventually he worked his way back to Albany. While there he learned of that tempting prize offered by the billiard-ball makers.

Always a born tinkerer, he had already a number of neat little gadgets patented in his name. One of them, a sharpener for kitchen knives, involved a new method of compressing powdered emery into a solid wheel. He went out for that ten-thousand-dollar prize by compressing pulverized wood, macerated rags, and paper pulp with various and sundry binders such as glue, starch, rosin, shellac, and collodion. He made a number of plastic compositions, but none good enough to win.

However, he did begin to manufacture checkermen and dominoes out of a wood-glue mixture. And he did continue to experiment. Three years later — this work was all done nights and Sundays — he made billiard balls out of a mixture of paper flock, shellac, and collodion. For considerably less than ten thousand dollars he sold this patent to the sponsors of the prize contest.

Nobody could work with collodion without being impressed by its peculiarities. Accidental spillings of the sticky stuff are credited with suggesting not only Chardonnet's artificial silk, but also the first idea of safety glass. Hyatt became interested in pyroxylin — which is the chemist's generic name for various nitrocellulose compounds — as the basis for plastic compositions. He knew as little about their chemistry as the sub-deb who paints her nails flaming red with pyroxylin enamel, and he was completely ignorant of much work along the same lines that had been carried on by Alexander Parkes, Daniel Spill, and other good chemists. None of these men, however, had had the courage to try molding guncotton by heat and pressure. Indeed, such a method appears to be a first-class way of committing suicide. Probably Hyatt lacked the means of combining high temperatures with great pressures, but even so, it is hard to see why John Wesley Hyatt was not blown to Kingdom Come. We also do not know just how he hit upon the idea that camphor and a little alcohol added to the nitrocellulose would serve as a plasticizer, creating Celluloid.

After he had learned to make and manipulate this strange material, his brother, Isaiah — from the names of his sons one suspects that Blacksmith Hyatt was a good orthodox Methodist — went down to New York to raise capital. Their pressed-wood business had prospered enough to take John away from the type cases and galleys forever, but it did not provide much surplus over operating costs and the proprietors' living expenses. From the first Isaiah saw this plastics business in much truer perspective than John, and his infectious enthusiasm interested the successful head of a very distinguished Long Island family.

The pioneering blood of his Dutch ancestors who settled in the wilds of Brooklyn in 1660 had not run thin in the veins of Colonel Marshall Lefferts. He himself pioneered in the establishment of the telegraph, constructing the lines between New York and Boston and Buffalo. Later he became president of the American Telegraph Company and built up one of the earliest large industrial organizations of the country. On the side he had a partnership in an importing house and was the owner of an ironworks. He devised many early instruments for the telegraph system and perfected the first practical method of galvanizing sheet iron. During the Civil War he was Colonel of the New York 7th Regiment, the famous " Dandy Seventh "; a big, handsome figure of a man, packed with energy, a strict disciplinarian, who nevertheless was never known to have lost his temper. He amassed a comfortable fortune.

It was Marshall Lefferts who saw the possibilities in this new material, Celluloid, and who backed it liberally. He relished a joke and delighted to tell how his bankers and his friends all pooh-poohed this new chemical idea, chiding him with recklessness, foretelling failure. He could well afford to laugh at their conservatism. The Celluloid Corporation was an enormous success. For thirty years it paid astonishing dividends.

A plant was built at Newark, New Jersey, and during the winter of 1872–3 the Hyatts moved down from Albany. John worked early and late designing all the special machinery needed to produce the pyroxylin plastic on a large scale, and during the next few years he continued to devise many machines for fabricating commercial articles and novelties out of Celluloid.

About 1880 Hyatt became interested in the purification of water by means of chemical coagulants. It was not a new idea, but till his time the process was clumsy, requiring large tanks in which the water had to stand many hours while the chemicals precipitated the sediments to the bottom. With his brother he devised a system whereby the coagulants were added to the water while on the way to a special filter. This eliminated the settling basin and saved much time, especially as the filter could be cleaned quickly and simply by reversing the flow of the water through it. Many paper and textile mills installed these Hyatt filters and the invention proved quite profitable. In 1891 the Hyatt roller-bearing was patented. This clever adaptation of the ball-bearing idea was his biggest money-maker, for he had in the meanwhile sold out his Celluloid interests to the Lefferts family.

As long as he lived Hyatt could no more stop inventing than he could stop breathing, and among many others he scored notable successes with a more economical sugar mill and a monstrous sewing machine for fabric machine belting. In the chemical field he put together a combination of bone and silica into a plastic compound and discovered a process for solidifying hardwoods for use in bowling balls, golf-club heads, mallets, etc. It is worth while to make a special mental note of that bone-silica compound.

Colonel Lefferts died on July 3, 1876, suddenly, of a heart attack while on his way to Philadelphia, where he was to lead his regiment in the parade at the opening of the Centennial Exposition. As head of the Celluloid Company he was succeeded by his son, Marshall C. Lefferts.

Their plastic was meanwhile marching on, invading new fields every year, upsetting all sorts of traditions. It was offered to the trade in sheets, rods, and tubes of various dimensions. It could be had in glossy jet black or opaque milky white or crystal clear; in all the colors and combinations of colors of the solar spectrum. It could be made to simulate tortoise-shell, coral, ivory, marble, onyx, agate, lapis, or turquoise matrix. It imitated perfectly either clear or cloudy amber.

In the workshop there had never been so versatile a raw material. It could be cut, sawed, drilled, milled, machined with any ordinary woodworking equipment. It softened when heated and could be molded into shapes which it retained upon cooling. It might be dipped over wooden cores or blown in bronze molds to produce lightweight hollow articles. Several excellent cements were discovered to fasten parts together or mend broken pieces.

Cellulose scrap could be recovered and reused. It was markedly cheaper than almost all of the natural products whose appearance it imitated so successfully. Furthermore its fabrication was notably less expensive than the manufacture of similar articles out of all other materials, with the possible exception of wood. It required no finishing, no painting, no polishing.

Celluloid has its faults. The worst of these is its inflammability. In the early days it was quite as easy to send it off in a flash and a puff of smoke as it had been to explode the Count de Chardonnet's nitrocellulose imitation silk. This

grievous fault has never been entirely cured, but the addition
of ammonium phosphate and other fire-retarding ingredients
have materially cut down this hazard. The flexibility of Celluloid, which is relatively great, is an advantage in that it
reduces the chances of breakage; but it is a distinct disad-
vantage when one wants accurately to machine it. Likewise
its high shrinkage during molding makes it almost impossible
to produce from Celluloid interchangeable parts or parts that
require exact fitting. This failure is exaggerated by the fact
that Celluloid continues to shrink a little long after it has
been molded and then cooled. While its mechanical strength
is fairly good, it is an infamously poor heat-resistant material.
In fact, its softening point is so low that Celluloid cannot even
be used in hot water.

Despite these shortcomings, however, Celluloid opened
the eyes of industry to the possibilities that might be found
in synthetic materials for manufacturing purposes. D. H. Killeffer, chemical editor of the *Scientific American*, was one of
the first to point out how poorly many of our natural raw
materials are adapted to the streamlined industrial processes
of modern production. Uniformity is vital in the interchange-
able-parts system that makes the belt-line assembly of the
automobile or the airplane or the rifle or the carpet-sweeper
possible. It requires that all variations be taken out of the
raw materials, an expensive task of sorting, or averaging, or
even of chemical purification.

Moreover, aside from this, the natural materials must still
be fabricated by essentially handicraft methods. Wood must
be whittled. Stone must be chipped. Metals must be pounded.
Our most cunning machines, automatic almost to the point
of displaying human intelligence, are essentially performing
these operations of whittling, chipping, pounding. And these
operations are discontinuous, not very adaptable to high-
speed, continuous manufacturing systems.

Compare the patient cutting, boring, polishing of grand-

mother's amber beads with the almost instantaneous molding of plastic beads for our daughters' costume jewelry and you will comprehend Killeffer's meaning. It is not only the difference in the intrinsic value of amber, which is based on its scarcity, and of a plastic molding powder, which becomes cheaper the more it is in demand; but there are also enormous differences in time and in human labor, savings that put the modern product on the counter of the " five-and-ten."

Certainly all of this is not pure gain. We have lost certain valuable skills and precious satisfactions that were enjoyed by both the craftsman and his customers. We have learned new skills and found different satisfactions; and all of us, rich and poor, have gained an immeasurable material wealth. But, even from the chemical point of view, all this is still the subject of warm debate. However you may wish to interpret all the sociological implications of the synthetics, industrially it is indisputable that Celluloid was the pioneer of this new type of fabricating material, the herald of the Plastic Age.

First paper, next guncotton and collodion, followed by rayon, then Celluloid, and now we come to the final link in the chain of progress in man's use of cellulose, the pyroxylin lacquers. One would be hard put to it to name any raw material that has made more significant contributions to our civilization than cellulose. Even iron, coal, and petroleum, great as their gifts have been, have not brought to us such a variety of benefits.

First paper: Shakespeare has said it for us: " He hath not eaten paper, as it were; he hath not drunk ink: his intellect is not replenished: he is only an animal, only sensible in the duller parts." Next guncotton — and if explosives have been perverted to uses of destruction, remember that over the years we employ more tons of them for getting out coal and iron, copper and zinc, for digging tunnels and leveling highways, than were ever used in war, and do not forget those eight thousand hapless slaves driven to death by stinging lashes that the Emperor's aqueduct might come straight through the mountain to Rome. In collodion were found medicinal agents and the secret of man-made fibers, motion-picture films, safety glass, sanitary wrappings, and new coatings which have helped make the cheap automobile possible and which literally save us millions of dollars' worth of iron and wood from the ancient enemies rust and corruption.

The first man to dissolve cellulose in the form of nitro-cellulose in a mixture of ether and alcohol was Louis Nicolas Menard, who was a better artist than chemist. The idea must have popped into his fertile brain that here was a promising material to varnish his imaginative Barbizon landscapes. Likely enough he tried it out, and what a mess he must have made! Alcohol and ether are not correct lacquer solvents. They do not evaporate quickly to leave a smooth, hard, clear film of cellulose. That was the rub, the right solvents. Many a chemist gummed up his fingers seeking liquids that would make cellulose a rival of shellac and the varnish gums.

Shortly before the first World War two such were found: amyl acetate, better known to most of us as " banana oil," and fusel oil, an indefinite mixture of amyl, butyl, and propyl alcohols produced along with good potable ethyl alcohol during the fermentation of whisky. These other alcohols of un-pleasant smell and flavor are partly removed by careful distillation and partly by the aging process, during which they either evaporate or are absorbed in the wooden cask. Chemically amyl acetate and amyl alcohol are both perfectly good pyroxylin solvents for lacquer purposes. Commercially they were impractical because of limited supply.

Amyl acetate was at that time prepared from the fusel oil, and the bottleneck was in the whisky distilleries. Even if the whole world decided to go on a permanent whisky spree — which when we look at the world today might not be such a bad idea — there would not be available sufficient fusel oil to make enough lacquer to keep the Ford " paint shop " running fifty-six hours. Produced now largely by synthetic chemical processes, amyl acetate is still used as a special solvent for particular coatings. You will recognize now the atrocious banana-like perfuming of the living-room when the painter "bronzes" the radiators. But before nitrocellulose lacquers could become industrial coatings, either the supply of amyl compounds would have to be greatly increased and their price much reduced or some other cheap, abundant pyroxylin solvent discovered. Here was again the same sort of chemical puzzle that baffled the Germans in their synthesis of indigo and that delayed for so many years the wider use of synthetic vanillin.

Francis P. Garvan was not quite within the strict limits of actual fact when he said that a coal-tar chemical industry was all that the United States got out of World War I. We also salvaged the modern lacquers out of our surplus war materials.

At that time everybody and his wife and children knew all about the shortages of dyes, of potash for fertilizers, and of certain coal-tar medicinals; but there were shortages of other key chemical products that did not get into the newspaper headlines for the very excellent reason that it was not smart military policy to let the enemy know too much about the Allies' weaknesses and how they were being bolstered up. One of these famine chemicals was acetone.

Germans and Allies alike underestimated the enormous chemical demands of modern warfare. In the case of the English the mistake in anticipated requirements for acetone was particularly serious. Not only was acetone vital to the production of the cordite which loaded their smallarms cartridges and the big shells of the Navy; it was also needed for "aeroplane dope" and for tear gas.

The principal source of acetone was then the wood chemical industry of the United States. When well-seasoned hardwood is thrust into a great iron kiln and subjected to destructive distillation, it produces besides methanol (wood alcohol) and charcoal, a crude acetic acid (vinegar) from which acetone can be recovered. The average yield of acetone is about fifty pounds to the cord of wood, and the total American yearly output was then about ten and a half million pounds. That sizable total was about a fifth of British war requirements. A wood-distillation plant with acetone-recovery equipment required an initial investment of about $3,000 per cord capacity, a hopeless overhead charge even when judged by war-time cost and necessity. Furthermore, any wholesale expansion of the wood chemical industry's capacity would have been utterly impractical. Only seasoned wood can be efficiently used, and the cutting and hauling of the raw material involved more men than were available.

There are two other chemical methods of making acetone. In the age-old, natural process of making vinegar, ethyl alcohol oxidizes to acetic acid. Calcium carbide treated with water produces acetylene (the basis of the old Presto-lite lighting systems of the primitive automobiles), and this acetylene can be converted to acetic acid. Made by either of these processes acetic acid plus limestone equals calcium acetate, which can be changed to acetone as is done in the original wood process. Both these processes were put to work. Still the supply was inadequate.

To make a bad situation desperate, in the battle off the coast of South America British naval officers discovered with dismay that there was something radically wrong with their ammunition. Shells fired for a range of 5,000 yards plunged into the ocean halfway to the enemy ship. An Admiralty Board of Inquiry fixed the blame on the poor quality of the acetone used as a stabilizer in the loading charge.

In the depth of the dark days of the gloomy winter of 1916 somebody thought of a clever Jewish chemist, professor at the University of Manchester, who might help. He had been monkeying with odd fermentations, trying to synthesize rubber or something, and there was some gossip of his having found acetone when he wanted something else. It was all rather nebulous, but grasping at straws, Dr. Chaim Weizmann was summoned to London.

Yes, indeed, he had obtained acetone by fermentation.

How? And could he do it again? And how quickly? — the questions shot at him like bullets from a machine-gun.

Quietly he explained that he was interested in rubber synthesis and he believed that if he could get a plentiful supply of butyl alcohol at low cost he should be able to work out a commercial process from butadiene. The ordinary fermentation of sugar or starch produces ethyl alcohol, but other bacteria had been noted from time to time that changed these carbohydrates into different alcohols. Accordingly, he had been searching for some bacteria that would produce butyl alcohol. He had found one, but unfortunately it also produced acetone: twice as much butyl alcohol as acetone, so that the yield appeared to be satisfactory enough to make his proposed rubber synthesis at least a promising possibility.

Never mind the butyl alcohol — what about the acetone?

He did not know. At least he could not be sure. He had not had time to isolate the bacteria that caused this strange type of fermentation. He had cultures; but one must have pure cultures to be certain, and obviously a pure culture would be necessary if the process was to be worked on a large scale.

Working under imperative orders to find the answers to all those questions, Dr. Weizmann found himself two days later in the famous Admiralty Laboratories with every possible facility at his beck and call. He is a man of prodigious powers, a stocky little Jew, packed with energy and determination. Within the month he had identified the strange bacteria, *Clostridum acetobutylicum Weizmann.* He had studied its habits and knew just the kind of mash (a thin soup of cooked, ground corn) that it liked best. He had carried on many distillations and figured accurately the yields of

butyl alcohol and acetone. It is a tradition that he worked on
the average about twenty hours a day during that month.

The British Minister of Munitions commandeered six
whisky distilleries and converted them to butyl-acetone
plants. As the U-boat campaign progressed, to conserve
edible corn in England similar plants were established in
Canada and India, and after we entered the war the British
bought a distillery at Terre Haute, Indiana, in the midst of
our Corn Belt, and our Government took over a similar plant
near by.

Chaim Weizmann had solved the British acetone problem
and Lloyd George sent for him. He richly deserved the thanks
of the nation, and the Prime Minister offered to recommend
him to the King for any honors he might wish.

" I have not the least desire to become Sir Chaim," protested Weizmann smiling at the very idea.

" A baronetcy, perhaps? " suggested Lloyd George.

" No, no. Believe me, I do not want any title."

" Ah yes, of course, I understand. How about a monetary
grant? Shall we say a hundred thousand guineas? "

" A hundred thousand — what would I do with so much
money? I do not need it."

" You are a real scientist, indeed," exclaimed the statesman.
" Let us show our gratitude by making it possible for you to
pursue your chemical studies in comfort all the days of your
life. Let me suggest to His Majesty an annuity — a generous
pension."

" Thank you. I thank you sincerely; but I do not want
money."

" What then do you want? " cried the astonished statesman.

" I want but one thing. I have wanted it a long time, ever
since I was a little boy in Russia. For a long time, too, I have
been convinced that it can come only from the British
Government."

Lloyd George was puzzled. What sort of man was this who

refused titles and money? The Welshman's caution was roused and he asked softly, " What is it, Dr. Weizmann, that you have wanted so long? "

" I want a national home for my people. Promise me that you will use your influence to give Palestine back to the Hebrews."

The Prime Minister was startled. Only the day before, it had been urged at the Cabinet meeting that it would be good international politics for Britain to adopt such a position. The Cabinet had not agreed. He himself was undecided. He looked at the earnest little man across his desk, and he made up his mind. Three weeks later the Balfour Declaration, promising that England would restore Palestine to the Jews, was made public.

Today Chaim Weizmann, a good deal more bald, but with the same little Vandyke beard, the same eager mannerisms, the same unflagging industry, the same dogged perseverance, lives in a beautiful home adjoining a perfectly equipped chemical laboratory at Rehoboth in Palestine. He is the true head of the Zionist movement throughout the world and ex-officio chief chemist of all the Jewish industries in Palestine. Today these are both important posts. The man who holds them is a world figure. More than ever, viewing the desperate plight of his people all over Europe, Dr. Weizmann is convinced that Zionism is a vital, a sorely needed movement, an inspiration and a haven. He is still the chemist, and no man has done more to develop the agriculture and the industries of Palestine. All Jews do not agree with him, but he still believes that their dream of the rehabilitation of the Hebrew nation in Palestine can only come true with the assistance of Great Britain, and he still has faith in the British pledges.

At the close of the war most of the Weizmann acetone plants shut down, but the American operations at Terre Haute and Peoria were bought from the Allied War Board by a small group of far-sighted capitalists who organized the

Commercial Solvents Company. Their business promptly
proceeded to go through one of those rapid transformations
which so distress bankers who shudder at technological
changes that disturb established equities and so delight
chemists who know that progress must mean change. Such
revolutionary transformations are a conspicuous feature of
the business of making molecules.

The war-time operation of these plants had been carried
on to produce acetone. The two-for-one output of butyl alcohol had been regarded as a bothersome waste. Small quantities of it had been used experimentally as a makeshift solvent
for airplane wing dope and a good deal had been chemically
turned into methyl-ethyl-ketone, which was in demand for
the manufacture of smokeless powder. Most of the stock,
however, had accumulated in storage tanks.

The war ended, as you remember, abruptly with the Armistice of November 11, 1918. Our Government forthwith suspended all work on plant construction; issued stop orders
against all current shipments of war materials; canceled all
contracts for future deliveries. Shortly afterwards they began
selling their surplus war supplies at public auction. These
prompt, drastic actions threw the chemical industry into a
whirlpool of confusion.

Following the Government's lead, obligations for equipment and raw materials were abrogated and deliveries were
refused point-blank. Many lawsuits naturally followed. Great
piles of surplus chemicals of many kinds hung perilously over
the market. Prices were demoralized. Our enormously expanded plant capacity for chemical production was turned
almost overnight from a pride and joy into a monstrous fear.
Yet looking back now on all that confusion and distress, we
can see that this incisive amputation of the whole war demand assisted a quicker, more healthy recovery.

Out of the great stocks of nitrocellulose that could be
bought at distressed prices was built the modern coatings

industry. Those tentative, makeshift experiments with butyl alcohol as a pyroxylin solvent for airplane dope led to careful work which demonstrated that at last an appropriate lacquer solvent had been found. Butyl alcohol worked well in nitro-cellulose lacquer formulas. It could be produced by the Weizmann process in any quantities that might be demanded. It was cheap and it was immediately available. The management of the new-born Commercial Solvents Company found suddenly that their former by-product had become their main product. Their acetone was now the by-product, almost a drug on the market. Like Minerva from the aching head of Jupiter, the cellulose lacquer industry sprang into existence out of the stock piles of nitrated cotton and butyl alcohol.

This new-born industry would have died of starvation if just at this time a great new demand for lacquers had not been created. The American automobile industry was just swinging into the stride of mass production. The six million motor cars made during the last year of the war more than doubled in 1923 and trebled by 1925. Henry Ford began applying the principle of interchangeable parts, devised by Eli Whitney to speed up production of rifles during the Civil War, and the assembly-belt system was being gradually built up. It jammed at the end when it ran into a " paint job " that was a relic of the horse and buggy era of industry.

Grandfather's brougham was a custom-made job, a triumph of the carriage-maker's art and skill. Its deep bottle-green finish was achieved by applying coat upon coat of fine varnish, each one baked and then rubbed down from top to spokes with oil and pumice. These operations were repeated at least half a dozen times. A thoroughly good job took six weeks. Now six weeks at the end of an automobile assembly line might just as well be six months.

It resulted in an intolerable delay that held up both production and prices. Automobile executives lay awake nights scheming to smash this jam. They resorted to all sorts of expedients, skimping here and cutting corners there, till the customers complained that deep maroons turned a delicate pink, that blacks and greens mottled to an effect that imitated a dapple-gray pony; that the varnish left hoods and fenders as skin peels off a sunburned nose. They were right. Nobody expected a " paint job " to last through the four seasons of a single year. It was a depressing situation for everyone.

What was obviously needed was a new kind of finish. Varnish was excellent over wood, but it developed more faults than a balky mule when applied to metal. Something that clung closer and dried faster was needed, and research was busy trying to find that new coating.

Just about this time one of the big executives of General Motors drove a young engineer named Charles Kettering downtown from the plant to lunch at the Detroit Club. On the way he wished that he might have his car refinished, but added that he simply could not afford to have it laid up three weeks.

" What color would you pick, if you could do it over? " asked Kettering.

" Black. This red fades so that it looks shabby in no time at all."

It was a protracted luncheon with much discussion of many engineering problems that were engaging the research department's energies. Kettering does not admit unduly stringing out that conference, but though he dearly loves a joke, he is also a cautious man. No doubt he was certain that the car had been returned from the experimental laboratory before they left the table. When they walked down the front steps, there it stood, no longer a shabby red, but new-finished a glossy black. It was an impressive demonstration of what the new lacquer finishes could do.

The pyroxylin lacquers not only broke the jam at the end of the automobile assembly line, but smashed also the ancient traditions of the paint and varnish industry. For rule-of-thumb methods they substituted chemical processes. Butyl alcohol was quickly followed by other solvents. Plasticizers were found that make the coating film tougher, more flexible, more adhesive to the metal surface. Lake colors prepared from coal-tar dyes, and later even the dyes themselves, took the place of the old natural mineral pigments. The time of drying was further speeded up. Paints and varnishes, purely physical mixtures of natural raw materials — linseed oil, turpentine, wood alcohol, pigments, shellac, and varnish gums — began to be superseded by elaborately formulated chemical compounds made from nitrocellulose, butyl acetate, tricresyl phosphate, ethyl and butyl phthalates, and others whose very names sounded as strange and uncouth as Choctaw or Hindustani to the old paint-grinder and varnish-cook. Modern coatings — made of chemicals by chemical processes and under chemical control — had arrived. Another new industry had been born.

CHAPTER XIX

MATERIALS FOR TOMORROW

◇◇◇

HORATIO ALGER enshrined in 119 books the American tradition of the office boy who marries the beautiful daughter of the big boss and becomes president of the First National Bank. The theme is changeless as the laws of the Medes and Persians: unflagging industry, perseverance in the face of insurmountable obstacles, virtue that succumbs to no temptations, win a sure reward right here on earth. The tale in the telling is one of infinite variety.

But this fecund author never hit upon the plot of the young chemical laboratory assistant who married his chemistry professor's daughter and invented Velox and Bakelite. Which goes to show that, after all, truth is stranger — sometimes — than fiction.

Leo Hendrik Baekeland was born on November 14, 1863, in the old Flemish city of Ghent, of poor but honest parents who made great sacrifices that their son should receive a splendid education. (From the very beginning, you see, the story is quite orthodox.) He was a brilliant student and was graduated at sixteen from the public high school with honors. At the University of Ghent, where he partly supported himself by tutoring less apt pupils and by serving as bottlewasher for the professor of chemistry, he accumulated more academic distinctions. He headed his class and won the Doctor of Science degree, *summa cum laude,* two years later in

1884. During his post-graduate work he was made instructor in chemistry and as soon as he had his doctorate he was appointed assistant professor. He had fallen in love with the pretty daughter of Professor Swarts, the head of his department. So to eke out his modest salary he took on in addition to his duties at the university the post of professor of chemistry and physics at the Government Normal School in Bruges. In 1887 he was named the Laureate of the four Belgian universities, a distinguished award made to promising young scholars, carrying with it a gold medal and a two years' traveling scholarship. Every sign pointed towards an academic career. One conjures up the picture of a serious-minded young man driven to extraordinary efforts by ambition and love.

It is a shock, therefore, to learn that the youthful Baekeland impressed a fellow American student as a jolly, happy-go-lucky chap who had come to Berlin, not to improve the opportunities offered by the great Technische Hochschule, but to see the sights and enjoy the night life of the German capital. Later Charles Herty was to revise this opinion, but when he and the big Flemish boy-professor first met in the Charlottenburg laboratories, he seemed to the hard-working youngster from Georgia to be a great grasshopper in a hill of busy ants. Evidently Baekeland carried both his high honors and his profound knowledge of chemistry lightly; but as Herty came to know him better, he learned that for all his casual manner, nothing escaped him in the lecture room and he managed somehow or other to get through an amazing quantity of first-class laboratory work.

"My real education began," Baekeland himself confessed years later, "only after I left the university and was confronted with the big problems and grave responsibilities of practical life, and this education I received mainly in the United States. I hope to remain, until I die, a post-graduate student in that greater school of practical life which has no

fixed curriculum and where no academic degrees are conferred, but where wrong, petty theories are quickly cured by
hard knocks."

This sounds suspiciously like the soliloquy of an Alger hero
in the last chapter. But it may well be true, for towards the
close of his traveling scholarship Baekeland returned to
Ghent, married Celine Swarts, and came to the United States
on a sort of combined honeymoon and scouting expedition.
He had by this time definitely made up his mind to renounce
an academic career. His reasons were chiefly financial, and
where was a better place to win a fortune than in the United
States?

Amateur photography had long been one of his hobbies,
and it was quite natural with his training that he should have
delved into the then mysterious chemistry of photography.
At a Camera Club meeting he met Richard A. Anthony, of
E. and H. T. Anthony and Company, manufacturers of photographic supplies, who promptly offered him a job as chemist.
Baekeland accepted and wrote to the Belgian Minister of
Education resigning his associate professorship at the University of Ghent. After two years with the Anthony firm he
resigned.

He had come to the second great decision of his younger
life, a resolve to work for himself. He opened an office and
small laboratory and hung out his shingle as consulting chemist. He had little money and few clients, but a great many
chemical ideas.

" I tried to work out several half-baked inventions," he has
explained; " the development of any one of them would have
required a small fortune. Fortunately for me, I was taken out
of this muddle by a serious illness that nailed me to my bed
for several months. Hovering 'twixt life and death, all my
cash gone, and with the uncomfortable certainty of rapidly
increasing debts, I had abundant time and good reason for
sober reflection. It then dawned upon me that instead of

keeping so many irons in the fire, I should concentrate upon the one single thing which offered the best chance for the quickest possible results."

Thus he came to the third turning-point in his career. His enforced period of reflection was employed to excellent effect. Since his student days he had been playing with the chemistry of photographic printing, and now he decided that his idea of a photographic paper which could be printed in artificial light was that one single thing which offered the greatest commercial possibilities in the least time. Velox was the result.

Holding fast to his resolution to work for himself, he did not peddle his invention for sale to any of the established makers of photographic supplies. He took to himself a partner, Leonard Jacobi of Yonkers, New York, who supplied the working capital for the Nepera Chemical Company, organized to make and market Baekeland's new photographic paper. They went first to the professional photographers, as offering the largest, most concentrated market, and ran up against that same conservatism that forced Muspratt to introduce soda ash to the English soapmakers by giving it away. Accustomed to sunlight printing, the professionals were reluctant to experiment. So Baekeland went to the amateurs and found them less conservative, and eager for any means of riding their hobby horses in the evenings. Gradually the new paper, which at first created so little interest, began to be discussed. Steadily the sales mounted.

Baekeland received a letter from George Eastman, who with typical frankness wrote that he was interested in buying Velox. " If you are interested in selling," the letter concluded, " come up to Rochester. We can talk it over and I am sure come to terms."

Being a good Fleming, Baekeland left the letter unanswered several days. It would not do to appear too anxious. Then he replied that he was perfectly willing to sell — for a price — and that he would be in Rochester the following Tuesday.

But for what price? The question gnawed at his brain day and night. All the way up on the New York Central sleeper he lay awake, adding up cost figures, figuring probable profits, wondering what the Kodak organization could do in the way of increased sales, speculating what Eastman would pay. Not till the train pulled into Rochester did he come to a decision. He would ask $50,000; he would not accept less than $25,000.

During breakfast at the Hotel Seneca and while driving out to the Kodak offices, he rehearsed question and answer of the forthcoming interview. He would be bold. He would be firm. Fifty and not less than twenty-five.

He was ushered at once to Mr. Eastman's private office and was greeted warmly: " Dr. Baekeland, I am delighted to meet you. You have a perfectly wonderful thing in that Velox paper of yours — wonderful, full of possibilities. I have the greatest admiration for your accomplishment. Won't you be seated? "

Baekeland sank weakly into a chair. This was not what he had expected from the man he knew well was a ruthless, powerful competitor bent upon dominating the camera field. None of his carefully planned speeches fitted this opening.

" Will you take a million dollars for Velox? "

It was fortunate that Baekeland was seated else he would have sunk through the floor.

Leo Baekeland now had ample means " to see the sights and enjoy the night life," as his friend Herty had suggested he might, for he is a man who lives with zest and relish. He did retire — to his laboratory in the rear of his home in Yonkers. He sat down again to figure out what was the most likely chemical idea that he could develop in the shortest time. He picked what an enthusiastic schoolboy would describe as a " lulu," an old chemical problem that many a good man had failed to solve; and the first thing he did was to repeat deliberately all the mistakes that his predecessors in this research had committed. He wanted to find out what not to do. Then he methodically went about learning what to do.

Like the Count de Chardonnet he set out to rival an insect, a minute bug, *Coccus lacca,* a native of India, which sucks the sap at the end of the twigs of certain types of fig trees, coating himself with a red resin, shellac. It takes 150,000 of these lac insects to produce one pound of shellac. We import some 40,000,000 of the 65,000,000 pounds total produced each year. In other words, Dr. Baekeland proposed to put about 10,000,000,000,000 lac bugs out of business by synthesizing a better varnish resin than their shellac.

Leo Baekeland is a fascinatingly contradictory personality — a true scientist who is a successful executive, a philosopher who is a poet. His big frame, slow movements, and careful speech hide the fiery vitality that burns within. He is friendly, humorous, a delightful companion full of pleasant little social graces; but he is stubbornly determined and capable of intense concentration focused upon a single objective for a long time. His approach to a chemical problem is a curious combination of scientific curiosity and commercial realism. The results of his researches have been sensationally successful.

When he came to grips with the problem of making a synthetic resin, he knew perfectly well that he was in for a nasty job. " Nasty " is the right adjective. A tarry mess which does not form crystals and cannot be dissolved can only be analyzed with exceeding great difficulty. If you do not know what you have in your test tube and how its molecules are constructed, you must work by the " by guess and by gosh " method. You become a sort of twentieth-century witch doctor brewing charms, which is neither scientific nor satisfactory. The chemical literature of the past century is full of records that such and such reactions " resulted in the formation of an uncrystallizable tar which was not investigated further." That means that a disgusted chemist dropped the mess in his laboratory slop jar and went on to something else.

As far back as 1871 the illustrious Adolf von Baeyer — he of synthetic-indigo fame — had investigated the reactions of several different phenols and aldehydes, members of the same two chemical groups that contain our familiar disinfectants, carbolic acid and formaldehyde. He had found them bad: that is to say, they formed tarlike substances that hardened into insoluble resin-like masses. Other good chemists, notably Kleeberg in the early nineties, gummed up their flasks and beakers with these shapeless, infusible, insoluble messes and consigned them to the drains.

Baekeland read all their notes. He had plenty of time. He repeated their experiments. He convinced himself that the chemical way to a synthetic shellac of commercial possibilities lay in the reaction of phenol and formaldehyde. Both were cheap and available, said his practical self. The scientist in him believed there was some way to control that reaction. He knew they combined and polymerized to join little molecules into big ones, and he was certain that the secret lay in stopping the polymerization at the right point. The trouble was that when the two reacted, almost anything might happen.

Baekeland's long hunt began by trying out every possible solvent. Nothing dissolved this phenol-formaldehyde gunk. For several months he experimented trying to impregnate various woods in the golden hope that he might thus transform hemlock into ebony, pine into indestructible zapote. Instead of hardening the woods, it softened them. He went back to the start again and instead of formaldehyde he tried out all the other methylene compounds. He found any of them could be used, and he began to get some suggestive variations. He tried adding small quantities of acids and alkalies. The former kept his messy product soft; the bases made it harder and reduced the violent foaming during the reaction so that his product looked less like a sponge cake. He filled notebook after notebook with carefully observed facts, some of which we shall see he was able to put to good use later, but he had not got anything like the product he sought.

Then one day there suddenly registered in the pragmatic section of his brain a new plan of attack. If these substances are so damnably tough, why not make a virtue out of this vice? He stopped endeavoring to make a shellac substitute and sought a resin that could be cast or molded into definite forms — one that would remain forever unchangeable in shape and substance, an unbelievably tough stuff. The world could use such a material.

Jubilantly he went to work anew. With the fresh objective in view he reversed his former methods. Previously he had been trying to hold down the violent reaction. Now he would step it up by every chemical and physical means at his command.

Day after day, late into the night, he tried out various chemicals to accelerate the union of phenol and formaldehyde. Where he had used cooling devices he now applied heat. He combined heat with pressure, and put into an autoclave, a sort of sealed kettle, equal parts of the two reagents, pumped in air, brought the temperature up to 200° Centigrade. Instead of the customary tarry mass he obtained a clear liquid which promptly solidified. He turned over the little retort and out plopped a clear, sparkling hemisphere, a miniature beehive of beautiful amber, its surface engraved with a perfect reproduction of the seam and bolt heads where the vessel had been joined together. The liquid had set perfectly, frozen as it were; obviously a grand molding material.

Eagerly he investigated its chemical and physical properties. It looked like amber, but it was much harder. He could not dissolve it. It did not absorb water. It cut with a knife, so he imagined that it could be machined. It was a poor conductor of heat and a worse one of electricity. It did not change its shape nor its substance. Now he was getting somewhere.

For the next two years Baekeland continued to work on this new resin-like material. Different alkalies, different pressures, different temperatures modified its characteristics. He wanted the best combination. He must learn how to use it, press it, machine it, try it out in every possible way so as to uncover its weaknesses and explore its possibilities. His neighbors noted that night after night the lights burned brightly in his laboratory till long after midnight. He took out over four hundred different patents.

During this period of patient trial, his old friend of the carefree student days in Berlin visited him. Herty, too, was making a name for himself. After the year at Zürich and Berlin he had come back to a teaching post at his alma mater, the University of Georgia, and began his study of the turpentine industry, which resulted in his invention of the famous Herty cup for collecting the resinous sap of the Southern pines. He had not sold this idea to a George Eastman for a fortune, but his patents produced a pleasant addition to his salary as professor of chemistry at North Carolina.

Proud as a mother of her new baby, Baekeland showed Herty billiard balls, phonograph records, a pair of dumbbells, electrical switches, a score of different-shaped cups and bowls, all made of his new material. He bounced the balls on the floor, threw the record into the corner, poured acids and alkalies into the containers, staging a pretty little informal demonstration of its astonishing toughness. He boasted that he had counted up as many as forty different industries which could make good use of this strong, inert material. Herty suggested a couple of additional ones. Neither of them dreamed that thirty years later it would be hard to name any industry that did not make use of this material. Both were chemists of exceptional vision, but they had no conception whatever of the importance of this discovery, of the multiplicity of synthetic plastic materials that were to be developed, or the repercussions of the introduction of these new materials, handled by a new fabricating technique, upon our entire manufacturing economy.

In a general way we all of us know what a plastic is. We ought to, for Nature made plastics long before man's most remote ancestor appeared on earth, say roughly 150,000,000 years ago, or four times as long ago as the silkworm began spinning cocoons. Admittedly that is a rough estimate, but what are a few million years between a pair of geologists arguing the chronology of the Paleozoic Era? At all events it was a long, long time ago, as we measure time in annual circuits around the sun, when the first evergreen, cone-bearing tree flourished on earth. These coniferous trees were distinguished then, as now, by needles instead of leaves and by the resinous sap they exude when the bark is bruised or broken. Amber and the best, hardest varnish gums, copal and kauri, are fossil resins from prehistoric pine trees dug out of the ground. Kauri oil is obtained by distilling the peat which remains from the antediluvian forests of kauri trees, a conifer that still abounds in New Zealand.

The caveman polished and bored and strung amber beads as early in his career as he chipped stone arrowheads. Before the Babylonians and the Egyptians and the Chinese, the Sumerians made varnishes by dissolving resins and gums in wine. The Phœnicians were probably not the first to calk their ships with melted pine tar. Yet, for all this ancient familiarity with plastics, we find difficulty in defining them neatly and exactly.

We have picked up a perfectly good technical word and given it a number of indefinite meanings. " Plastic " literally applies to anything which possesses the physical property of plasticity; that is, anything that can be de-formed or reshaped under mechanical stress — pressing, pulling, twisting — without losing its coherence, and which keeps the new form given to it. Plastic materials are amorphous, not crystalline.

Applied to the molded articles — cups, ashtrays, and what not — " plastics " is a misnomer, for such rigid forms are in reality anything but plastic. Indeed, any material that is truly plastic at ordinary temperatures, as fresh putty or a gum eraser is plastic, could not possibly be used for the very articles most of us commonly think of as " plastics."

Such articles must be made out of substances that are either thermoplastic or thermosetting. Thermoplastic substances can be re-formed repeatedly by softening them with heat, like Celluloid. A thermosetting material, on the other hand, while originally formed by heat, becomes permanently infusible, like Bakelite, and, once set, cannot be re-formed.

By some three thousand years Hyatt and Baekeland were not the first to make a synthetic plastic of this type. By the curbstone definition, glass is a synthetic thermosetting plastic. It was discovered so long ago that we know as little about its origin as we do about the first smelting of ores or the earliest weaving of fibers. Pliny tells a good story about Phœnician sailors wrecked off the mouth of the Belus River with a cargo of natron from Egypt. Natron is a crude, natural form of sodium carbonate, the soda ash that Le Blanc learned to make economically and Muspratt introduced to the soap- and glass-makers of England. On the sandy shore they built a little fireplace out of the blocks of these soft, white stones. On this fireplace, in a great kettle, they cooked their evening meal. In the morning they found among the ashes tiny vitreous beads, glass made from the fusing of the silica of the sand and the alkali of the natron. This is the regular way to make glass; but, alas for the tale, this fusion takes place only at a temperature of 1,832 degrees. A picnic fire on the beach, even in a carefully built stone oven, does not generate half this heat. Still there must be something in the story. Glass must have been found first by some such lucky accident — probably in a charcoal fire fed by a bellows for smelting copper

or tin — and extensive glassworks, for which natron was imported from Egypt, were located on the banks of this same
Belus River during Roman times.

However man discovered glass, it was so long ago that we
quite forget its chemical origin and we never think of it as
a synthetic plastic. Yet today, under the quickening influence
of the chemists, glass is being tailor-made for special purposes and even, like the other plastics, being spun and
stretched into fibers for weaving.

Likewise we forget that while the great use of the natural
resins has for long ages been as protective and decorative
coatings — varnishes and lacquers — nevertheless molded articles have long been formed out of them. They have also
been employed as adhesives and for impregnating materials,
especially for impregnating fabrics. Half the shellac brought
into the United States goes into phonograph records, and
goodly quantities of it, and of the fossil varnish gums too, are
used in stiffening felt and straw hats and the canvas or burlap
backings of oilcloth and linoleum, in printing inks, for electrical insulation, as a binder of many things from match-heads
to structural cements.

All old stuff: some of it as old as the pyramids! So why
then, asks the inquiring citizen, all this pother about the new
synthetic resins? Because they no longer imitate the natural
resins, but offer unique combinations of more useful properties. Their thermoplastic and thermosetting characteristics,
for example, have created molded articles.

Dr. Baekeland may not have dreamed of half that lay hidden in his Bakelite, but during the long months when he
explored its possibilities he did not miss any of the great
essentials. When he introduced his chemical child to his
chemical peers at a meeting at the Chemists' Club in New
York, on February 6, 1909, he showed samples of molded
articles in both the " gadget " and the electrical fields and of
synthetic varnishes. Pipestems and cigarette-holders — imi-

tation amber — were the first Bakelite articles to reach the store counters. It was plastic electrical goods, however, that first invaded the industrial field. In those days of dusty, bumpy, jerky motoring, the chances were about three to one that it was " ignition trouble " that forced the driver to get out and get under. Most frequently the cause was a cracked distributor head. These, like the electrical connection plugs, were then made of porcelain. Exact-fitting parts were impossible. The material was as susceptible to shock as an old bachelor to flattery. Bakelite removed this nuisance. It can be molded to within two thousandths of an inch. Reinforced with a powdered wood filler, it is largely shock-proof. It is an even more perfect electrical non-conductor than porcelain. During the World War there was a big expansion of such uses in motor cars and airplanes. The famous Liberty motor featured a number of new efficiencies because of its use.

During that earlier struggle the frailties of the wood propeller made it an Achilles' heel of dangerous vulnerability. So the first step in the long development of the plastic airplane was made at the Westinghouse plant in East Pittsburgh when experts set out to design, make, and test a propeller of Bakelite. The first idea was to mold it, but this quickly proved impractical. Accordingly, laminated plastics had their first real trial. Sheet after sheet of Bakelite-impregnated canvas was hand-cut to fit the intricate pattern, each laid layer upon layer until the great bundle was placed in a mold matching the blueprints of the wooden wing to the last iota. The lid was clamped down; hydraulic power turned on; then heat.

It came out a perfectly good-looking propeller, smooth as glass, hard, the canvas weave visible beneath the thin plastic veneer. Because Bakelite has a higher specific gravity than wood, it was overweight for the exacting army specifications, and so they gambled on its strength and omitted the steel hub. It more than met all the tests that had proved wood a weakling. They spun it at 2,500 revolutions a minute and kept

In the viscid, reddish " gunk " that clogged his test tube Leo Baekeland saw all the beauty and utility of a true synthetic plastic.
— Courtesy Bakelite Corporation

it at top speed overnight. They ran it in a tunnel through which an air-blast blew sharp sand, and the Bakelite was unmarred in this synthetic sandstorm that tore the wood to shreds. They peppered it with twenty machine-gun bullets, which hopelessly shattered wood, and afterwards it ran without a murmur. All this was a sensational demonstration of that toughness the inventor had sought. Incidentally it was a grand publicity stunt that convinced many people that this new material was something a lot more important than an imitation amber cigarette-holder.

Phenol, primary ingredient of this new plastic, was an explosive necessity, for picric acid (tri-nitrophenol) was a favored ammunition of both the French and English. One of the great American triumphs of that war was our production of phenol. From scratch it reached over 100,000,000 pounds annual capacity, and when the Armistice was signed our Government had on hand a reserve stock of over 40,000,000 pounds. It was another case of triumph turned to problem.

On the morning of the first Armistice Day phenol was selling for 55 cents a pound. By New Year's it was offered at 8 cents, with few takers, for the only peace-time uses were in sheep dips, as a disinfectant, as raw material for aspirin, and other salicylates used in medicines; all told, about 3,000,000 pounds a year.

That 40,000,000-pound mountain of steel drums, packed full, not of the dilute, brownish liquid carbolic acid we get in the drug-stores, but of the concentrated, pinkish-white crystals of pure phenol, was turned over to the Monsanto Chemical Company to unload gradually. The price was set at the bargain figure of 12 cents. To everybody it looked like a five- or six-year job. Within two years that big stack of drums had vanished.

The phenol had gone into Bakelite. And the Bakelite had gone into radio receiving sets. In 1920 there were less than 12,000 radios in all American homes. By 1922 there were

100,000; by 1923, 500,000; by 1924, 1,550,000: and in 1940, 11,800,000 house sets and 7,500,000 automobile sets. As the radio grew, Bakelite became big business. From about 4,000,-000 pounds in 1920, our synthetic resin output has grown to 150,000,000 pounds in 1940.

Only half this tidy tonnage is now of phenol-formaldehyde resins of the general Bakelite type, for the Belgian chemist who became the American inventor had blazed a trail to another new industry. Other men found other plastic materials.

The hunt is still on and new materials with special qualifications of usefulness are found almost every year. The perfect plastic, the ideal synthetic coating, is still in the offing. Still every effort is being strained to discover cheaper raw materials, more economical processes. The future of the molded goods particularly depends now more and more upon their ability to compete on a cost basis with wood and metal and cement. The vision is of a plastic that can be extruded and set as the rayon and nylon filaments are pumped through the spinnerets. That would mean baseboards, moldings, paneling, window-frames, what not, fire- and warp-proof, that no termite nor mold would attack, that would never have to be painted.

Twenty years before Bakelite quite a different type of synthetic plastic material had been made for a special purpose. It is still produced for very special purposes. Dr. Adolf Spitteler of Hamburg was asked to produce a " white blackboard." He performed this legerdemain by pouring formaldehyde into the curds of sour milk. Thus he created the first casein-derived plastic, which every now and again puts Elsie Borden in the newspapers as a chemical worker and inspires jokes about the pounds of cheese used in the latest models at the automobile show. As a matter of fact, the casein plastics are now confined pretty strictly to the button field. Here, having ousted the ivory nuts from Brazil, they have almost a monopoly.

The phenol-formaldehyde compounds are still at the head of the class of moldable resins. However, another series, the urea-formaldehyde plastics, because of their crystal clarity, are a real rival. Not only glasslike objects, but also a fine array of goods in delicate pastel shades are thus possible. Both these series are distinguished by a characteristically rapid cure in the molding presses, an important cost factor in mass production.

Stockings out of coal, air, and water are hard enough to believe; but that the pretty blue cups and saucers in the picnic hamper are made literally out of four gases is a practical joke almost beyond the realm even of miracles. Yet it is a sober fact. Urea, which Wöhler synthesized out of mineral materials in the classic experiment, knocked the " vital element " out of organic chemistry. The laboratory-born chemical is now made by the ton by the reaction between ammonia and carbon dioxide. This ammonia is the gas which dissolved in water becomes the "household ammonia" in its round-topped, flat bottle with the rubber stopper. Formaldehyde is made from methyl alcohol, made in turn by the hydrogenation of the carbon dioxide: the gas of soda water treated with hydrogen gas. Thus the blue cups and the pretty white case of your new radio — charming things, but indubitably hard and solid — are products out of thin air.

During the past fifteen years another series of synthetic resins has become exceedingly important. A polybasic acid (the same prolific chemical group that combines with the polyamines to make nylon) reacts with a polyhydric alcohol (you remember the glycerin-mannitol family with a sense of moisture) to form resinous products.

These are the so-called alkyd resins which you can thank for coating your fenders with a finish that clings tightly even if your parked car is mauled by a passing truck. Not so long ago, if you but lightly flicked the edge of the garage door, you flaked off a chip of lacquer as big as your hand. That expresses all the difference between the two types of finish. A lacquer, or spirit varnish, is simply a solution of a resin in a volatile solvent which evaporates, leaving behind a thin film. An oil varnish is a combination of drying oil with a resin dissolved in it. Both are combined in the resulting film. The drying oil alone leaves a film, which is tough, adhesive, and elastic, but lacks the hardness and gloss which are contributed by the resin.

The natural oil-resin finishes, such as were baked onto grandfather's carriage, are complicated to prepare, hence costly, and they dry very slowly. The natural fossil resins are not soluble in drying oils till they have been melted. This is a tricky operation, and on top of it comes blending with thinners and driers, maturing the mix, and filtering it, so that the difficulties of making a good oil-resin varnish are not to be sneezed at.

They can be eliminated by synthetic resins in two ways. First, the oil-drying element can be actually incorporated in the synthetic resin molecule. Second, resins of superior hardness, toughness, and elasticity can be synthesized for use in the lacquer type of coating with exceedingly quick-drying solvents. In both directions progress in the synthetic coatings rushes forward at a speed that bewilders even the manufacturers who use them in their business.

Not long ago an industrial scout from one of the big refrigerator companies dropped in on the director of development work for one of the larger lacquer companies. In answer to his question: " What's new? " a " swatch " of a new coating was put into his hands. It was a sheet of metal, four by eight inches, painted on one side with a rich white finish as thick and smooth and soft-feeling as a porcelain tile.

" Just bend that strip double," said the research man.

He did so, flexing it over the edge of the desk and forcing it between his knees into a sharp, narrow U. Being wise in his generation, he bent the swatch with the coated side inwards. In the trough-like crease the finish was still smooth and firm — not a crack, not a flake.

" Do you remember, Bill, that three years ago was the first time you ever had a finish that would stand up under that treatment? But now straighten it, and bend it over till the coating's on the outside, and then straighten it out again."

The inquiring visitor did so. Still that coating remained flawless.

" About a year ago we perfected a finish that would stand that; but this new one goes farther. If you want a lot of exercise, bend that swatch back and forth till the metal breaks. Till it does, that coating stands up."

So our new coatings, like our new fabrics, are being tailor-made to suit the exacting conditions of their particular use, be it a mine timber deep underground or an airplane high in the sky. The coatings outside and inside of your refrigerator are as different as cheese and chalk because they must stand up under almost contradictory conditions. Protective coatings on a divebomber must cling to the surface at four hundred miles per hour. At that speed wind resistance strips off ordinary coatings like a blow-torch, and defective finishes not only increase wear on exposed parts, but also cut down speed — as much as ten per cent in the case of wings. And ten per cent means thirty-five miles an hour in fighting planes, which is too much handicap to give an enemy.

About threescore different types of synthetic resins, dissolved in more than a hundred different solvents and plasticizers, are the raw materials out of which the gentlemen of that brand-new profession, the formulation of coatings, are creating specialized " dopes " for the turrets of a battleship and the baby's rattle. It is astonishing what a beating the finish of a wooden toy must take and how exacting the requirements are for a perfectly harmless, lick- and bite-proof coating.

From " A–K " through the alphabet to " Zyl " it takes

thirty-eight pages of fine type in Carleton Ellis's two stout volumes, *The Chemistry of Synthetic Resins,* merely to catalogue the trade-names of the plastic molding powders and resins. To the date of this writing at least, it is here, in this distinctively American chemical development, that we find the last words spoken in the practical application of the underlying principle of the synthetics: materials made to order to suit man's needs.

Looking into the future of plastics, as Larry Livingston of du Pont said to Christy Borth, historian of the chemurgic movement, " is just like watching a four-ring circus: you never can tell what will happen next in which ring."

CHAPTER XX

OUR CHEMICAL ARMORY

◇◇

HITLER's war is essentially like the Kaiser's. Its objective — a German-dominated Europe — has been heightened from political control to economic slavery and the vision of Teutonic power more sharply focused before the German people; but *Deutschland über Alles* has still the same sinister ring that no other national anthem sounds. This war's technique, too, is quite similar. Then and now a quick victory to be won by any means, fair or foul, is the key alike to German international policies and German military tactics. Nowadays the policies are better planned and more ruthless: the tactics have been modernized and mechanized.

How anyone was fooled; why anyone should be surprised; that is the wonder, matched only by the blind stupidity of a people which can still believe that the rest of humanity will let go unchallenged Thor's bloody boast:

> *I am the War God —*
> *Force rules the world still,*
> *Has ruled it; will rule it.*
> *Meekness is weakness:*
> *Strength is triumphant.*
> *Over the whole world*
> *Still it is Thor's Day.*

In America the situation is essentially unchanged. The United States is always prepared for the war before. Chroni-

[353

cally we lack the modern munitions. Regularly, almost religiously, we forget that when Washington told Congress on January 8, 1790, that " to be prepared for war is one of the most effectual means of preserving peace," he was but repeating the ancient wisdom of Horace, who warned the Romans: *In pace, aptarit bello.* It follows naturally that in the first World War we were unprepared chemically and in World War II we are unprepared mechanically.

You need only change a word or two to bring these flaming headlines, culled from the newspapers of 1918, right up to date:

SABOTAGE SUSPECTED IN DYE PLANT BLAST

WAR TRADE BOARD TO RATION SULPHUR

HUNS USING NEW POISON GAS

TNT LACK STOPS ALLIED DRIVE IN WEST

FARMERS ASK CONGRESS TO FIX POTASH PRICES

As an antidote to the sinking feeling at the pit of the stomach that the repetition of these familiar facts causes, nothing is better than a spanking dose of cold figures. The record of our chemical accomplishment in the last war is a tonic. What we made in 1914 and what in 1918 was a defense program accomplished under greater handicaps than we face today. What we make now speaks eloquently of chemical progress, despite the depression, since the earlier struggle. What we need for total defense today is a goal that, in the case of chemicals, we know can be reached.

Behind that array of figures is a story as dramatic as the adventure of the Lost Battalion; a struggle as bitter as Ypres and Verdun.

Then and now, the chemical picture is clear enough. Under " 1940 " we see that our present peace-time consumption, which is not by many jugfuls up to our capacity to produce most chemicals, is, generally speaking, greater than the peak of the war-time effort of 1918. Let the chemical production figures, then and now, speak for themselves:

U.S. CHEMICAL PRODUCTION [1]

	1914	1918	1940	Defense Needs
Sulphuric acid, tons	3,200,000	9,500,000	9,400,000	12,000,000
Synthetic ammonia, tons	none	none	260,000	550,000
Nitric acid, tons	80,000	500,000	200,000	1,000,000
Toluol, gals.	1,500,000	14,100,000	25,000,000	65,000,000
TNT, lbs.	7,200,000	192,000,000	10,000,000	600,000,000
Smokeless pwdr., lbs.	1,800,000	513,000,000	30,000,000	800,000,000
Chlorine, tons	6,000	45,000	485,000	700,000
Potash, tons	none	54,800	350,000	375,000
Coal-tar dyes, lbs.	7,000,000	66,000,000	140,000,000	145,000,000
Bromine, lbs.	50,000	210,000	38,000,000	50,000,000
Caustic soda, tons	215,000	330,000	1,000,000	1,250,000

[1] Published in Chemical & Metallurgical Engineering, XLVII, 11 (November 1940).

In certain instances our chemical resources are today enormously greater. Bromine production, for instance, has to be expanded since it has become an ingredient in the preparation of the tetra-ethyl lead for motor fuel. Two seashore plants of the Dow Chemical Company now extract bromine from sea water. During the period chlorine has replaced bleaching powder in the textile and paper industries. Its greatly increased employment in water-purification has virtually banished typhoid fever from the country. Nowadays a lot more of this poisonous, yellow gas is used in various chlorination processes in chemical synthesis. Hence the big jump in chlorine output.

At the head of the list of famine chemicals in the earlier war were toluol and potash. The first is the coal-tar crude from which the pet disruptive high explosive, tri-nitrotoluol is made, and the latter is one of the three essential plant food elements. Today the ordnance officers talk glibly about a toluol need thirty, maybe fifty times as great as in 1918; and the chemical executives are not thrown into a dither by hints even of a hundred million gallons. As for potash, the item has simply been stricken from the list of " critical " chemicals.

And thereby hangs a tale, or rather two fables in chemistry that have each their own motto.

In 1914 all of our scanty supply of toluol came from the by-product recovery coke ovens of the steel industry. It was then used exclusively as a solvent, not a chemical. Most of it went into paints, varnishes, and rubber cements. Since there was so little call for the coal-tar crudes, our metallurgical coke was produced in those crude little cones of stone, the beehive ovens, which wasted their chemical sweetness upon the surrounding communities in what was unkindly called "Pittsburgh fog." After the opposing armies dug into the trenches on the western front, artillery created the number-one munitions problem by their insatiable demand for shells loaded with TNT or the mixture of TNT and ammonium nitrate known as Amatol. In response to that demand, and quite without any planning in Washington or checks from the U.S. Treasurer, eight American steel companies installed thirty million dollars' worth of recovery ovens, sufficient to boost our output of toluol to 9,600,000 gallons, almost a six-fold increase in three years. When the Armistice closed hostilities, five additional mills were being equipped with this expensive recovery system.

This heroic effort did not furnish enough toluol, so some gas companies began stripping it out of their product. The good citizens of eighteen American cities began in the spring of 1918 to make their war contribution by burning gas that had six per cent less heat value. But still toluol was short of requirements and so a third source was tapped.

California petroleum contains an appreciable amount of toluol, so the General Petroleum Company and the Standard Oil Company of California, on their own initiative, unprompted by either bureaucratic bidding or bribery, installed stripping apparatus at a cost of five million dollars. These operations were just getting under way at the close of the war. Both were scrapped. Furthermore a couple of experi-

mental projects were afoot to change the petroleum hydrocarbons to the coal-tar hydrocarbon series of which toluol
is a member and so synthesize the sorely needed munitions
material.

Since those feverish days toluol has become a real chemical
and our coal-tar chemical industry has created a steady demand for it. Accordingly, the steel industry has forsworn its
former wasteful habits and scrupulously collects the by-
products of its coking operations. When steel activity is lively,
we are actually producing right in the regular stride of business about twice as much toluol as at the top of that extraordinary war effort twenty-five years before. All would be as
merry as a wedding feast if it were not for the air force. They
have turned the extraordinary 1918 demands of the artillery
for TNT into something that beggars the vocabulary of a
circus press agent. Even " super-colossal " does not quite describe the quantities of high explosives that the air chiefs call
for when they are planning an all-out attack.

In two ways they have stepped up their requirements. A
big shot in artillery attack is the shell from a 14-inch gun,
1,560 pounds of projectile packed with 450 pounds of high
explosives. This is small potatoes in bombs. A big one is two
tons and it carries to earth a load of 2,500 pounds of TNT. In
other words, artillery shells carry 10–20 per cent of their
weight in explosives, while the bombs carry 50–60 per cent.
When you are arming air armadas of thousands of ships, you
can see that the TNT requirements become inordinate.

The groping experiments to twist the petroleum hydrocarbons into those of the coal-tar series had in the meantime
uncovered several proved processes for the production of
toluol from crude oil. Three of these have been tested through
the pilot-plant stage, and two plants, those of the Humble
and Shell companies, both in Texas, were actually operating
before the defense program got under way. As in the case of
rubber, we have " know how " to the point of large-scale pro-

duction. How little time and how much money, which are
reciprocal elements, answer how quickly and to what ton-
nages our toluol capacity shall be expanded.

The cost of toluol from petroleum would initially be higher
than from coke — engineering gossip says half again higher —
but when Mars is the customer, price is seldom the finally determining factor. However, once initial research costs have
been amortized and experience raises efficiencies of operation
and larger output shaves down overhead, no chemical man
doubts that petroleum toluol can be made quite as cheaply;
unless, as is always possible in any by-product operation,
there is some monkey-business in the allocation of the various costs. The vastly larger demands of the air forces for
toluol can be met, and even for an all-out war it is a solvable
problem.

It would be hard to plot a chemical drama more different
from this than the rise of the American potash industry. First,
potash is almost exclusively an agricultural chemical. Nine
out of ten of the 3,500,000 tons produced in the world go into
fertilizers. It is one of the three great elements — nitrogen,
potash, and phosphorus — essential to plant health, yet apt
to be deficient in farm soils. This trio is, therefore, the basis of
commercial fertilizers. Potash enters the fertilizer business as
several different salts — potassium chlorides and sulphides
and sundry mixtures — but what the plant needs and the
farmer wants to buy is K_2O — the actual potash content.
Accordingly, these salts are sold on a unit basis of how much
K_2O they contain, and potash statistics are commonly reduced to this basis. Thus the 3,500,000 tons mentioned above
mean tons of actual potash, a total of some 13,000,000 tons
of the salts. So eagerly do plants take up this element that
wood ashes by leaching provide the potashes (potassium
carbonate), which were the world's standard alkali until Le
Blanc showed how to make the cheaper sodium carbonate
out of salt.

In 1914 the Germans had a world monopoly on potash salts. Neither chemical skill nor business acumen had built this up. It was a perfect " natural," a great bed of salts from the bed of an ancient sea, near Stassfurt, from which common salt, sodium chloride, had been extracted since Roman times. At greater depths in this salt bed was discovered a rich layer of potassium salts.

Since 1861, when the potash salts were first mined, the German syndicate that controlled these mines controlled the world trade in this essential fertilizer material. They controlled it completely since the only other known workable beds were in adjacent Alsace, which was one of the prizes of the Franco-Prussian War. During the early stages of World War I, as a spur to encourage us to induce the British to loosen their blockade, the Germans embargoed the export of their potash. It quickly became a real famine chemical here and the price went from $44.25 a ton to $483.63. In terms of K_2O plant food, this meant that while the American farmer was paying 76 cents for each unit of potash before the war, at the peak in December 1915 he was forced to pay $10.06.

After a whole year of World War II, when no more potash came out of Germany and France than in 1914–15, he paid 53½ cents — roughly fifty per cent less than when the German monopoly was effective — and only .027 cents more than he paid when the Nazi panzer divisions rushed into Poland. In its own way — and a very practical way towards American economic independence and farm prosperity it is — that accomplishment overshadows all that has been done at Muscle Shoals. That well-publicized experiment in cheaper fertilizers has cost the American taxpayer uncounted millions. Our potash industry, quite to the contrary, in addition to taxes pays royalties to the U.S. Treasury for the lease of public lands.

There is plenty of potash in little odd lots all about here and there, and in 1915, when the price soared, frenzied efforts were made to recover it from wood ashes, cement-mill flue dust, distillery slops, from minerals such as the New Jersey greensands, Wyoming leucite, Utah alunite. The natural salt deposits and briny lakes of the West were the sites of scores of prospective potash plants. On the Pacific coast the giant kelp was dragged in, to become a chemical raw material, a return to the day when Scottish seaweed was an important source of both potash and iodine. At the top of this potash boom, 128 different companies produced 207,000 tons of various potash salts containing about 54,000 tons of K_2O, about a fifth of the amount normally fed to American crops. Of the 128 only three survived. Two of these, by-product recoveries from molasses by the U.S. Industrial Alcohol Company and from flue dust by the North American Cement Corporation, while operating producers, are not important.

Having rewon Alsace, France became an important producer in the post-war period. Other factors in world trade appeared, for the same frantic 1914–18 hunt for potash went on the world over and bedded deposits were found and worked successfully in Russia, Poland, and Spain. In Palestine an English company began extracting potash from the brine of the Dead Sea.

The first and still the most important American enterprise conducts a similar operation in Searles Lake, California. So concentrated is the mixture of salts (sodium chloride, gypsum, borax, potash, and others) that this so-called lake is a great field of white slush. It can be scooped up in shovels. The borax and potash are recovered by a clever process. These different salts have varying degrees of solubility, hence they are thrown out of solution — precipitated, as the chemist says — at different temperatures. Thus by carefully heating or cooling the rich mother liquor they can be separated, and by a subsequent refinement of the same treatment, purified.

This is another up-to-date trick of hoary antiquity, just about as old as the pioneer manufacture of resins by the cone-bearing trees. At the same time that the first true conifers appeared, when the Appalachians were baby mountains and the Rockies had not been born, a map of the United States would show the Gulf of Mexico reaching way up into Nebraska. It was the Permian epoch, the thousands upon thousands of years beginning the lush Carboniferous Age, one continuous warm, moist August afternoon of centuries' duration when the vast forests that have been turned into our coal beds flourished, when gnats as big as chickens were snapped up by huge, clumsy lizards with foot-long spines down their backs and great bristly ruffs round their ugly heads. Periodically cut off from the open ocean by the rise and fall of the land, that great shallow Permian Sea stretching from Texas to Nebraska evaporated to slush. As it dried up completely, the various sea salts (chiefly sodium chloride, gypsum, and potassium chlorides and sulphates) were deposited in selective layers. It was that identical process of selective precipitation which John Teeple (the same who refused to worry about our wood supplies) adopted with consummate chemical engineering skill for the Searles Lake operation.

In the hot Permian days evaporation was quick and continuous beyond anything we can conceive in nature; but you can get some glimmering notion of the quantities of sea water and the periods of time involved when you figure on these facts. Near Carlsbad, New Mexico, three companies are mining beds of sylvinite, a mixture of sodium and potassium chlorides from the residues of that Permian Sea. These potash-bearing seams are from 8 to 14 feet thick. They lie a thousand feet underground, beneath 200 feet of pure rock salt, above another bed of rock salt 2,000 feet thick. Above the upper bed of salt lie 500 feet of calcium sulphate, the white, natural gypsum, the makings of the alkali deserts of the Southwest. How much sea water, how many centuries to lay down a thousand feet of salt? One geologist guesses five million years.

Throughout the American Permian Basin, as geologists call the bed of that ancient sea, are scattered deposits of various combinations of potash-bearing salts: vast quantities of polyhalite, a mixed sulphate not so easy to separate as the sylvinite. These potash beds appeared from time to time in oil-drilling cores, and after the Snowden-McSweeney Oil Company had found the rich Carlsbad sylvinite bed, Congress appropriated half a million — this was back in 1926 — to explore for potash on Government-owned lands in the region, "because," so explains a Government publication dated May 1, 1940, "of the slowness of private enterprise to undertake drilling operations in the Texas and New Mexico regions." Between 1926 and 1930 the Snowden-McSweeney interests spent over $600,000 in core-drilling in this area, and three other private prospectors were also actively exploring in the region. Official reasoning is askew since there was proved up an area of some fifty square miles beneath which lie beds of sylvinite four or more feet thick. Estimated reserves are close to 200,000,000 tons, a quarter of which runs 28 per cent K_2O or better — material, that is, about twice as rich in potash as the famous Stassfurt deposits.

Today within this area three independent, privately financed American companies are mining potash on public lands under leases authorized by the Federal Potash Lease Act of 1917. These leases require that the property shall be actively developed, and provide a definite schedule for the investment of determined sums in plant and mine shafts. It is possible that these very proper but very rigid financial prerequisites delayed the initial development for years.

German and French producers had buried the hatchet of competition and formed a cartel that sold in this country through a single agency. American chemical people had learned thoroughly the lessons of German cartel competition. Foreign potash can be landed at Baltimore, Norfolk, or Charleston (the biggest fertilizer centers) for $5 a ton, while the rail rate to the Gulf port nearest Carlsbad plus charter rates to the fertilizer ports totals $8.70. That differential in delivery cost must be absorbed by an American producer, who thus is forced to accept $3.70 less per ton at the mine than his foreign competitors. As well expect water to run up-hill as to hope for any tariff protection on potash. However sorely such assistance might be needed by the producers, however provident it might be to assure our national self-sufficiency in this key chemical, any tariff on any fertilizer raw material is fought tooth and nail by the farm bloc in Congress, and its chances of enactment would have been minus zero. All in all, a venture into potash production, even from the highly promising Carlsbad beds, was fraught with extraordinary risks.

Two groups of courageous chemical pioneers accepted those risks and began operations in 1931. Almost immediately they faced an unexpected hazard. For several years the price of imported potash had been maintained somewhat lower than before the war at close to 70 cents a unit. Reasonably enough, they had undoubtedly used this figure in calculating their selling price at the mine in competition with imported material. Spain and Russia, both new potash-producers outside the cartel, began dumping potash in our markets. The price dropped as low as 32 cents a unit. This merry price war broke out just as the American mines were getting into operation and continued for four years. The outbreak of the civil war in Spain abruptly cut off exports from that country. The Russians, although their production of potash has mounted steadily, evidently have decided that it is wiser to use this fertilizer material on their own crop lands than to sell it abroad for gold credits. At all events they have not exported potash in recent years. With dumped material off the market, the price settled down at about 50 cents a unit.

Since then a third company has begun mining the Carlsbad beds. And today there is not even a rumor of a potash famine.

POTASH, WORLD WARS I AND II

	Total Supply	U.S. Production	Price Range
1913	255,101	——	.76
1914	193,878	——	.78
1915	42,609	1,090	1.18–9.87
1916	11,446	9,720	5.98–9.27
1917	33,077	32,573	6.75–8.66
1918	55,063	54,803	5.64–6.90
1919	60,958	32,474	2.17–5.54
1920	245,872	48,077	2.13–2.93
1937	603,240	283,497	.471
1938	510,560	316,951	.471
1939	410,050	312,201	.471
1940	497,335	379,679	.471

Total supply in the above table is imported plus domestic production of potash salts in tons, and it is seen at a glance that while we have been increasing our use of this element, our American output has been growing till in 1941 it is able to fill all requirements. Especially interesting is the course of prices which are quoted in dollars per unit of K_2O, as explained in the text. The price in 1939 was 40% less than it was when the German monopoly was operating in peacetimes before the first World War. Figures from the U.S. Bureau of Mines and Dale C. Kieffer, " Potash Report," 1941.

Furthermore, the American farmer is buying this essential fertilizer ingredient at about two thirds as much as he paid in the days of the German monopoly.

Another essential fertilizer ingredient was a famine chemical during the last war. Unlike potash, however, nitrogen is an essential element also in explosives. Unlike potash, too, we were not then cut off from the sole source of supply, for although the Chilean monopoly of sodium nitrate was quite as perfect as the German monopoly of potash, nevertheless, thanks to the British Navy, there was no blockade of our trade routes to the west coast of South America.

However, every belligerent had underestimated the nitrogen requirements of modern warfare. The demand for Chile nitrate, to be converted to nitric acid from which to make explosive nitrates and nitrated organic compounds, became fantastic. What was much more serious, there were not enough ships available to bring up the tons upon tons of material needed. In this country the need for fertilizer nitrogen, too, was greatly increased by the war. Besides, anyone with half an eye could foresee that some day we might be at war with an enemy who could cut the line to Chile, and Germany was giving the whole world a splendid demonstration of how nitrogen independence could be won through the Haber synthetic-ammonia process and all that it might mean to a nation.

Even before we entered the war this problem was pondered by a commission of experts. It was upon their recommendations that the Government decided to supplement our supplies by building synthetic plants to operate both the proved cyanide and the guessed-at ammonia processes. Having accepted the finding of that original, competent commission of chemical and military men, our Government under five Presidents, three Republicans and two Democrats, has made the astonishing record of having ignored in this matter every subsequent recommendation of disinterested chemical experts and frequently of having adopted the diametrically opposite or specifically opposed course of action.

President Wilson personally picked the Muscle Shoals site for the experiment in synthetic-nitrogen production. He was told plainly that half a dozen power companies had rejected it, and shown why, and offered three other locations that the hydro-electrical and chemical experts agreed were better. He insisted upon Muscle Shoals. His reasons were political.

When the 1941 defense program was being planned the T.V.A. put in a bid for a proposed 150-ton synthetic-ammonia plant. They argued that they had the land, utilities, and an obsolete ammonium nitrate plant, also that since they were already producing phosphate fertilizers, a nitrogen plant would enable them, after the war emergency passes, to extend their educational work to complete fertilizers. The Army and the Defense Commission were convinced, however, that Muscle Shoals was in the first place an unstrategic location for an explosives plant. Secondly, the figures showed that an additional synthetic ammonia supply could be more quickly and more cheaply secured by extending either one of three existing privately owned ammonia operations. President Roosevelt insisted that the Ordnance Corps contract with T.V.A. to design, build, and operate a synthetic-ammonia plant in connection with a contract to supply an ammonium nitrate. It was a purely political victory in a strictly chemical field.

On the other hand there have been some striking chemical victories in defense. In the last war Boy Scouts trudged from door to door collecting peach pits to be charred for an absorbent for gas masks. Later this special charcoal was made from coconut shells. Again we have an essential material that must be imported and again the molecule-makers have found a way to tear up geographies. By starting with sawdust and ending with a particular chemical treatment, which for obvious reasons is not being broadcast, the National Carbon Company have perfected a new type of activated carbon. Two plants to make it are being built in Ohio by the Government to be operated by them and the Barneby-Cheney Company.

Though tales of new gases so destructive that a few drops will exterminate every living creature in a whole city are fictions, gas is still an important weapon. During the first war over three thousand possible gases were investigated. Only four — dichlor-diethyl sulphide (mustard), phosgene, chlorpicin, and brombenzyl cyanide (tear) — are now considered to have met all the exacting requirements of available raw materials, ease of handling, and tactical effectiveness. Of these incomparably the most important was and is mustard gas. These gases, with the addition of Lewisite, discovered during that war but too late for it to be used, are still the mainstays of gas warfare. So far as anyone knows, no nation has perfected any chemical agent markedly more effective.

Gas is an effective weapon, not, as most people suspect, because of its deadliness, but because it is an economical and efficient way of disabling men. The casualty lists tell the story. On both sides in World War I, 32.9 per cent of the non-fatal casualties were caused by gas; but only 8.9 per cent of the deaths. Compare this with 32 per cent non-fatal and 54.6 per cent fatal casualties from gunshot wounds. It is evident that the effectiveness of gas is from its disabling not its lethal powers. This is increased by the lengthy hospitalization of gas cases, and it takes four men to care for and feed one field-hospital patient. It is an economical weapon too, since each of those casualties on the enemy required 5,000 pounds of TNT, but only 60 pounds of gas. These grisly figures go far to explain the colossal quantities of munitions set up for our defense program.

The new chemical weapons of this present ultra-modern, mechanized war are paradoxically not new at all, but they had been almost forgotten. From what is now the Iraq oil field the Assyrians collected seepages of petroleum which they used as liquid fire, the ancestor of our incendiary bomb. The pious Æneas, of Troy, is said to have formulated from pitch, sulphur, tow, and pine shavings an excellent mixture for pouring down on the heads of the attacking Greeks, and A.D. 660 Callinicus, the Syrian, developed the famous Greek fire, which is credited with having repeatedly saved Constantinople from the attacks of the Saracens. For generations that formula was a secret, and we are not now quite sure of the proportions. His big idea was to add crude quicklime and petroleum to the classical recipe. Quicklime in contact with water generates additional heat, partly nullifying its extinguishing effects. Light vapors of the petroleum cause explosions which scatter the flames far and wide.

These principles of Callinicus still prevail. Naturally materials and technique have been enormously improved by the misuse of scientific research diligently applied to finding materials whose flames are difficult to put out with water or carbon tetrachloride, or by smothering in sand. The technique of rapidly spreading the fire has also been greatly perfected. In both ways progress, a terribly misdirected but also terrifically important progress, is rapid, for the incendiary bomb is now one of the most important weapons at the command of the air forces.

Phosphorus, sodium, and magnesium are all metals that burn in the air with intense flames exceedingly difficult to extinguish, and they have taken the place of pitch and sulphur. Phosphorus, used with devastating effect by the Japanese on the flimsy wooden buildings of Chungking, is not highly effective against brick and concrete cities because of the low temperature of its flame. Sodium has the advantage of burning vigorously in water, so that it is used to ignite naval bombs and for strafing docks and waterfront warehouses. It is also used to ignite illuminating bombs. These are loaded with petroleum, emulsified with soap to keep it from splattering too widely, a mixture that burns brightly on a paved street or the concrete runways of an air field.

The "visiting cards" of the Nazi airmen are diabolically clever adaptations of the properties of phosphorus, which, as every high-school chemistry student knows, is quite harmless when kept in a bottle under water, but dangerously explosive on exposure to the air. Two disks of wet guncotton are filled with a little finely divided phosphorus. Dropped from a plane, they remain where they fall for hours until the guncotton dries out and the phosphorus, no longer protected by moisture from the air, catches fire. The guncotton bursts into

Cross-eyed stepchild to fairy princess: magnesium, lightest of all metals, is today in exorbitant demand for many uses.
— *Courtesy The Dow Chemical Company*

a long, hot flame of short duration, very effective against easily ignited materials. These little fire cards weigh an ounce each so they can be dropped literally by the tens of thousands over a wide area, not only over cities and factory districts, but on forests and farm crops. They are dangerous, too, because they may be picked up innocently by children, or even adults, attracted by the bright colors, pictures, or messages printed on them, and carried indoors.

Magnesium has become the most favored incendiary loading material. Its flame is intense and it is exceedingly difficult to extinguish. When touched off by a cap made of "thermite," it soaks up water poured upon it by burning the oxygen, thus liberating the hydrogen, which also burns and adds to the flame. The thermite mixture, originally perfected for industrial welding, consists of metallic aluminum and iron oxide, which burn together with a white-hot flame. They must be set off with a primer, which is commonly made of powdered magnesium and barium peroxide. Obviously, it is not only as lightweight metals for airplane construction that war now makes heavy demands upon the elements aluminum and magnesium.

Ordinary incendiary bombs weigh about two pounds, and while their design has been streamlined to get better penetration, still dropped from five thousand feet they only penetrate a slate or composition shingle roof to the top floor. Nevertheless, the accepted technique is still to count upon great numbers rather than to concentrate in larger bombs. In the Finnish campaign of 1939 the "Molotov breadbaskets," light metal frames in which are packed several dozen incendiary bombs, were a pioneer in group distributing of firebrands. Since only about 20 per cent of a city area is covered with buildings, about 80 per cent of the incendiary bombs will fall harmlessly upon open ground. Fully half of those that do strike buildings will glance off or fail to penetrate the roof. Only 10 per cent can be counted upon to start fires, and no doubt this figure is optimistic. Fire attacks must therefore be heavy and extensive to produce results, a double-barreled example of the wastefulness of war.

All the modern tactics demand more and yet more munitions. Our own defense-needs totals tabulated at the beginning of this chapter were based upon the requirements for an army of 2,000,000 men. Already the figures all round are being doubled. Still there is not a vital chemical that cannot be supplied.

In many cases existing plant capacity will have to be vastly increased. Already, as an example, we have in operation at Charlestown, Indiana, seventeen miles from Louisville, the largest smokeless-powder plant in the world. It cost close to $75,000,000. It was financed by the Government and is operated by the du Ponts. It stands in the midst of 5,400 acres surrounded by 15 miles of protective fencing. It uses 100,-000,000 gallons of water a day and employs over 1,000 men. It went into operation on May 1, 1941, the first of three, the two others at Radford, Virginia (Hercules Powder Company), and Childerburgh, Alabama (du Pont).

The outstanding difference in our chemical situation now and in 1916 is that today we know how. All the chemicals we need have actually been made here. The plant processes, the apparatus, the set-up, are all familiar. And we have available the largest staff of competent, trained chemists and chemical engineers in the world. That is important, and the confidence that we may place in their skill and resourcefulness is exceedingly comforting.

Chemistry is no national monopoly. The carefully fostered myth of German chemical omnipotence has long since ceased to be a bugaboo. The record shows that for all their great contributions to applied chemistry, most notably in the coal-tar derivatives and in air nitrogen, Germans have been conspicuously weak in that inventive vision which laid down the first principles of chemical theory and which followed through by making the great original discoveries in the practical application of those fundamental laws. The first coal-tar dye was discovered by an Englishman; the first synthetic fiber by a Frenchman. The initial discoveries in plastics were made right here in the United States by native-born Americans.

Nor do we need to be nervous at the astronomical numbers that the Army and Navy write down as their requirements for toluol and ammonia, for chlorine and bromine, for caustic soda and soda ash and sulphuric acid. It did not need war to accustom our chemical industry to big figures. Since long before the last war, because we have the largest consuming market, we had incomparably the largest heavy chemical production. The soberly calculated figure that the single little mill town of Pawtucket, Rhode Island, normally uses more chemicals than the entire continent of South America is a significant fact. However much it may distress those who are wishfully thinking about a greater, mutually profitable, reciprocal trade between the Americas, it is nevertheless enheartening evidence of our chemical self-sufficiency upon a grandiose scale.

The statistics of our own domestic chemical consumption in many instances reveal figures greater than all the rest of the world added together. To make our soaps we use 198,000 tons of a soda ash; for glass, 830,000 tons; for paper, 105,000 tons; to make other chemicals 1,356,000 tons. That is more soda ash than all the rest of the world uses for all purposes. Over 2,000,000 tons of sulphuric acid go into making our fertilizers, and yet our application of fertilizer per acre of farm land is far below that of the more intensively cultivated countries of Europe and Asia. In addition we use a million tons of this same acid each in petroleum refining and chemical making. We consume 127,000,000 gallons of alcohol — not a drop of it drunk, all of it poured into vats and percolators as a chemical reagent or a solvent. And the list could go on and on till, with examples, we should have another book.

Nor do we lack the raw materials to feed this enormous chemical enterprise. In their endless hunt for the most abundant and economical atoms our molecule-makers use more and more air and water, and after these they have built upon five great basic raw materials: salt, sulphur, lime, coke, and cellulose.

Of salt — source of the atoms sodium and chlorine — they use each year some 4,000,000 tons in the form of brine and half as much again as rock salt. Big quantities, but remember that all along the Texas Gulf coast the oil prospectors have time and again run their drills into beds of pure salt and given up in disgust after pounding away for a thousand or more feet. Sulphur consumption totals about 2,000,000 tons a year. Almost all of it is used for chemical purposes. Again we have enormous deposits of pure sulphur in that same Gulf coast country and a wonderful American process for melting it below ground and pumping it to the surface. Lime, for its calcium atom and its carbonate radical, and coal as a source of carbon and the coal-tar hydrocarbons, have both other important uses. About two thirds of the 3,500,000 tons of limestone quarried each year go into chemicals, glass, paper, tanning, and water-purification. Some 2,000,000 tons of coke are used in our chemical and illuminating-gas plants every twelvemonth. There is no prospective shortage of either lime or coal in our national economy. As for cellulose, it is the skeleton of every living plant; and if perennial cellulose from trees should fail, we can grow immeasurable quantities of cellulose from annuals.

Peering into the future, Dr. William J. Hale, the father of the farm chemurgic movement, sees a plastic age, now in its initial, experimental stages, which, beginning about 1950, will become a serious competitor with the dominant metal alloys. Into the extremely complicated latticework of plastic molecules he forecasts the introduction of the element silicon, the sand of the glass melt. You recall that Hyatt made a plastic material of bone and silicon. In nature silicon plays an important role in imparting resistance and rigidity to the ordinary tree; incorporated into the plastic structure it would add needed strength. Besides, silicon is one of the most abundant and cheapest of chemical elements. And cheaper plastics are quite as important for the future as stronger plastics.

One dares not dream what plastics and lightweight alloys, synthetic fibers, and a full range of chemotherapeutic agents will do for the human race. We know there is not one material which we use today that is absolutely perfect for its human purposes. And yet there are those who dare to tell us that the salvation of the race depends upon a moratorium upon chemical research, that there are no horizons for our children, that the frontier is closed, that we are all washed up.

IF YOU WANT MORE—

A BRIEF BIBLIOGRAPHY

◇◇

THE CLASSIC among many popular chemistry books is Slosson's *Creative Chemistry*, which though far from up to date is still the best simple introduction to the science. Another is Ellwood Hendrick's *Everyman's Chemistry* (Harper & Brothers, 1917), delightfully written with a sly sense of humor. Both are out of print, but can be found in most public libraries. Of numerous more recent books, *The Romance of Chemistry* (second edition, D. Appleton-Century Company, 1936) is among the best. Written by a Princeton professor, William Foster, it is complete and authentic. *Man in the Chemical World* by A. Cressy Morrison (Charles Scribner's Sons, 1937) and *Out of the Test Tube* (Ray Long & Richard R. Smith, 1934) by Harry N. Holmes review the practical accomplishments of chemistry.

In the lives of the great chemists Bernard Jaffe has told chemistry's story in *Crucibles* (Simon & Schuster, 1930) and told it exceedingly well. More complete, in a less popular vein, is Sir William Tilden's *Famous Chemists* (E. P. Dutton & Co., 1921). De Kruif's well-known *Microbe Hunters* (Harcourt, Brace & Company, 1926) has a good deal of chemical material, especially in the chapters on Pasteur, Koch, and Ehrlich. This is also true of the excellent *Industrial Explorers* (Harper & Brothers, 1928) by Maurice Holland. The development of the chemical industry in England has been biographically traced in Allen's *Some Founders of the Chemical Industry* (Sherratt, 1906) and in the United States by Haynes in *Chemical Pioneers* (D. Van Nostrand Company, 1939).

Four books published by the Chemical Foundation, *Chemistry in Industry* (2 vols.), *Chemistry in Agriculture,* and *Chemistry in Medicine,* are all excellent. For a briefer, crisper book, try *Men, Money and Molecules* (Doubleday, Doran & Company, 1935) by Williams Haynes, the story of the chemical business, and *Magic in a Bottle* by Milton Silverman (The Macmillan Company, 1941), the story of medicines.

A classic in its own way is William J. Hale's *The Farm Chemurgic* (The Stratford Company, 1934), and for a good journalistic account of the whole chemurgic movement read Christy Borth's *Pioneers of Plenty* (Bobbs-Merrill Company, 1939).

For peeps into the chemical past: *Prelude to Chemistry* (The Macmillan Company, 1937) by John Read, and *Ancient Egyptian Materials* (Longmans, Green & Company, 1934) by A. Lucas. For a peep into the future: *The Next Hundred Years* (Reynal & Hitchcock, 1936) by C. C. Furnas.

If you want still more, in the back of Jaffe's *Crucibles* is a long list of his references, which is full of good titles.

WORDS THAT PUZZLE—

A SIMPLE GLOSSARY

◇◇◇

THEORETICALLY, this book should need a Glossary even less than an Introduction. It is certainly the author's obligation to define for the comfort and satisfaction of his reader any technical terms he uses, and I have been conscious of this responsibility.

Practically, the following pages may be quite a convenience. For while I have endeavored to make all technical words clearly understandable, nevertheless some are used several times in different chapters and repeated definition would have been clumsy and boring.

Furthermore, some words that seem quite simple to a chemist, such as "acid" and "synthesis," often badly confuse one who has no chemistry. These are frequently words which have come out of the laboratory into common use. The technical man employs them in a definite and exact sense that the layman guesses he understands. Thus is confusion worse confounded.

ACID: a large group of inorganic and organic chemical compounds containing one or more hydrogen atoms which can be replaced by a metal forming a salt, as sulphuric acid plus lead yields lead sulphate and hydrogen. Acids are usually sour or bitter in taste: they turn blue litmus paper red.

ALCOHOLS: a large family of organic compounds containing one or more OH (hydroxyl) groups: the commonest is the drinkable ethyl alcohol, or ethanol (C_2H_5OH); wood alcohol is methyl alcohol, or methanol (CH_3OH); glycerin is an alcohol, more properly called glycerol, with three hydroxyls, $C_3H_5(OH)_3$.

ALKALIES: a series of compounds, called also "bases," containing an

OH group: commonly soda, potash, and ammonia; soluble in water. They neutralize acids to form salts, turn fats to soaps, change red litmus paper blue.

ALKALOID: one of a group of organic compounds that contain nitrogen and react chemically like the alkalies. Many are found in plants and have poisonous or therapeutic properties: quinine is an alkaloid found in cinchona bark; morphine, nicotine, codeine, and atropine are all of this class of compounds.

ALLOY: a mixture or compound of two or more metals made by melting them together; usually with different physical properties from their component metals. Brass is an alloy of copper and zinc; bronze of copper and tin.

ANALYSIS: the process of determining the chemical composition of any material: qualitative analysis finds only the elements present, while quantitative analysis determines the quantity or percentage of all the atoms in the substance analyzed.

ATOM: the smallest stable part of a chemical element that can exist in combination or take part in a chemical change. Though atoms are composed of still smaller parts (see Protons and Neutrons), they act as units in chemical reactions.

ATOMIC WEIGHT: a number indicating the relative weight of an element as compared with hydrogen = 1 or oxygen = 16. Each year an international committee publishes the most accurate and reliable determinations of the atomic weights of all elements.

BACILLI (sing. BACILLUS): a genus of microscopic vegetable organisms, known also as bacteria, having power of motion, causing fermentation, putrefaction, and some malignant diseases.

BASE: see Alkali.

BIOCHEMIST: a chemist who studies particularly the processes and products of living matter, especially of the human organism, as the assimilation of food, the elimination of wastes, etc.

CARBOHYDRATE: a large group of compounds synthesized by plants, containing carbon, hydrogen, and oxygen, the latter two elements in the proportion of water, 2H to 1O; sugars, starches, cellulose, gums, and tannins are all carbohydrates.

CATALYST: a substance that promotes or exhilarates a chemical reaction without being used up in it. Some catalysts do enter into reactions, but are re-formed. The enzymes and ferments catalyze reactions in the human body.

CELLULOSE: the material that composes the solid framework or cell walls of all plants.

CHEMOTHERAPY: the treatment of infectious diseases based on the specific action of chemicals upon the invading bacteria.

COATINGS: modern name for paints, varnishes, lacquers, etc., as a group of protective and decorative materials.

COMPOUND: a substance composed of two or more elements that are united chemically; distinguished from mixtures in which each element retains its original identity and properties.

CONCENTRATE: a trade-name for certain natural perfume or flavor principles isolated and strengthened by diminishing the bulk of the material.

CO-POLYMER: any one of two or more compounds which are polymerized at the same time and jointly.

CRUDES: the primary products, hydrocarbons derived by distillation from coal.

DECOMPOSITION: the breaking down of a substance into simpler compounds or more usually into its component chemical elements.

DENIER: originally a measure for the fineness of silk yarn, being the amount of yarn equal in weight to a gold coin, the denarius; the finer the thread, the greater the length necessary to attain the fixed weight; now a measure of the fineness of silk and rayon expressed as the weight in grams of a length of 9,000 meters of the yarn. If 9,000 meters of an individual filament or a yarn weigh 50 grams, it is said to be 50 denier. Obviously the higher the denier, the coarser (because heavier) the material.

DERMATOLOGIST: a physician who specializes in diseases of the skin.

DISTILLATE: the product of the process of distillation, the liquid which has condensed from its vapor.

DISTILLATION: the process of heating a substance to the boiling-point; then condensing again and collecting the vapors; used to purify and separate.

ELECTROLYSIS: the process of breaking up or decomposing a substance in a solution by means of an electric current.

ELECTROLYTE: a compound which in solution will conduct an electric current.

ELECTRON: the negatively charged unit in all atoms, found in the outer shell of the atom and playing an important part in all chemical reactions.

ELEMENT: matter consisting entirely of one kind of atoms, which thus cannot be further decomposed by chemical means.

EMPIRICAL FORMULA: a chemical formula showing only the number and kind of atoms in a compound, which does not show how these atoms are linked together, as $Fe_2S_3O_{12}$ contrasted with the structural formula, $Fe_2(SO_4)_3$.

EMULSION: intimate mixture of two liquids not normally soluble in each other; smaller drops of one are held dispersed in the other by means of an emulsifying agent which is partly soluble in both liquids.

EQUATION: chemists' shorthand to summarize the results of a chemical reaction, as $HCl + NaOH = NaCl + H_2O$. While a chemical equation must " balance " — i.e., all atoms must be accounted for in the result — it has little relation to a mathematical equation.

FILTRATE: the liquid that passes through the filter when a mixture of solid and liquid is filtered.

FLOTATION: the process of concentrating ores by grinding them, treating with a frother (called flotation agent), and floating on water usually agitated with compressed air. The ore floats away and the dirt settles to the bottom.

FORMULA (chemical): shorthand representation of a compound using symbols of the elements and sub-numbers to indicate the number of each element present in the molecule of the compound, as H_2O or 2 atoms of hydrogen combined with 1 of oxygen equals water.

HEXAHYDRIC: alcohols having 6 OH groups, as mannitol and sorbitol.

HUMECTANT: chemicals employed to maintain moisture in tobacco, transparent wrappings, leather, etc.

HYDROCARBON: any compound of only the elements hydrogen and carbon, a very numerous and important chemical family found in coal, natural gas, petroleum, and other organic materials.

INTERMEDIATES: chemicals used in the synthesis of organic compounds such as dyes, medicines, etc., and prepared from the so-called crudes.

ISOLATE: trade-name for a class of perfume materials, commonly the active principle of plants, purified and concentrated.

ISOMER: any compound having the same composition, but different properties from another compound. Isomers have the same empirical formula, but different structural formulas.

LACQUER: (1) a natural varnish containing shellac; (2) a coating made of a solution of synthetic resins or cellulose.

MOLECULAR WEIGHT: the addition of all the atomic weights of the elements in a compound, multiplying each atomic weight by the number of times that atom is in the formula and adding all together.

MOLECULE: the smallest unit of a compound or element that enters into chemical reactions. The chemical formula is a perfect representation of the molecule; as H_2O for water.

MONO-HYDRIC: having only one OH group.

MORDANT: a chemical used to fix dyes upon textiles by absorption; commonly used mordants are the soluble salts of aluminum, chromium, iron, and tin.

NEUTRALIZE: to add an acid to a base, or vice versa, till the reaction of forming a salt and water is complete, as $HCl + NaOH = NaCl + H_2O$. The resulting solution is neither acid nor alkaline.

NEUTRONS: the surcharged (electrically) units which with positons make up the nucleus or dense central part of each atom.

NITROGENOUS: any compound containing the chemical element nitrogen.

ORGANIC CHEMISTRY: formerly the study of compounds of living organisms; now of the compounds containing the element carbon.

PATHOLOGIST: one who studies diseases, especially the functional and structural changes produced by disease in the human organism.

PHOTOSYNTHESIS: the synthesis of compounds by means of light-rays, more definitely the synthesis of carbohydrates by plants through the agency of chlorophyl and sunlight.

PIGMENT: any finely powdered, insoluble coloring matter, used suspended in a vehicle, as in the oil of paints.

PLASTIC: (1) soft, pliable; (2) a group of synthetic materials which are shaped when soft and afterwards hardened into more or less permanent forms.

POLYHYDRIC: alcohols having more than one OH radical.

POLYMERIZATION: a reaction in which two or more molecules of the same substance combine to form a new compound whose molecular weight is a multiple of that of the original compound.

POLYMERS: compounds that have the same elements in the same percentage, but contain a different number of atoms, which may or may not be arranged in a similar structure, as C_4H_4, C_8H_8, $C_{12}H_{12}$, etc.

PRECIPITATE: (n) the insoluble matter formed during a chemical reaction in solution; (v) bringing two soluble compounds together in solution to produce an insoluble compound.

PROTON: a positively charged sub-atomic particle, the basic unit of the atomic nucleus; with an electron in close contact it becomes a neutron.

PROTOZOA: any one-celled animal, a member of the lowest class of the animal kingdom, as infusoria, amoeba, etc.

RADICAL: any group of atoms that act in chemical reactions as a unit or as a single atom: (NH_4) ammonium, (OH) hydroxyl, (C_2H_5) ethyl, etc.

RAYON: generic trade-name for synthetic fibers.

SOLUTION: the mixing of a solid or gaseous substance (the "solute") with a liquid (the "solvent"), forming a homogeneous mixture from which the dissolved matter can be recovered by crystallization or distillation: a physical, not a chemical change.

SOPORIFIC: an agent producing sleep.

SUBSTITUTION: any chemical reaction in which an atom or a radical in a molecule is exchanged for another atom or group of atoms.

SYMBOL: the abbreviation, a letter or letters, used to represent a chemical element, also in formulas to represent one atom of an element, hence also one atomic weight of the element.

SYNTHESIS: the process and operations necessary to build up a compound, generally a reaction or series of reactions in which complex compounds are derived from the elements or simpler compounds.

TERPENES: hydrocarbons of the general formula $C_{10}H_{16}$, that occur in resins, essential oils, and other vegetable, aromatic products; related groups are sequiterpenes, $C_{15}H_{24}$, and diterpenes, $C_{20}H_{32}$.

TRYPANOSOMES: a group of micro-organisms causing sleeping sickness.

TYMPAN RED: an azo dye found by Ehrlich to have bacterial action against trypanosomes.

VISCOSITY: the state of a liquid of being glutinous or sticky, a slight resistance to change in form; fluid friction.

WATER GAS: a mixture of hydrogen and carbon monoxide obtained by the action of steam on glowing coal, used for fuel.

ACKNOWLEDGED WITH THANKS

◇◇◇◇◇◇◇◇◇◇◇◇

It is trite, but true, that many people — literally hundreds — have helped write this book. During the past twenty years chemists and engineers, salesmen, purchasing agents, attorneys, and executives in all chemical fields have supplied much material for the foregoing pages. Many will recollect facts and figures, anecdotes and bits of characterization that they have contributed. I cannot thank all individually; but I have directly called upon the following for data or criticism. For their liberality and candor I am deeply grateful:

Horace M. Albright
U.S. Potash Co.

Robert T. Baldwin
The Chlorine Institute

L. N. Bent
Hercules Powder Co.

Marston T. Bogert
Columbia University

Elmer K. Bolton
E. I. du Pont de Nemours & Co.

Reginald A. Brewer
MacManus, Johns & Adams

Benjamin T. Brooks
B. T. Brooks Labs.

Gordon Brown
Bakelite Corp.

Kenneth R. Brown
Atlas Powder Co.

Arthur D. Chambers
E. I. du Pont de Nemours & Co.

C. C. Concannon
U.S. Dept. of Commerce

Sallie E. Coy
Westerly (R.I.) Library

H. Jermain Creighton
Swarthmore College

M. L. Crossley
American Cyanamid Co.

[383

George O. Curme
*Carbide & Carbon
Chemicals Corp.*

Francis Despard Dodge
Dodge & Olcott Co.

Willard H. Dow
Dow Chemical Co.

Gaston du Bois
Monsanto Chemical Co.

Gustav Egloff
*Universal Oil Products
Co.*

Gustavus J. Esselen, Jr.
G. J. Esselen, Inc.

F. Miller Fargo
American Cyanamid Co.

C. C. Furnas
Yale University

William C. Geer
B. F. Goodrich Co.

William J. Hale
Dow Chemical Co.

Carl H. Hazard
Hazard Advertising Corp.

Maurice Holland
National Research Council

J. K. Hunt
*E. I. du Pont de Ne-
mours & Co.*

Stanley B. Hunt
*Textile Economic Bu-
reau*

Eric C. Kunz
*Givaudan-Delawanna,
Inc.*

Arthur Langmeier
Hercules Powder Co.

Ira P. MacNair
Soap

Theodore P. Marvin
Hercules Powder Co.

E. C. Kenneth Meese
Eastman Kodak Co.

Charles L. Parsons
*American Chemical So-
ciety*

Cesare Protto
*E. I. du Pont de Ne-
mours & Co.*

William M. Rand
Monsanto Chemical Co.

H. W. Rose
Viscose Co.

Norman A. Shepard
American Cyanamid Co.

S. J. Spitz
Newport Industries

John Swenehart
Atlas Powder Co.

M. V. von Isakovics
Synfleur Scientific Labs.

Theodore P. Walker
*Commercial Solvents
Corp.*

To Florence Williams of *Time* and Pelham Barr I am especially indebted for valuable suggestions and most particularly to Mrs. William H. Robey, who has read the entire manuscript. The question marks and exclamation points, the crosses and double checks, and the staccato comments with which she " blue penciled " the margins were a very real help. Besides compiling the Index, Dorothy Farrand Haynes has checked dates, confirmed quotations, fended off visitors, and been from the first page to the last, a painstaking and friendly critic. My debt to her is beyond words. Last, but not least, Mildred Brown, my secretary, has labored early and late over manuscript and proofs; and I more than appreciate her loyal enthusiasm.

WILLIAMS HAYNES

INDEX

Index

A NOTE ON THE TYPE

The text of this book is set in Caledonia, a Linotype face designed by W. A. Dwiggins. Caledonia belongs to the family of printing types called " modern face " by printers — a term used to mark the change in style of type-letters that occurred about 1800. Caledonia is in the general neighborhood of Scotch Modern in design, but is more freely drawn than that letter.

The book was composed, printed, and bound by The Plimpton Press, Norwood, Massachusetts.